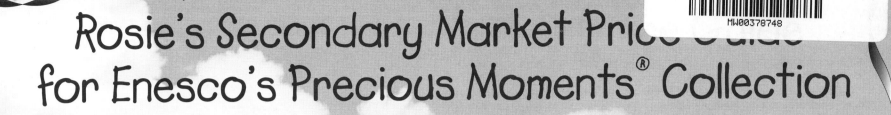

Rosie's Secondary Market Price Guide for Enesco's Precious Moments® Collection

14th Edition

Editor: Rosalie "Rosie" J. Wells

Published by Rosie Wells Enterprises, Inc.
22341 East Wells Road, Canton, IL 61520
Ph. 1-800-445-8745

Rosie

"To God Be The Glory"

*Sam designed this piece
for his recognition to the Lord for his "gift" of
creating Precious Moments® figurines. In this
piece he acknowledges that his works cannot be
compared to God's. God receives the glory for
Sam's gift. "To God Be The Glory" is
Sam's favorite piece. See page 16.*

*We thank Precious Moments Incorporated for the use of special line art
drawings in this guide and for the use of the Precious Moments® design
logo on the front cover. We thank Enesco for their assistance in providing
information as well as line drawings. Also thanks goes to our Precious
Collectibles™ subscribers who contribute yearly to this guide and to Sam
Butcher for special art work and his dedication to the
Precious Moments® Collection.*

Table of Contents

Hundreds of hours of labor
have gone into this guide...
Oh no! There may be an error or an omission.
If you find one, please let us know.

Total Count of Pieces

1978	11
1979	18
1980	40
1981	64
1982	66
1983	60
1984	48
1985	64
1986	80
1987	65
1988	68
1989	48
1990	42
1991	50
1992	52
1993	58
1994	68
1995	95
1996	75
Birthday Club figurines and Membership Pieces (through 1996)	35
Membership & Club Figurines, Ornaments, etc. (through 1996)	76
Dolls	24
Century Circle Exclusive Figurines, Ornaments, etc.	3

♥**Retired Through 1995**

Figurines	67
Ornaments	12
Musicals	7
Bells	1
Dolls	1

♥**Suspended Through 1995**

Figurines	175
Ornaments	44
Musicals	24
Frames	14
Bells	10
Dolls	9
Containers	6
Plates	5
Candle Climber	2
Night Lite	2
Thimbles	4
Plaque	1

Did you know...

... that 1,210 Precious Moments porcelain pieces have been produced by Enesco? This sounds like a lot, doesn't it? But have you ever really stopped to think about the fact that out of those 1,207 pieces, approximately 687 pieces are no longer available? We have! Wow! Included in the 687 pieces which are no longer available are 296 Suspended pieces, 88 Retired pieces, as well as Birthday Club, regular Club, Dated Annuals and Limited Editions. Nearly 57% of all Precious Moments porcelain pieces ever produced are now only available on the secondary market. This is another good reason to stay in tune with what is happening on the secondary market and our guide will help you do just that!

...About the Editor

Rosie Wells came down with Precious Moments® fever in late '82 and the "fever" still exists. In the early years of Precious Moments collecting, there was not much information available for collectors. Rosie saw the need for a publication that would inform collectors and, at the same time, bring them together in friendship. Rosie's goal has always been to "Bring Collectors Together."

It has been exciting to look back to the humble beginnings of the first eight page newsletter written at Rosie's kitchen table and to realize just what the Lord has done. Rosie Wells Enterprises, Inc., is now housed in a beautiful office building with a scenic view of one of the farm's lakes, situated across the road from the Wells' farm. Twenty-five employees work together to offer readers the latest in collecting news through several publications including *Precious Collectibles™, Collectors' Bulletin™, The Ornament Collector™* magazines and the *Weekly Collectors' Gazette™,* a Weekly All Collectibles newsletter which provides readers with the latest, up-to-the-minute collecting news on most "Hot Collectibles," including Precious Moments news and retirement announcements! In addition to the guide for The Enesco Precious Moments® Collection, Rosie Wells Enterprises, Inc., also publishes guides for Applause Precious Moments® Dolls, Hallmark Keepsake Ornaments, Hallmark Merry Miniatures and The Enesco Cherished Teddies™ Collection. A future guide for Precious Moments Company dolls is on the drawing board. Rosie Wells Enterprises is now represented by over 110 reps throughout the USA and Canada. The magazines are now on newsstands across the country and on military bases overseas "Bringing Collectors Together"!

Rosie and her husband, Dave, have hosted ten conventions across the United States for Precious Moments collectors. They also host the semiannual Midwest Collectibles Fest, now held each March and October at the Inland Meeting and Exposition Center in Westmont, Illinois. These shows in past years were held at the Pheasant Run Resort Pavilion in St. Charles, Illinois. These shows usually consist of over 150 collector tables, nearly half of which are older Precious Moments figurines.

Rosie and her staff answer the many questions that come to the office by phone or mail. If you have a question or comment, please feel free to call 309/668-2565 for assistance. Write us at 22341 E. Wells Rd., Canton, IL 61520, or E-mail us at RosieWells@aol.com. Enjoy this guide and thank you for purchasing it.

Insuring Your Collection

One purpose of this guide is to assist you in evaluating your collection's monetary value for insuring, investing, estate planning or reselling. We recommend that you record your collection's value and store the records in a safety deposit box, etc., so you have a record of your collection available at a location other than your home in case of fire or other catastrophic damage. Another excellent tool in recording your collection is a video camera. A video tape would be a valuable resource if questions arise when filing an insurance claim. By all means, insure your collection. You will want to take a detailed inventory. We have included space in this guide for you to enter your own inventory. Computer programs are also available for this purpose. Whatever method you choose, it is very important to give this information to your insurance agent. Collectibles usually are not covered with a general homeowner's insurance policy, but require a "rider" policy. Check with your agent for all important details and double check to be sure that your insurance agent has copied your list correctly when the policy is written.

Insure your collection at replacement value and not retail cost, but keep in mind that some pieces stay at retail cost for several years. (You also may want to include the amount of state tax you paid, too.) Use this guide to determine what the replacement value is. There is no need to over-insure, as this just adds to the cost of the policy.

Above all, enjoy your collection. Display your pieces and share the meaning of Precious Moments® with others. This "Loving, Caring and Sharing" has a value which cannot be measured in dollars and cents.

What is the Collectibles' Secondary Market?

The term secondary market refers to the buying, selling or trading of collectibles, most generally for a price other than original retail. This secondary market price is usually higher than original retail, but at times could be lower. People involved with the secondary market include those who buy specifically for this purpose (secondary market dealers), those who happen to have a few extra pieces they want to sell or collectors who decide to liquidate their entire collections. Some retailers are also involved in the secondary market.

Factors such as scarcity, age, errors, changes, retirement, suspension, over production and whether or not a piece is dated or a limited edition contribute to the secondary market value.

What about the value of club pieces on the secondary market? The secondary market value of club pieces rose quickly in the early years of the club's existence, especially in 1982-1984. As new members joined the club, hundreds of new collectors sought early club pieces. At present, club pieces increase in value but not at the rate of the '81-'82 pieces. Many avid collectors today have been club members since the early 1980s and have more than one membership. They may buy several club pieces, making extras readily available for future collectors. If a current club piece is broken, Enesco now has a replacement policy which also affects the secondary market. Many of the club pieces are very special and I feel it's of real benefit to join the National Club.

Today's coveted piece still remains the 1981 retired *God Loveth A Cheerful Giver* (E-1378), also known as "Free Puppies." Only a few people bought extra pieces at the time of this piece's retirement. (Many of these buyers were insiders who knew about the retirement announcement before the collectors did.) In 1982 more Ice Cream Cone Boys (E-1374B) were bought up by collectors than any retirement piece to date. As of 1989, the secondary market has just begun to show a demand and a rise in value for this piece. Not all Precious Moments® collectibles increase in value, although not many have decreased.

This 14th Edition Guide debuted in March, 1996.

Of course, as in the past, prices could drop... just like the stock market. We can't always predict the future, but I've never seen anyone selling their collection for less than the original retail. Precious Moments® figurines have been stable on the secondary market since a year or two after they debuted in 1978.

Precious Moments®

• Avid collectors still love to find the "first Twenty-one" pieces in a "No Mark." These are E-1372B through E-2013.

• The early figurines were darker in color than today's pieces. In 1982 pieces were produced with a very pale color, then somewhat darker in 1983-1984. A darker color was favored by many collectors.

• The box to "Free Puppies" (E-1378) has added as much as $50 to the value of this figurine in the past, but pay the top price if you want the piece, even without the box. Other boxes only add around $3 to the resale value. I do not keep my boxes any longer.

• Pieces produced in 1978-1984 and licensed by the Jonathan & David Company have smaller heads than pieces relicensed by the Samuel J. Butcher Company and Precious Moments, Inc. Jonathan & David was co-owned by Precious Moments artist Samuel J. Butcher and his former partner Bill Biel until 1985. J&D closed its doors in late 1988.

• Since 1985, "Sam B" has been embossed on pieces which are licensed through the Samuel J. Butcher Company. Pieces still in production which were originally licensed through the Jonathan & David Company are not marked Sam B. and do not have the larger heads. Many of these Jonathan & David pieces have been suspended. E-1381 was suspended in 1984, which means it was no longer produced but could be brought back into production at a later date. It was brought back in 1992 as E-1381R, with some changes. (The "R" after the original number signifies a piece that was reissued after suspension.) This reissued piece was licensed under the Samuel J. Butcher Co. and is embossed with "Sam B." It's not unusual to find a current figurine which is missing the Sam B. logo. Precious Moments, Inc. (PMI), is now the licensee of Sam's artwork to Enesco, the licensee.

• Pieces were produced with an embossed mark from mid-1981. There are fewer Triangle marks (the first mark) than any other mark. A newly released piece may have the previous year's mark as its first mark because of production schedules.

• Style/stock numbers did not appear on the bottom of the bases until mid-1982, so No Marks, Triangles and some Hourglass marks do not have a style number. There have been errors on the bottom of the bases, with some being totally blank. Some marks (usually the Fish and the Hourglass marks) are decals. Small stickers imprinted with the words "Sample: Prototype" have also been found on pieces. Sample pieces are given to company sales representatives to display at store events. Earlier, the sales reps were able to purchase these pieces or return them to the company when the shows were over. Many of these samples are in the hands of collectors now. It's my opinion we have underestimated the value of these pieces in the past. Prototypes are from molds which may or may not

have been the accepted molds for the collection. Prototypes may deserve a value of $500 up.

• There are figurines still being produced with Jonathan & David as the Licensee... (figurines initially produced before 1985).

• The Enesco Precious Moments Collectors' Club began in 1981 with Charter Memberships issued to members joining the first year. The Charter Members continue to receive pieces that are imprinted with "Charter Member." An error was found on some Charter Member pieces produced in 1985; these pieces were marked "1985 Charter Membership" instead of "1981 Charter Membership." This error was corrected later in 1985.

• Sometimes a mold is changed after a piece has been produced and marketed. For example, *Nobody's Perfect* (E-9268), known as the Dunce Boy, was first produced with a smile. The mold was changed to give the piece a frown. The "smile" piece is the errored piece and is "rare" (approximately 5,000 pieces bearing this error were produced; see page 43 for further information).

• Different types of errors have occurred on Precious Moments® figurines; some are more significant than others. Generally, the more valuable errors are those which are visible while viewing the piece and not the errors on the bottom of the figurine (unless the error is a double mark). Two highly visible errors collectors have found are the large Columbus piece missing the dog and the spyglass, and *Friendship Hits The Spot* missing the table. A decal error on the base of a piece is usually not significant, although some collectors collect these pieces. For more information about errors, read our publications, *Precious Collectibles*™, *Collectors' Bulletin*™ and *Weekly Collectors' Gazette*™.

• Many paint variations occur on pieces now since painting takes place at more than one factory. Usually paint variations do not affect secondary market values unless the variation is markedly different.

• In May 1993 the little boxing girl, *Faith Is A Victory,* was retired. January 1994 found her being shipped to retailers. We received calls by collectors and retailers alerting us of this "eight months later" shipment. When a piece has been retired, look in stores first before buying on the secondary market. At times certain pieces which are retired are very hard to find in stores; these pieces will rise in value more quickly than those easily found. Collectors look for the older marks on retired pieces. Many desired pieces may be found at large swap meets and collectibles shows. (Especially at our Midwest Fest held in the spring and fall in Westmont, Illinois. Hundreds of PMs are there!)

• The 9" Easter Seals pieces: 1,000 were produced in 1988, 1,500 in 1989, and 2,000 in 1990, 1991, 1992, 1993, 1994, 1995 and 1996. The regular sized Easter Seals pieces are abundant and have been

readily available for several years after production. The second year Girl on Crutches piece did not have the Easter Seals logo on it; this error was found on each one of this particular piece. The 1997 Boy in Wheel Chair Easter Seals figurine may be as popular as the 1992 Girl Hand-Signing "I Love You" (527173).

• The 1989 first in series porcelain dated ball ornament is scarce as over 45% of these ornaments were ruined in the kiln. The 1990 dated porcelain Easter egg was also hard to find. The 1990 dated ball ornament was produced in two variations; one with the boy in a yellow shirt and the other with the boy in a blue shirt.

• More and more Precious Moments® accessories are being produced these days. These items are fun for collectors to have, but do not generate much interest on the secondary market.

• In 1995 Goebel introduced hand painted bronze miniature Precious Moments sculptures. Barely an inch tall, the first pieces to debut included seven designs from the "Original 21," plus a limited edition Christmas figurine. Each miniature "cameo" is enhanced with accents to help express its message and the sculptures are designed to fit into a larger vignette. It's too early to evaluate a secondary market on these pieces.

• Precious Moments® unpainted Jonathan & David pewter is collectible, although the Precious Moments® Company has reissued pewter which is very similar, making it difficult to distinguish between the two. In addition to figurines, Precious Moments Company has produced gold and silver-plated pewter charms, pewter key rings, magnets, spoons and thimbles. Painted pewter debuted

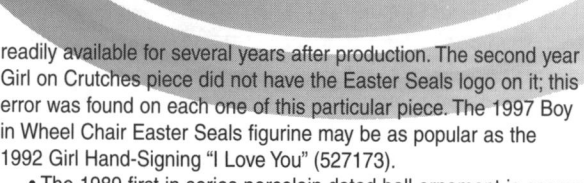

Jonathan & David Logo

Precious Moments® Logo

Samuel J. Butcher Co. copyright

Precious Moments Inc. copyright

in 1989. Chipping has been a problem with these pieces.

• Although not as collectible to date as the figurines, the PMC dolls are very popular. Many of these doll collectors do not collect figurines.

• Several of the large Columbus pieces that debuted in 1992 were reported to have paint that flaked off and some were reported with kiln cracks.

• In 1992 the Precious Moments® logo was missing from the base of the Fall pieces and the Members' Only pieces. This logo was included on the Spring 1992 pieces with the Vessel marks.

• Debuting in 1993 was the 15 Year Anniversary figurine *15 Happy Years Together: What A Tweet* and the 15 Year Anniversary ornament *15 Years: Tweet Music Together*. The special dealer display dome for the figurine included a commemorative medallion and plaque attached to the dome.

• In June 1995 the Enesco Corporation invited 35 retailers to an all expense paid weekend at Enesco's Chicago-area location for a mysterious special event. These special retailers became charter members of Enesco's new Century Circle Retailers, an elite group recognized by Enesco as being extraordinarily committed and supportive of the Enesco Precious Moments Collection. A new line of limited edition Precious Moments collectibles (LE of 15,000) will be available exclusively at these retailers. The first piece was a figurine, *Love Makes The World Go 'Round* and the second was an ornament, *Peace on Earth*. As of early 1996 these two pieces were still available at retail. *God's Love Is Reflected In You* (175277) is this year's Century Circle figurine. Other special event pieces may be available to these retailers this year, including a figurine of a girl holding a string of sunflowers and two Christmas ornaments.

• Precious Moments® artplas ornaments debuted in 1992. However, these have not seen much secondary market activity. There's talk of limited edition artplas, crystal and pewter pieces being produced in 1996 for Signature Stores.

• artCentral in Carthage, Missouri, commissioned a bronze bust of Sam Butcher to be created there. It was a special tribute to Sam, and collectors donated money to this project. Those making donations had their names engraved on a plaque which is displayed by the bust.

• Something new at the Precious Moments Chapel will be the Fountain of Angels. This impressive tiered fountain will feature 120 four-foot bronze angels in many different poses. Look to Spring 1997 for its debut. There will also be a lazer light

show at the Fountain area. A portable ice rink was constructed in the winter of 1995. Over 750,000 Christmas lights twinkled brightly during the holidays at the Chapel in 1995.

• Visit the Precious Moments Chapel to view some of Sam's modern artwork. The Chapel, with its continually changing exhibits, is very unique and inspirational.

• In 1991 the first Amway Precious Moments Christmas doll, *Jessica*, was a sell-out. *Melissa* was available in 1992 from Amway. The 1993 doll, *Rebecca*, was shown in the Amway catalog as having a yellow dress and plain yellow headband. None were actually produced this way but were changed to a cream dress and ruffled headband. The 1994 Amway doll was *Maddy*, a blond beauty with a bouquet of flowers, wearing a light blue and pink party dress. *Marissa*, with her dark blond curly hair and brown eyes, debuted in '95 wearing a long-sleeved pink satin dress accented with lacy white tights and bright pink ribbons tied in her hair, around her neck and at her waist.

• Several collectors have reported at various times having figurines with only half of a Butterfly mark.

• 1994 marked the last in the series of dated Precious Moments Easter Eggs. In 1995, Easter figurines debuted with a large cross as a central theme.

• Remember, if you have any collecting questions or comments, you may call us at the office at 309/668-2565. Keeping collectors informed is our specialty!

• An exciting collectibles annual event will be held April 26 - 28, 1996, in Tulsa, Oklahoma. This is the show's third year and Sam will again be present to sign figurines for collectors. Plan to attend; Tulsa is beautiful in the spring and only a two hour drive from the Chapel in Carthage, Missouri.

• Use care in cleaning your figurines. Lay a towel in the bottom of your sink to protect them from breakage. We suggest placing a finger over the air hole in the base of the figurine to keep water from going inside (this prevents drips on furniture later). Use a mild soap or Dow Scrubbing Bubbles. Don't use glass cleaner as we have heard that some Disney porcelain collectibles were damaged by such a cleaner. Lay each piece on its side to dry.

• New factories in Bangkok, Thailand, are producing Precious Moments figurines. Factories in Mexico did not prove to be successful. Other gift and collectible lines by Enesco are produced at the same factories.

A Precious Moments® Message

By Todd Swanson

I guess I always knew how meaningful and appropriate the sayings are on the bottom of the figurines we all love, but I never really knew how strong an impact one particular piece would have on my life and the life of my family. I guess my story begins when my wife, Lisa, received her *GoodNewsletter* and we learned of the upcoming June 17th retirement. We wrote the date on the calendar and kept the 800 number in a place where it would be accessible for that early morning call to see which figurines would be retired. We also had this particular time in June circled on our calendar as my wife and I were expecting our first child on June 12th. The first two weeks of June really seemed to drag by, but finally we reached our due date... and nothing happened, the 13th, 14th, 15th and 16th all came and passed without even the tiniest contraction. As we went to bed the night of the 16th, I kidded Lisa by saying that she had better not go into labor until after the stores opened and we purchased whatever pieces we would need. I set the alarm for 3:00 a.m. and set my sharpened pencil and pad of paper right next to the phone, ready to take down the valuable information. I'm like a little kid on the night before Christmas when it comes to retirements or getting up the next morning to attend a collectible show, so falling asleep was not an easy task. Eventually I did nod off. Around 11:30 p.m. we were awakened by the telephone ringing. I answered the phone and heard my mom's voice on the other end. She said she was calling with bad news as my grandpa, her father, had just passed away. He had been struggling with a heart condition for the last two years, but he had been feeling so well recently, the news hit us very hard. I think the saddest thing for me was knowing he would miss the birth of his first great-grandchild. Now, neither my wife nor I could sleep, and the next thing we knew it was almost 3:00 a.m. In order to take our minds off things, I picked up the phone and called the retirement number. We only needed two of the four figurines, *Puppy Love Is From Above* and *The Lord Giveth And The Lord Taketh Away*.

Thirty-six hours after we received the phone call from my mom about Grandpa, our son, Aaron Todd, was born. To top it all off, Aaron was born on Father's Day. Talk about your range of emotions! Lisa and Aaron came home on Monday the 19th, and I made the difficult decision to leave my wife and newborn son to fly to South Dakota to attend Grandpa's funeral. Thankfully, Lisa's parents were able to stay with her while I was gone. After the funeral, mom told me she felt like she had to give up her father to get her new grandson. She and my dad felt very sad as they had missed the birth of their first grandchild. Mom and I decided to go for a walk and we ended up in the town's only drug store. There, sitting right in front of us, was a display case with Precious Moments figurines, and staring at us from the top shelf was the newly retired *The Lord Giveth And The Lord Taketh Away*. I immediately told the sales clerk I wanted to purchase the piece, and gave it to my mom right there in the store. As I said earlier, **what a powerful statement these little figurines can make!** A little bit of healing took place at that moment, and it all came from a little girl, a sly cat, a missing bird and an empty bird cage. I will forever think of my grandpa and my new son every time I look at this piece.

Precious Moments® Figurines
Give God The Glory

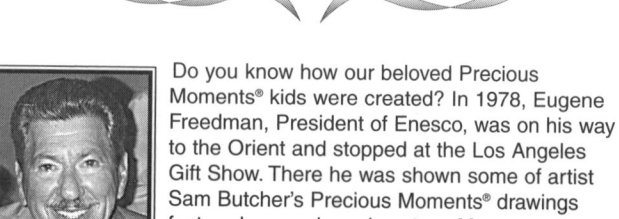

Gene Freedman

Do you know how our beloved Precious Moments® kids were created? In 1978, Eugene Freedman, President of Enesco, was on his way to the Orient and stopped at the Los Angeles Gift Show. There he was shown some of artist Sam Butcher's Precious Moments® drawings featured on cards and posters. Mr. Freedman immediately recognized the potential of Sam's work and felt confident this work could be produced in porcelain. Mr. Freedman had Yasuhei Fujioka of Japan in mind as the master sculptor.

When Mr. Freedman first contacted Sam and his partner Bill Biel about the possibility of producing Sam's artwork in porcelain, Sam was not in favor of the idea. But Mr. Freedman commissioned Yasuhei Fujioka to sculpt a prototype of Sam's art *Love One Another* (boy and girl on stump) and persuaded Sam and Bill to meet with him.

Sam was very protective of his work and wanted to ensure that it stayed in a medium which would glorify the Lord. But after seeing this first sample figurine, Sam fell to his knees, overwhelmed by the realization of the impact these figurines could have in the lives of people. He knew his artistic ability was a gift from God and wanted to use his talent to share the message of God's love. Sam felt this could be accomplished with the porcelain figurines.

We have seen the popularity of Precious Moments® spread across the United States and abroad as people fall in love with Sam's "little kids" and their message of hope and inspiration. Hundreds of local Precious Moments clubs have been formed, allowing collectors to share God's gift of friendship together. These clubs also are involved in sharing with others outside of the club walls as members participate in many volunteer activities such as Easter Seals fund-raisers, nursing home and children's home visits, the giving of Christmas baskets and gifts for those in need and much more.

My husband Dave and I have made many wonderful friends as we travelled around the country hosting Precious Moments conventions (ten since 1984) and shows. Our goal has always been to "Bring Precious Moments Collectors Together" and we actually thought of our conventions as family reunions.

With a definite leading from the Lord, I started *Precious Collectibles™* magazine as an eight page newsletter in February of 1983 from my kitchen table "down on the farm." This magazine has grown and now reaches collectors across the United States, Canada, Puerto Rico and foreign countries where American servicemen and women are stationed. We publish several magazines and price guides on various collectibles. In 1995, our publications were being introduced on many newsstands across the country. Who knows where this adventure will take us?!

Rosie

Remember, when purchasing Precious Moments, buy what you enjoy. Yes, many pieces escalate in value on the secondary market, but if you buy the pieces that are special to you, you'll never be disappointed if they don't rise in value. If you want to try your hand on the secondary market, remember that not all pieces will be traded easily. Study the information which *Precious Collectibles™* magazine, the *Weekly Collectors' Gazette™* and this guide offer. Read the classified ads, keep your ears tuned in at club meetings to learn about the pieces collectors are looking for and attend collectible shows. Many times you will find a bargain when purchasing a large collection (if you can afford to do this). You'll be buying hundreds of pieces and, in time, a profit will be made. Keep detailed records and don't forget to pay Uncle Sam his share! As Christians, the Bible tells us to render unto Caesar what is due him and unto God what is due him!

Precious Moments® are all about Loving, Caring and Sharing. Rosie and her husband Dave have made many wonderful friends through their involvement with the Precious Moments® collection.

Also remember, *Lay not up for yourselves treasures upon earth, where moth and rust doth corrupt, and where thieves break through and steal: But lay up for yourselves treasures in heaven, where neither moth nor rust doth corrupt, and where thieves do not break through nor steal: For where your treasure is, there will your heart be also.* Matt. 6:19-21, KJV.

Keep everything in perspective. *For what is a man profited, if he shall gain the whole world and lose his own soul?* Matthew 16:26a, KJV.

For God so loved the world, that he gave his only begotten Son, that whosoever believeth in him should not perish, but have everlasting life. John 3:16, KJV.

We want to express our gratitude to the many retailers and book dealers who make this guide available to their customers. We also appreciate our sales representatives and the hundreds of clubs and collectors promoting our publications.

Thank you for purchasing this guide. If there is any way we may be of service to you, please feel free to call or write to us at Rosie Wells Enterprises Inc., 22341 E. Wells Rd., Canton, Illinois 61520; e-mail RosieWells@aol.com; phone 309/668-2212. We'll do our best to help you. Remember to subscribe to *Precious Collectibles,™* our magazine published especially for Precious Moments collectors since 1983. The *Weekly Collectors' Gazette™* newsletter and *Collectors' Bulletin™* magazine also will keep you updated on Precious Moments news and ads between issues of *Precious Collectibles.™* Hundreds of older pieces may be found from other collectors through ads in *Precious Collectibles™* and the *Collectors' Bulletin™*! We also have an ad sheet you may request by sending a self-addressed stamped envelope. On this ad sheet you'll find names of dealers to call when trying to find that special older piece!

Our 900 collector line offers another way to buy, sell and trade. Leave your ad on line in your own voice ad for less than $5.00! (1½ minute ad for 21 days.) Hot tips which change every Thursday also are available on this line by Rosie! Call 1-900-740-7575; $2 a minute; use a touch-tone phone. You must be 18 years old. Press 1 to hear hot tips, Press 3 to advertise or locate Precious Moments Collectibles, Press 49 to advertise or locate Precious Moments PMC Dolls or press 50 to advertise or locate Precious Moments Applause Dolls.

We want to encourage you to visit the Precious Moments Chapel (off Rt. 44) in Carthage, Missouri. A real blessing awaits you there! Every year you'll find that something new has been added.

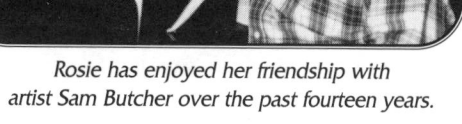

Rosie has enjoyed her friendship with artist Sam Butcher over the past fourteen years.

Precious Collectibles™ Congratulates

A Tie!

1995 COLLECTORS OF THE YEAR

Collectors of the Year are chosen because of their dedication to Precious Moments® collectibles. Ed and Millie Carey are very deserving of this award. In addition to being an avid collector, Millie has helped to organize several clubs. She also writes to several PM pen pals, is there with hot tips for us and always has the Precious Moments collector at heart. The Carey's travel extensively to events across the U.S. and truly exemplify Precious Moments in their lives – *Loving, Caring and Sharing.*

Ed & Millie Carey

1995 MOUSE REPORTERS OF THE YEAR

A trusty Mouse Reporter is one who is constantly on the watch for new and exciting Precious Moments news. Our most special Mouse Reporters spread the word about *Precious Collectibles™* and our other publications so that others may join in on the fun and friendship of Precious Moments collecting. This year we had a tie for Mouse Reporter of the Year. Both Sharon Barb and Gwen Stark have done a great job. Thanks for all your help, Sharon and Gwen! Oh yes, that's Gwen's hubby with her! He has attended several special events with Gwen!

Sharon Barb

Gwen Stark

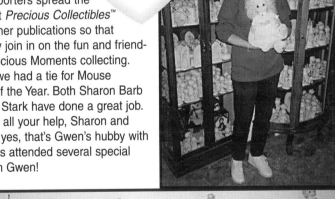

V

Errors
– and –
Omissions

"My figurine is different from the one pictured in Enesco's brochure. Do I have an errored piece?"

"The hand on my girl isn't painted. Should I return her to the store where I purchased it?"

"I have two mothers in my Family Thanksgiving set. Is this an error worth keeping?"

These questions and many more come into our office on a regular basis. What constitutes an error worth keeping and which pieces should be returned? What are some errors or changes that an avid collector would seek to add to his or her collection? From the early stages of collecting, changes have occurred on several pieces. I have come to the conclusion, however, that several "errors" didn't reach the market except for sample prototypes which were photographed for Enesco's brochures or for their representatives to show. Some talked-about errors were seen in these photos only.

Sought-After Errors

While a retailer was unpacking a new shipment of figurines, he found a glazed over, unpainted Sugar Town Dog and Cat Sitting on a Bench (529540)! This type of error may sell to a collector for $500 and should be insured for more, but it would definitely be irreplaceable!

Several collectors have reported that the heart with the age numeral from the *Growing In Grace Age 6* is missing. Most pieces with decals are occasionally found missing the decal, but this piece is missing the entire heart!

The Dunce Boy was incorrectly sculpted for the 1982-1983 market. Approximately 5,000 of these pieces were produced smiling. He appeared around Christmas of 1982. *Precious Collectibles*™ was able to get this word to our subscribers before the company announcement was made. This was the "first" real stampede of collectors looking for a **rare** piece! It took only three to four weeks for the retail price ($21) to rise to $400 on the secondary market. When a *Precious Moments*® figurine is hot, it's hot! If you have patience, the price generally drops six months to a year later, but usually not more than 10-15 percent. You may save some money if you wait to purchase it but the price could go up. Even though the Dunce Boy is retired "Smiley" will remain between $400-$500 as he was actually "retired" after 5,000 smiles!

Pretty As A Princess (526053) has been found with one of the points on her crown not painted gold. This error is quite evident and is considered rare.

The patch on the 1981 dated ornament was either missing or not painted within the outline of the patch. Avid collectors eagerly seek this piece.

The Indians' hair on 520772 has been darkened since first issuance. This piece

was retired in 1990 and has been one of the most sought after retired pieces. It was not a popular piece due to its original price, poor quality and lack of color in the hair and clothes until after it was retired.

The mold for *May Only Good Things Come Your Way* (524425), has the butterfly on top of the net on the left. The piece shown at left has the butterfly on the right side of the net, upside down.

The Girl Looking at Globe *What The World Needs Now* has been found missing the Bible which should be on the table.

Two more figurines have had smiles changed to a frowns: *Faith Takes A Plunge* and *My Days Are Blue Without You*. Both debuted with a smile and have since been changed to a frown or puckered mouth. Because so many were produced these cannot be compared to the 5,000 Smiling Dunce Boys.

Whenever a figurine has more than one piece, it is possible to find a part of the figurine omitted.

I'm Sending My Love Your Way (528609) has been found with a variety of errors. Several reports have been received that the kitten and kite strings are missing and we have also heard reports that the green stripes on the kite are missing.

An interesting error has been found on *Friendship Hits The Spot* (girls at tea party). This piece has been found more than once with the table missing!

Also missing.... *Loving Is Sharing* (E-3110B) has also been found without the dog. This piece has also been found with the boy's lollipop unpainted. Woof!

Other Reported Errors

Figurine sets with errors in duplicated pieces, such as two mothers and no father in the Family Thanksgiving set, is more of a defect than a desired error. This type of error should be returned to your retailer.

Another defect which does not add to the value of a piece is chipped paint. There have been several reports received that the paint on the back of Columbus' hat (the large piece) is chipping or flaking off. The chipped paint decreases the value of this figurine.

Different choices of paint were used on the Ice Cream Cone Boy (E-1374B). Most of the dogs had a black nose but many received a brown nose in 1982 at retirement time. This piece was overproduced for the retirement announcement. It took approximately five years to see its secondary market value climb (on the 1982 mark) to today's price.

Sugar Town's Grandfather figurine is being found with only half of his glasses painted on.

A Reflections Of His Love (522279) has been seen with both a white water reflection and a blue water reflection.

One of the first errors thought to be made was the Sad Boy with the Teddy (E-5200). The original picture shows him with a smile. Collectors, however, have only found him with a little circle mouth.

It's been said the three large camels (E-5624) came without blankets but has anyone actually found these? If so, I would say only one or two sets, if that many, are all that were produced.

There was a mold shrinkage problem with the Goose Girl figurine. This piece has been found with the goose's bill touching or not touching the girls face - this doesn't affect the value. Collectors have enjoyed finding the 9" Goose Girl with the touching goose. See page 6 for more details about the shrinkage problem.

The Groom with no hands was changed to have hands. There were so many "no hands" that collectors felt they would never be in demand. Several years later its price is now rising on the secondary market.

The first Chapel piece initially came with "no eyebrows." The Angel by the Cave Chapel exclusive figurine was found with the abbreviation of Matthew misspelled as "Math." instead of the correct "Matt." This was later corrected.

When Boy in Santa's Cap with Dog (E-2805) was retired, on pieces produced for retirement shipments both of the dog's eyes were painted. Previously only one eye had been painted.

Errors with Decals

Any time a figure contains a decal it is possible for it to be accidentally omitted. This also occurs with the inspiration decal. Another problem with decals is that they occasionally are put on "inside out" or "backwards." It appears that these types of errors have occurred more frequently in the last five years than before.

One error I have seen and would love to own is Boy with Slate ornament (E-0535), with "Merry Christmas" upside down on the slate. I am sure there are very few of these errored pieces!

The wrong inscription ("Crowns") appeared on the miniature *Clowns* (12238). Collectors seek this errored piece.

The Five Year Anniversary piece has been found with both bowls for Mrs. Fido and none for the "Mr."

The Lord Is Counting On You (531707) has been found with the decal upside down. This unusual error would increase the insurance value by $100.

There have also been problems with the decal on *Dropping In For The Holidays* (531952). This piece has been found without the "Egg Nog" decal and also with the decal upside down!

Some Heaven Bound ornaments (12416) appeared on the 1987 wreath with decaled words "Heaven Bound" upside down. This mistake adds approximately $50-$75 to the value of that wreath.

There is always the possibility of a decal being put on incorrectly or being omitted entirely, such as on the Birthday Club animals. Dates have been omitted from "dated" pieces or have been placed incorrectly on others such as OVEP on *Jesus Is The Only Way* (520756).

Prayer Changes Things (E-5214), Girl and Boy at Table, the title on the Bible was on the figurine upside down. It wasn't an error at the factory as the original drawing was drawn this way. It was changed. The same error is on the Pilot's book, but the Pilot's book title was not changed as the book actually would have to be turned to have the title on the correct side.

On the Boy and Girl with the Book (E-2013), there is talk of pieces that had words placed on the pages incorrectly. I have not actually heard of anyone owning one of these. I feel this may have been on sample pieces only. If there are several out there, I feel they are not in the hands of someone who is in touch with other avid collectors or we would know about it.

Errors Occurring on Bases - Marks and Inspirations

We often receive reports from collectors about errors on the underside of their figurines. Quite often people owning these pieces think they have a rarity. In the past, any piece with an "error" on the underside has not done handsprings on the secondary market. Some exceptions are inked marks that come off when rubbed, decaled

This puppy appears to be eating air instead of ice cream. After looking at the photo and comparing it to other figurines, it appears that the dog was turned incorrectly when placed on the base of the figurine. This error adds at least $50 to the current secondary market value of the figurine.

marks, double incised marks (good ones!), completely "bare" bases, and pieces marked "sample" with nothing else. Another "error" being noted frequently in the last few years are "Missing Marks." It is becoming more common to find that the mark has been omitted from a piece.

Errors with wrong inscriptions have not been highly sought after. Exceptions are "Crowns" instead of *Clowns*. Errors or changes visible to the eye without picking up the piece are the errors that have increased the value of the figurine on the secondary market.

The 1982 membership figurine (E-0202) was produced in 1985 by mistake with an embossed Dove mark. Approximately 700 of these figurines were shipped to Canada. Avid collectors tried to obtain this piece also!

Inspiration decals may be incorrectly placed or misspelled. A collector wrote that her *Friendship Hits The Spot* figurine is spelled *"Freindship"* on both the box and on the figurine. This type of error is usually worth $25.

All *Merry Christmas Deer* figurines with the Bow and Arrow mark had no *Precious Moments*® logo. There is no secondary market significance.

It's not uncommon to find recently produced figurines with the embossed "Sam B" unintentionally left off. Also, nearly every piece produced since 1985 has been found without a mark.

All figurines shipped to Canada had Taiwan "ink" stamped on the bases due to Canada's import laws.

What The World Needs Now with Bible missing from the table.

Errored Boxes, Musicals, Miscellaneous

Line art on boxes is sometimes different than the piece inside or the inscription may be different. Errored boxes have **NO** added value of their own.

The box for the 1982 Bell showed the date on the bell, but none of the bells had the 1982 date on them.

Keep the boxes if you have space to store them. They protect the pieces when storing and shipping and keep the secondary market value MIB. (The prices in this guide are MIB prices - Mint in Box.) Most boxes add from $3 - $5 value to a piece.

The Plates, Bells, Musicals and Dolls have not been produced in as large quantities as the figurines due to less collector demand for these. It seems the larger the piece, the higher the price, the less the demand. The secondary market usually stabilizes almost at the retail level, taking longer for a secondary market increase. This is unusual but true for this collectible. If buying for investment purposes, it is better to buy Club pieces or dated ornaments than to buy one large piece at $175. The Club piece, if popular, may double in price within a year or two, but very seldom has a large piece of $175 doubled to $350 in the same amount of time. I have yet to find any regular sized piece selling for $1,000 as was predicted by some for certain pieces. It may happen in the future, but it has not happened to date, not even for Free Puppies! (Not including the 9" pieces.) It's my opinon a limited edition of 1,500 retailing for $200 up will escalate on the secondary market. However, it takes more time to sell at retail.

Musicals with the wrong music selection have not yet increased on the secondary market.

Call our office with any additional reports of errors or unusual pieces. We would love to receive photos of these pieces to share with our readers.

MARKS

1996

Sam has signed many figurines during special visits to stores and conventions. His signature is found on more figurines than possibly any other artists' to date! He meets with collectors often, especially now that he has his own jet!

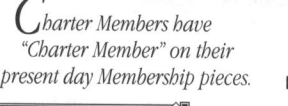

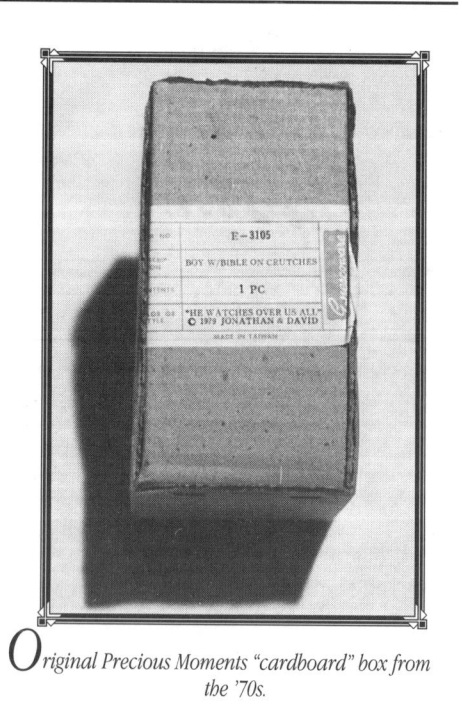

Charter Members have "Charter Member" on their present day Membership pieces.

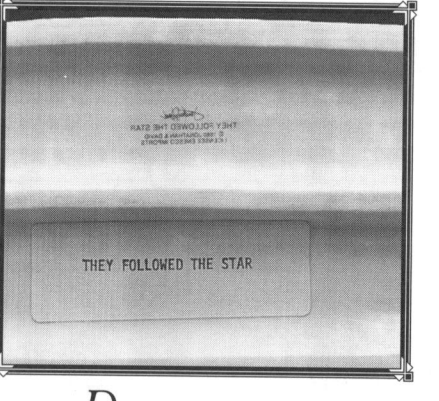

THEY FOLLOWED THE STAR

Decal applied backwards on figurine base.

Love One Another
by
Bill Biel & Sam Butcher

This is plate number 15674
certified to be a true first issue in the

Inspired Thoughts Series

It has been faithfully crafted in fine porcelain and painted by hand to our exacting standards in a collectors' edition limited to fifteen thousand plates

Bill Biel   Sam Butcher

Bill Biel   Sam Butcher

©1980 Jonathan & David license Enesco Imports Corporation
Elk Grove Village, Illinois, 60007
E-9215

Insignia on back of a plate during early days when Sam and Bill owned Jonathan & David Company together; this business partnership dissolved in 1984-85.

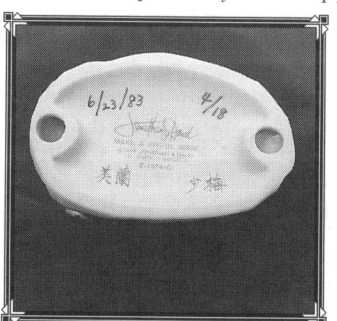

Figurine signed by Artisans

Original Precious Moments "cardboard" box from the '70s.

Decaled Fish Mark

Erasable Fish Mark
These can be easily removed. The Secretary was the first to be found with this mark and it's my opinion that less than 100 had this mark (mainly found in central Iowa at one location).

Double marked figurine
Rosie asked the project managers in Taiwan how double marks occurred on the figurines. They said they had never heard of this and didn't know why, since the mark is in the mold.

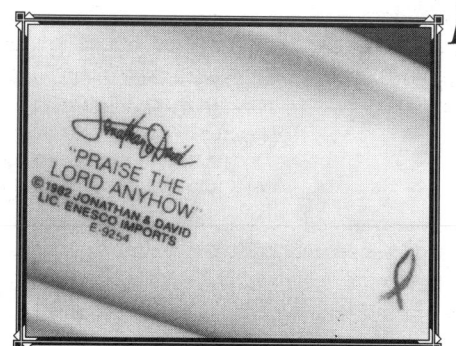

HIS BURDEN IS LIGHT
©1977 JONATHAN & DAVID
L/C ENESCO IMPORTS
TAIWAN

"Taiwan" is stamped on figurines entering Canada for retail.

"PRAISE THE LORD ANYHOW"
©1982 JONATHAN & DAVID
LIC ENESCO IMPORTS
E-9254

The Story of the ♡

Sam Butcher chose the heart as the production mark for 1996. According to him, *"Precious Moments® subjects have a way of reaching deep into the human heart. Through the years I have had the pleasure of meeting many people. They have shared stories of how Precious Moments® figurines met a need in their hearts and completely changed their lives. I have selected the heart as a symbol because it is the heart that so freely responds to the message of each Precious Moments® figurine."*

Precious Ann Calamusa

Although little Precious Ann is only 22 months old, she already has quite a collection, and her collection will grow as she does.

Precious Moments Are For Giving

Precious Moments figurines mean so much more than monetary value to many. These li'l children's inspirational messages are one of the leading reasons why this collectible continues to grow. Precious Moments are collected by many but maybe more are purchased for gifts to non-collectors. I recommend the following figurines for you to give to that special person for the following occasions:

Birthday

May Your Birthday Be A Blessing	524301
May Your Every Wish Come True	524298

For the young, any piece from the *Birthday Train Series* and for girls ages 1-10 and 16, the corresponding years from the *Growing In Grace Series*.

Sorrow

No Tears Past The Gate	101826
The Lord Is With You	526835

Illness

Make Me A Blessing (Retired)	100102
Bless-um You	527335

Thank You

To My Deer Friend	100048
You Deserve A Halo – Thank You	531693

Promotion

Cheers To The Leader	104035
Dreams Really Do Come True	128309

To the Discouraged

Sweep All Your Worries Away	521779
We Are All Precious In His Sight (LE '97)	102903

Remembering The Good Times

Hallelujah Country	105821
Hallelujah Hoedown	136836

To Combat Doubt – Losing Faith or Hope

Tell It To Jesus	521477
Take It To The Lord In Prayer	163767

Happiness News

Make A Joyful Noise	E-1374G
All Sing his Praises	184012

Just Because

I Get A Bang Out Of You	12262
Sweeter As The Years Go By	522333

McCoon's County

McCoon County Fair

Samson's Studios, a company which existed less than two years, produced these unique porcelain figurines. A total of nine figurines and ornaments were produced.

A sharp contrast to the teardrop-eyed Precious Moments figurines designed by Sam Butcher, the colorful cartoon-like characters of McCoon's County reflect the laid-back life-style in the Ozarks. The first figurines shipped in 1986 were signed by Sam.

Because Sam created these figurines, many Precious Moments fans are interested in adding them to their collections. See these at the Chapel Art Gallery with other works of art by Sam. "The Chapel hosts the McCoon County Fair."

**Wishing You A
2 Ton Christmas**

Checker Board Square

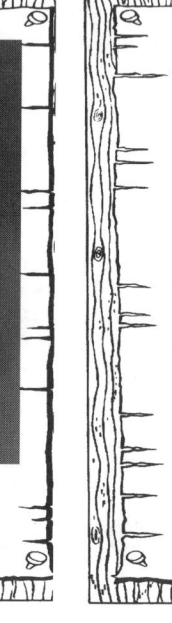

Saturday Night Ho Down

Box Social

X

Comments

Numerals correspond to those listed in the "Comments" section on various figurines throughout the guide.

 PRECIOUS MOMENTS® PLATES were produced in several series but were "slow sellers" and not as collectible as the figurines. Prices in this guide reflect the same lack of demand. Most earlier plates had "no marks." The first dated plate, the 1982 Drummer Boy, was the most popular; the dated 1985 plate was the most scarce. There is no dated annual plate for 1996. However, a Mother's Day plate series began in 1994. Plates do not cause "collectible fever" as do the figurines, probably due to the space required to display them. Plate collectors enjoyed collecting the "shiny glass" plates. These had gray, yellow borders, etc., and retailed for $35-$40 each ($65-75 secondary market value). Bisque plates are enhanced if displayed in an enclosed glass plate frame with light wood edging! The Hamilton Company owned by Stanhome, as is Enesco, produces today's "shiny glass" collector plates selling directly through mail order.

 Girl with Snowflake Ornament (142662) and others have been found without the decal date on them. It doesn't happen often, but usually when a piece requires a decal, a report comes to our office sooner or later from a collector who found one without the decal. Omitted decals such as dates, words and numerals on the *Birthday Train Series* animals are errors and we recommend adding $50-$75 to the secondary market price for insuring purposes. Decals have been missing from the underside of the bases also. Those decal errors which are visible to the eye rather than under the bases are of more value to the avid collector. "Wrong inscriptions" have been found more often but these errors are not of great importance to the collector compared to visible errors such as missing decals or unpainted figurines. Still, to be properly insured, add $25 to the book price of a figurine found with a "wrong inscription."

 Several pieces were produced without eyebrows and then later eyebrows were added in the production. The first Chapel piece debuted without eyebrows. Most avid collectors bought this piece in 1989. (Most avid collectors were able to obtain one.) The Chapel piece has been produced as a No Mark, Vessel Mark and G-Clef.

 Errors found include: one eye not painted, add $100 to value of piece; both eyes not painted, add $200; no white dots in eyes, no added value; different colored clothing or colors of clothing changed from one production to the next and smiles to frowns, value would depend on piece and quantities, etc. Color variations have been noticed on several pieces of *May Your Birthday Be A Blessing* (E-2826), Girl at Table with Dolls, such as black eyes, brown eyes, black nose and brown nose.

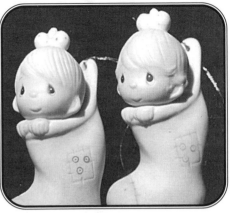

The "Baby's First Christmas" ornament came with several variations. Is the one on the left a girl with straight hair or a boy with a bow? This ornament was also produced with curly hair and a bow.

 The embossed **"SAM B,"** which has been required on all pieces licensed since 1985 by the Samuel J. Butcher Company, has been omitted on many pieces. The embossed marks are placed in the molds. Many figurines are produced from one mold and evidently the embossed **"SAM B."** sometimes is left from that mold. Many molds are produced of the same figurine. Avid collectors who look for errored pieces probably would not pay more for this omission.

 TWO MARKS have been found on the base. While touring the factory, I asked the production managers how this happened and they had no idea! They were very much surprised by this question. Double-marked pieces are rare. Most double-marked pieces had the Fish and Hourglass marks. Other errors have occurred, but less often than these first double-marked pieces. Two different Butterfly marks were found on one piece and a double Flame mark was found. Add at least $100 when insuring these errors.

Praise The Lord Anyhow was found with the Flower and Cedar Tree marks, one on top of the other!!

New! for Fall 1996

192368
Give Ability A Chance
1997 Easter Seals
Commemorative

183342
Peace On Earth... Anyway
1996 Dated Annual

183857
Color Your World With Thanksgiving

522333
Sweeter As The Years Go By

 **7** Sometimes collectors get excited about their rare find on new pieces but then learn no error has occurred. The original photos in the Enesco brochures usually are prototype or "sample" pieces and many times a change was made after the sample was produced. An example of this, I feel, was E-5200. The sample had a smile and the original brochure photo had the smile, but actual production consisted of a sad face. The same may be true of E-2013 with the words written across the two pages instead of down each page. Another example is the '92 Girl in Tree Swing (524085). There are three differences between the photo and the figurine... placement of bird and leaves, hair bow, and no heart on the tree. The same is true for the Enesco line cuts used in this guide.

8 **FRAMES** were very slow retail sellers in the late '70s and early '80s. Because they are not as easily available as before, we have seen a slight spark of interest since '93 and continuing through now. I feel they are very special.

9 Corrected or changed inscriptions (under base) or "visible" writing that changes usually are in the avid collector's collection. Examples include *I Picked a Special Mom* to *I Picked A Very Special Mom* and "he" to "He," "him" to "Him" on pieces E-9261 and E-9262. On the Boy Graduate with Scroll (E-9261), Enesco changed the word "Him" to a capital "H"... *Precious Collectibles*™ was first to announce this "error," but was it actually an error? The Holy Bible does not capitalize the word in the King James Version. A similar "error" occurred on Girl Graduate (E-9262) with the word "He" not capitalized in the verse on the scroll. The *Clowns* (12238) debuted with the inscription "Crowns" instead of "Clowns." There was a mistake on the "interpretation" from the Orient. In 1994 a mistake was made on a members' only figurine, Girl with Book (530980). The title was incorrectly printed as *You Fill The Page Of My Life.* The error was corrected to *You Fill The Pages Of My Life*.

10 Boy with Teddy (E-1372B) has been used extensively as a "logo" for the collection, along with the Girl with Bunny (E-1372G). The Kids on the Cloud artwork (E-3115) is the official logo for the collection. E-1372G was produced as a 9" Girl. The Boy would be a perfect 9" to match. A 9" version of him is on display at the Chapel Gallery.

11 Some "Black Eyes" on E-1373B were dark gray, yellowish-brown and, in '82, were so faint that collectors thought they had an error piece without a black eye. (The '82 pieces were all very faint in color until another change was made back to more color in mid '83 and early '84.)

12 Indeed, the avid collector's "must have" is *God Loveth A Cheerful Giver* (E-1378). Enesco's first retirement announcement in 1981 ended production for this favorite piece. Unlike today's retirement procedures, none were produced after the announcement. Thus, due to the lack of availability, retirement status and being such an adorable piece, this is the most sought after "jewel" of the collection. Most refer to this piece as Free Puppies. She was originally shipped in a cardboard box with white label (see photo of similar box on page VIII). This is the only piece that has sold in the past for $50 less without a box. She's special! Several years back she was projected to be the $1000 piece. To date she still can easily be found from $750 to $800 with or without a box!

13 Angels in Chariot, *Jesus Is Born* (E-2801), has been a very hard piece to find since it has been suspended! Figurines have been found with errors such as the "Holy Bible" decal missing from the Bible. Birthday Club pieces have been found without numerals; add $50-$75 to the value when insuring. Errors of wrong inscriptions on bases have not influenced the secondary market to a great extent except for *Crowns* instead of *Clowns* (12238). Add $25 to the secondary market value of the piece with the wrong inscription. This happens from time to time every year.

14 Earlier No Mark and Triangle marked pieces licensed by Jonathan & David Co. (such as E-2802) were darker in color than present-day pieces. During 1982 Sam requested lighter pieces. The collectors did not like these "faintly" painted pieces, so in late 1983-1984 the pieces were given more color. The heads on the original J&D pieces were also smaller than the new pieces which have been licensed by the Samuel J. Butcher Co. from 1985 to 1995. The license now is issued to Enesco for the figurines by Precious Moments Incorporated (PMI). Same folks, different name.

Collectors have found the word "polish" missing from the bottle on *This Is Your Day To Shine* (E-2822). Again, most pieces with decal print have been found without the "decals." (They're fun to find!) There was no decal on the Bandaged Boy by Sign (E-7159). Add $100 to his secondary market value. Some decals were placed incorrectly on the figurine, such as "OVEP" on the sign on *Jesus Is The Only Way* (520756). The R is P and the decal should be placed closer to the edge... those not are OVEP. In 1994 two figurines were produced with decal errors. *You're As Pretty As A Christmas Tree* (530425) has been found without an inspiration at all, and *Dropping In For The Holidays* (531952) has been found with its "Egg Nog" decal placed upside down. We'll probably hear from someone with a "messy" Egg Nog decal.

Avid collectors enjoy finding variations on figurines. Not only was this little piggy found without the inspiration decal on the front, if you look closely, you'll see that his coins are positioned differently as well.

 From 1985 to now, the Bride and Groom pieces (E-3114) were changed to have larger heads and other minute changes with Samuel J. Butcher Co. as the licensee and Sam B. embossed on the base. A new figurine, *I Give You My Love Forever True* (129100), introduced for 1995 will make a great wedding topper. Possibly *The Lord Bless You And Keep You* (E-3114) will be suspended... In 1996, new Anniversary figurines were also introduced which "age" with the years.

 BELLS were not as collectible as the figurines in the beginning, thus Enesco later decided to produce only annual dated bells. The collection of bells is a very outstanding collection in itself. Most were not marked for several years' production. To date the 1993 bell was the final bell produced in the regular style. The bell for 1994 is totally different and bells were discontinued in 1995.

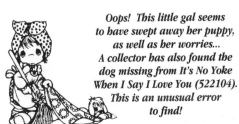

Oops! This little gal seems to have swept away her puppy, as well as her worries... A collector has also found the dog missing from It's No Yoke When I Say I Love You (522104). This is an unusual error to find!

 Some earlier figurines, such as E-5378, have been found with different license dates on the bases. There is no added value for these errors.

 UNPAINTED PIECES have been found. Approximately three of E-5379 and twelve of the Five-Year piece (12440) have been found unpainted. It has been reported by Enesco that twelve of 12440 were shipped to "who knows where"?! Retailers finding the unpainted 12440 very likely returned these priceless collectibles to Enesco!! We have not heard of any "unpainted" pieces selling on the secondary market to date.

 The "Follow Me" Angel with Three Kings (E-5641) is an **EXTRA LARGE PIECE** with four figurines on the base. We have found from research that it takes suspension or retirement to cause the secondary market value on such large pieces to increase compared to pieces with lower retail prices. Some examples are the Dealers' Nativity, Mother Sew Dear Doll, Wedding Party figurine, the Five Year Anniversary piece and probably the Fifteen Year Anniversary piece.

 Most **MUSICALS** resemble a similar figurine. *Silent Knight* (E-5642) was the first that did not.

 "R" by the style number means the figurine has "returned" from being suspended. E-7156, E-1381, 100153 and 100145 are the only figurines to have this status to date. "R" does not mean Retired.

 When pieces are suspended by the company, they are no longer produced but can be reissued at a later date. If a Jonathan & David piece is suspended, we know that it will have changes if returned. All pieces licensed by the Samuel J. Butcher Co. since 1985 have been produced with larger heads. PMI (Precious Moments, Inc.) is now the licensee, not Samuel J. Butcher Co. Compare E-1381 with E-1381R (*Jesus Is The Answer*), as well as E-7156 with E-7156R (*I Believe In Miracles*).

24 **DECAL MARKS** on *Love Is Patient* (E-9251) appeared as Hourglass, Fish and Cross marks. Why were decal marks used? No one has the answer. I feel the embossed marks were left from the mold and this was just a way to get the piece marked. ***A similar mark appeared on the Secretary (E-9254) but was called an erasable mark; one could wipe it away very easily*** (see photo, pg. VIII).

25 Girl w/Butterfly (E-9258) appeared as the 1991 **EASTER SEALS 9" PIECE** with a Limited Edition of 2,000, retailing for $500. Some of the 1990 Easter Seals pieces remained unordered and by late fall Enesco gave an incentive to retailers; if they purchased another 1990 piece, they would get an identical number for the 1991 Easter Seals Butterfly Girl (to offer as matched numbers). A 9" Easter Seals figurine has been produced each year since. Retailers do not profit from these pieces but hold raffles and sell to collectors at their cost ($500). The collector purchases the piece from the retailer, writes their check to Easter Seals and receives credit for giving. The first Easter Seals piece was the Girl with Bunny and production was limited to 1,000. While visiting the Orient I saw a "white" Three Kings and the Bride 'n Groom as 9" pieces. Will they be produced later? The President of Enesco, Eugene Freedman, has several 9" pieces similar to the regular line of Easter Seals pieces on display in his office.

26 Boy/Girl in Horse Costume (E-9263) was one of the first pieces which alerted collectors that new pieces could come with the prior year's mark. *Precious Collectibles*™ was the first to announce that 1983 pieces had 1982's mark! The other pieces which were hard to find that year with the Hourglass mark were *Press On* (E-9265) and *Nobody's Perfect* Dunce Boy (E-9268).

27 To date, **THIMBLES** have not been as collectible as the figurines. The only scarce Thimble was the '85 dated one. Thimbles are "precious" displayed in small shadow boxes. The "Four Seasons" thimbles have been a popular set, too.

28 **IDENTICAL DATED ORNAMENTS** are no longer being produced in consecutive years. This practice is not favorable for a collectible; they're not in demand the second year. In my opinion, color changes should be made if an ornament is produced for two consecutive years.

The production of identical dated ornaments for two consecutive years reduces the demand on the secondary market for several years.

29 **DATED ORNAMENTS** began in 1981 with *Let The Heavens Rejoice* (E-5629). The 1988-1991 dated ornaments were not overly abundant due to less production time at the factories (less space, fewer employees, etc.).

30 **BIRTHDAY TRAIN SERIES** - Many pieces have been found without the numerals on the birthday animals. Add $50-$75 on such pieces. The first four pieces are the hardest to find on retailers' shelves as this is the age group for which most figurines are purchased. When "Jimmy" becomes older, he wants toys and mom or gramma will most generally be the one to finish the collection. *Birthday Train Series* pieces with the first marks have risen 50% on the retail market since they were first issued in 1985. Retail prices on the Birthday Train increased in 1995.

31 Expect **EARLY SPRING PRODUCTIONS** to debut with the previous year's mark. Production time must begin before the new year's pieces debut, thus embossed marks must be put into molds and produced before the new year's delivery. All pieces in the 1996 Spring production have debuted with the 1995 Ship mark.

32 It's surprising, but **SPORTS AND OCCUPATIONAL PIECES** must not be selling or be as popular because so many are being suspended. The exception to this is the Policeman (12297) and the Navy Boy (526568) which have become more scarce since suspension. Navy Boy's secondary market value is now at $115 and the Policeman is valued at $145-$165, depending on the mark. Several new sports figurines will debut in 1996.

33 As these pieces debuted later in 1996, they have been listed only with the Heart mark. It is possible that they may debut with the 1995 Ship mark.

34 A new publication that is a sure source of current news including Retirement and Suspension news is *Weekly Collectors' Gazette*™ direct from Rosie Wells. Also, the Hot Line for Precious Moments® Hot Tips in the U.S. and now in Canada is always a source to keep the collector informed on Retirement and Suspension pieces. For more information see color ads at the back of this publication.

35 Most pieces which were produced for four years or less and then suspended are rising more quickly on the secondary market than pieces produced for more than five years; they are also rising more quickly than some retired pieces. It appears several '93 retired pieces were still on retailers shelves in late '94.

The "Original 21" or the first 21 pieces to appear on retailers' shelves were E-1372B through E-2013. These "No Mark" pieces are considered by many avid collectors as the most desired to own and enjoy.

 To God Be The Glory (E-0527), was withheld from the market due to production problems and suspended in 1985. When it was returned to production the order number was changed to E-2823.

 Individual figurines in sets may contain more than one mark (one piece in a set may come with a Triangle mark and another piece may have an Hourglass mark); see E-2386.

 Many of the ornaments, because of their small size, are found without a mark (Missing Mark) and an inspiration.

 Some pieces may be found without a mark from time to time. Those pieces produced before '81 are considered No Mark because no mark was intended. Earlier Chapel pieces debuted with a No Mark. Now marks are being used. A Missing Mark is considered an error. This means the mark has been left off the mold due to human error. This does not happen very often because of strict quality control. During early productions one mold would be used to produce around 75 pieces. Because of advancements in technology, more pieces can now be produced from a mold. Therefore, there would be fewer earlier pieces with Missing Marks and the replacement value or insurance value would be higher. We are the only source that recognizes the possible insurance value of Missing Mark figurines.

 Occasionally, figurines are found with missing or incorrect parts. The large Members' Only Columbus Ship has been found without the dog and spyglass. One collector purchased the 1992 *Friendship Hits The Spot* which was missing the entire table! The Tenth Anniversary figurine has been reported being found with two bowls for Mrs. Fido and none for Mr. Fido.

"Precious Moments" by Avon

Have you seen the Avon "Precious Moments Collection"? In the early 1980s the Avon Company produced a collection of porcelain figurines which were called The Precious Moments Collection. The name of this collection was then changed to Cherished Moments Collection to avoid infringement. Fun to own!

Top Left to Right:

1983	*Come Rain or Shine*	$65
1980	*Ready for an Avon day* (First figurine in the set)	$55

Bottom Left to Right:

1982	*Collector's Corner*	$60
1980	*Which shade do you prefer?* (Third in set)	$75
1980	*Merry Christmas Avon '80*	$65
1980	*The day I made President's Club*	$60
1980	*My First Call* (Second in set)	$55

Mini awards were also given to representatives for sales goals in 1982. They were called *Small Treasures* and were created in Japan exclusively for Avon Co.

Not Pictured:

1982:	*Going Avon Calling Award 1982*	$100
	(Rabbit in yellow car, given to reps for Recommendation prize.)	
1985	*We Did It Together* (two rabbits)	$95

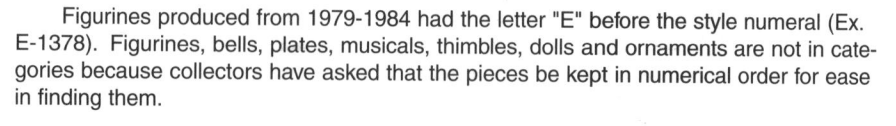

How To Use This Guide

You will find this guide to *Precious Moments*® collectibles very easy to use. It has been compiled in numerical order.

Figurines produced from 1979-1984 had the letter "E" before the style numeral (Ex. E-1378). Figurines, bells, plates, musicals, thimbles, dolls and ornaments are not in categories because collectors have asked that the pieces be kept in numerical order for ease in finding them.

An alphabetical index by inspiration which includes every porcelain collectible is located at the back of this guide. If you don't know the style number, you probably know the inspirational name of the collectible. This guide also features an alphabetical listing **by description** (© copyrighted index). Here are examples of how it works: Girl with Goose, Girl with Plunger, Boy with Ice Cream Cone. If all else fails, we have line drawings from Enesco to further assist you!

Following this paragraph are the abbreviations for each year's mark which is normally embossed on each porcelain piece. Pieces produced before mid 1981 had no embossed marks and are regarded as "NM" or No Marks. The Triangle was the first actual mark (and the least produced of any mark) placed on the earlier No Mark licensed pieces released after mid 1981 plus new pieces produced during this time. Pieces produced each year thereafter are marked accordingly. The style numbers first appeared on the bases of the figurines in mid 1982. Artwork was licensed by the Jonathan & David Company until 1985, when the Samuel J. Butcher Company started licensing the artwork. Remember, it is not the date on the base, but the embossed mark that determines the year of production and secondary market or insurance value of the collectible.

Marks Appearing on Figurines and Their Abbreviations as They Appear in This Guide:

Before '81	No Mark (NM)	♟ 1990	Flame (FLM)
▲ Mid 1981	Triangle (T)	♟ 1991	Vessel (V)
⏳ 1982	Hourglass (HG)	♪ 1992	G Clef (GC)
🐟 1983	Fish (F)	� 1993	Butterfly (B)
✝ 1984	Cross (C)	📯 1994	Trumpet (TRP)
🕊 1985	Dove (D)	⛵ 1995	Ship (S)
🌿 1986	Olive Branch (OB)	♡ 1996	Heart (H)
🌲 1987	Cedar Tree (CT)	♦ Special	Diamond
🌺 1988	Flower (FL)	🌿 Special	Rosebud
➶ 1989	Bow & Arrow (BA)	⚑ Special	Flag (FLG)
Error	Missing Mark (MM)	⚑ Special	Flag w/star (FLG☆)

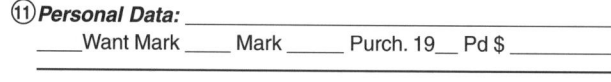

① E-1374B ② ③ **Ice Cream Cone Boy** *One of the "Original 21"*
④ *"Praise The Lord Anyhow"*

⑤ *RETIRED 1982 - 14 YEARS AGO*

	NM	$125
⑥	T	$100
	HG	$90
Brown Nose	HG	$95

⑦ *Comments:* 1976; Original Retail $8.00/$17.00 ⑧
⑨ Dog found with brown nose. "Overproduced" after retirement announcement. (My first piece – that started it all for me.) ⑩

⑪ *Personal Data:* _____
____Want Mark ____ Mark ____ Purch. 19__ Pd $ _____

1. This is the style/stock number. Numbering for earlier pieces began with "E" -- this is no longer the case. **The style number did not appear on pieces until mid '82.**
2. If nothing is written here, then the item listed is a Figurine. All others such as Ornament, Musical, Doll, Plate, etc., are listed here.
3. Short description of the piece.
4. Inspiration or "name" of the piece.
5. This is the location for noting whether a piece is dated, retired or suspended, followed by the year. **DATED 1984** indicates that the piece was produced only during 1984. **SUSP. 1986** means the piece was suspended in 1986. Suspended pieces are taken from production until further notice. They may or may not return to production. To date, only four figurines have been returned to production from the suspended list (E-7156R, E-1381R, 100145R and 100153R). The "**R**" after the number represents a reissued piece. **RETIRED 1991** means the piece was retired in 1991. A retired piece is no longer in production and will not be reproduced again. **LE 1986** means the piece is a **Limited Edition** and is produced only during 1986. Some Limited Edition pieces are produced for two years, and some have a specified edition size (LE 15,000). Secondary market prices differ according to the mark on the piece. Price information has also been included for "error" pieces. A secondary market value has been entered for each mark.
6. Prices to follow to insure your collection. Pieces are easily found from sellers at these prices.
   "**NE**" after marks means a secondary market price is "**Not Established**" to date. The piece has not sold or research has not found sufficient known sales to establish a secondary market price. Insure at retail unless scarce or rare. **Current** after a mark means the piece is new and is still available at original retail.
   The value listed for each **1996 Heart** mark is the current retail price, effective January 1, 1996. At press time, all of the Spring Introduction pieces had been found with the 1995 Ship mark. If a piece listing the H mark is suspended in 1996 before production, we may list this piece with Heart mark and find by mid year the Heart mark was never produced (no significance on secondary market). We will keep you updated in *Precious Collectibles*™ and the 1997 guide.
7. This is the year the original artwork was licensed to Enesco, not the date the figure was produced. Artwork was licensed by the Jonathan & David Co. from 1976 to 1984 and from 1985 on by the Samuel J. Butcher Co. Older pieces still have the J&D name on them in 1996, although most have been suspended or retired.
8. **RETAIL PRICE:** The first amount is the retail price of the figurine when it debuted. The next amount listed is current retail price or final retail price if the piece has been suspended or retired. Over the years some pieces have seen more than one price increase which explains the seemingly large jump on some pieces from original retail to current retail price.
9. **COMMENTS** have been added explaining errors and other variations for each piece. Other information is also included here to explain if the piece is part of series, Limited Edition, etc. Space has been added for your personal comments.
10. *See #36, page XV.* If this is in the comment, it is a reference to an item number and page listed under the "COMMENTS" section which will give greater detail about that particular piece.
11. Space is provided for use for your personal record keeping. List pieces you have, price paid, or which piece (and mark) you want.

E-0501 Boy Pushing Girl on Sled
"Sharing Our Season Together"

SUSP. 1986 - 10 YEARS AGO	F	$160	D	$145
	C	$150	OB	$145

Comments: 1983; Original Retail $50.00
Also appeared as Musical (E-0519).

Personal Data: _____
____Want Mark ____ Mark _____ Purch. 19__ Pd $ _____

E-0502 Boy in Nightcap/Candle
"Jesus Is The Light That Shines"

SUSP. 1986 - 10 YEARS AGO	F	$70	D	$55
	C	$60	OB	$50

Comments: 1983; Original Retail $22.50/$23.00
Very few collectibles honor Jesus as Precious Moments® collectibles do.

Personal Data: _____
____Want Mark ____ Mark _____ Purch. 19__ Pd $ _____

E-0503 Girl in Snow Looking at Bird House
"Blessings From My House To Yours"

SUSP. 1986 - 10 YEARS AGO	F	$90	D	$80
	C	$85	OB	$80

Comments: 1983; Original Retail $27.00
Nice piece to have in your collection - produced only 4 years. This is one reason first marks for such pieces are more valued on the secondary market than pieces produced for 8 or 10 years.

Personal Data: _____
____Want Mark ____ Mark _____ Purch. 19__ Pd $ _____

E-0504 Boy Giving Teddy to Poor Boy
"Christmastime Is For Sharing"

RETIRED 1990 - 6 YEARS AGO	F	$115	OB	$95	BA	$85
	C	$100	CT	$95	FLM	$75
	D	$95	FL	$85		

Comments: 1983; Original Retail $37.00/$50.00
Same figures on 1983 Dated Plate (E-0505).

Personal Data: _____
____Want Mark ____ Mark _____ Purch. 19__ Pd $ _____

E-0505 *PLATE* - Boy with Teddy
"Christmastime Is For Sharing"

DATED 1983	MM $80	F $60

Comments: 1983; Original Retail $40.00
Second Issue of *Joy of Christmas Series*. Some were not marked as they should have been, thus this guide uses MM for Missing Mark. More MMs were reported in late '95. **See #1, page XI.**

Personal Data: _____
____Want Mark ____ Mark _____ Purch. 19__ Pd $ _____

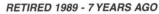

E-0506 Boy with Wreath
"Surrounded With Joy"

RETIRED 1989 - 7 YEARS AGO						
	F	$90	OB	$80	BA	$70
	C	$80	CT	$75		
	D	$80	FL	$75		

Comments: 1983; Original Retail $21.00/$27.50
Not dated as ornament is (E-0513). A similar figurine (531677) of a girl with wreath was produced for sale by the Chapel in '93 and was still available as of late '95.

Personal Data: _____
____Want Mark ____ Mark _____ Purch. 19__ Pd $ _____

E-0507 Girl Looking into Manger
"God Sent His Son"

SUSP. 1987 - 9 YEARS AGO	F	$95	OB	$80
	C	$85	CT	$80
	D	$85		

Comments: 1983; Original Retail $32.50/$37.00
Adorable piece! Becoming very hard to find.

Personal Data: _____
____Want Mark ____ Mark _____ Purch. 19__ Pd $ _____

E-0508 Angels Preparing Manger
"Prepare Ye The Way Of The Lord"

SUSP. 1986 - 10 YEARS AGO	F	$150	D	$135
	C	$135	OB	$135

Comments: 1983; Original Retail $75.00
Six-piece set. Seemed to be a slow seller. Collectors' opinions were "heads too large."

Personal Data: _____
____Want Mark ____ Mark _____ Purch. 19__ Pd $ _____

E-0509　**Girl Angel Pushing Jesus in Cart**
"Bringing God's Blessing To You"
SUSP. 1987 - 9 YEARS AGO

F	$95	D	$85	CT	$75
C	$90	OB	$75		

Comments: 1983; Original Retail $35.00/$38.50
Paper-covered wand and star not remaining in "good condition" on many pieces. Do not see many of these at secondary market shows. Becoming hard to find.

Personal Data: _____
____Want Mark ____ Mark _____ Purch. 19__ Pd $ _____

E-0511　**Pig with Hen on Back**
"Tubby's First Christmas"
SUSP. 1993 - 3 YEARS AGO

F	$45	CT	$25	V	$25
C	$40	FL	$25	GC	$25
D	$30	BA	$25	B	$22
OB	$30	FLM	$25		

Comments: 1983; Original Retail $12.00/$16.50
Several reports of broken birds from this very fragile piece.

Personal Data: _____
____Want Mark ____ Mark _____ Purch. 19__ Pd $ _____

E-0512　**Boy Angel with Red Cross Bag**
"It's A Perfect Boy"
SUSP. 1990 - 6 YEARS AGO

F	$65	OB	$50	BA	$40
C	$55	CT	$45	FLM	$40
D	$55	FL	$45		

Comments: 1983; Original Retail $18.50/$27.50
Many added this piece to the original Nativity set. In very little demand.

Personal Data: _____
____Want Mark ____ Mark _____ Purch. 19__ Pd $ _____

E-0513　**ORNAMENT - Boy with Wreath**
"Surround Us With Joy"
DATED 1983　　　F　$60

Comments: 1983; Original Retail $9.00
Date omitted on several - add $50 to secondary market. Similar figurine, E-0506. Chapel piece that debuted in '93 was a little girl in a wreath (531685). ***See #2, page XI.***

Personal Data: _____
____Want Mark ____ Mark _____ Purch. 19__ Pd $ _____

E-0514　**ORNAMENT** - Mother in Chair Sewing
"Mother Sew Dear"

						DECALED C-	$85		
F	$40	CT	$25	V	$18	S	$18
C	$35	FL	$25	GC	$18	B	$18
D	$30	BA	$20	B	$18	H	$18
OB	$30	FLM	$20	TRP	$18		

Comments: 1983; Original Retail $9.00/$17.00
Similar to figurine E-3106. No space for inspiration on base of ornament. Good candidate for suspension.

Personal Data: _____
____Want Mark ____ Mark _____ Purch. 19__ Pd $ _____

E-0515　**ORNAMENT** - Boy in Dad's Duds
"To A Special Dad"

SUSP. 1988 - 8 YEARS AGO　　　　****INKED C***　$80

F	$55	D	$50	CT	$45
C	$50	OB	$50	FL	$45

Comments: 1983; Original Retail $9.00/$12.50
*Found with Inked Cross.
Personal Data: _____
____Want Mark ____ Mark _____ Purch. 19__ Pd $ _____

E-0516　**ORNAMENT** - Grandma in Rocking Chair
"The Purr-fect Grandma"

						DECALED C	$50-$55		
F	$40	CT	$22	V	$18	S	$17
C	$30	FL	$22	GC	$17	H	$17
D	$26	BA	$18	B	$17		
OB	$22	FLM	$18	TRP	$17		

Comments: 1983; Original Retail $9.00/$17.00
Produced for 13 years. Excellent "gift item." Easy to find.

Personal Data: _____
____Want Mark ____ Mark _____ Purch. 19__ Pd $ _____

E-0517　**ORNAMENT** - Grandpa with Newspaper
"The Perfect Grandpa"

SUSP. 1990 - 6 YEARS AGO　　　***DECALED C***　$55

F	$45	OB	$35	BA	$30
C	$35	CT	$35	FLM	$30
D	$35	FL	$30		

Comments: 1983; Original Retail $9.00/$15.00

Personal Data: _____
____Want Mark ____ Mark _____ Purch. 19__ Pd $ _____

E-0518 ORNAMENT - Baby in Cradle
"Blessed Are The Pure In Heart"

DATED 1983   F $45

Comments: 1983; Original Retail $9.00
Fewer dated E-0518 were produced than dated E-0513. Similar *Baby's First Christmas* dated ornament (E-5392) was produced in 1984. Also produced as figurine (E-3104). Somewhat plentiful in '83! ***See #28, page XIV.***
Personal Data: _____
____Want Mark ____ Mark _____ Purch. 19__ Pd $ _____

E-0519 ♪ MUSICAL - Boy Pushing Girl on Sled
"Sharing Our Season Together"

RETIRED 1986 - 10 YEARS AGO
F $160   D $145
C $150   OB $140

Comments: 1983; Original Retail $70.00
Produced in 1983 as figurine (E-0501). Plays *Winter Wonderland*.
Personal Data: _____
____Want Mark ____ Mark _____ Purch. 19__ Pd $ _____

E-0520 ♪ MUSICAL - Three Kings on Base
"Wee Three Kings"

SUSP. 1986 - 10 YEARS AGO
F $140   D $125
C $130   OB $120

Comments: 1983; Original Retail $60.00
Plays *We Three Kings*. Came on a base. Not easy to find.
See #9, page XII.

Personal Data: _____
____Want Mark ____ Mark _____ Purch. 19__ Pd $ _____

E-0521 FRAME - Baby in Cradle
"Blessed Are The Pure In Heart"

SUSP. 1987 - 9 YEARS AGO   MM $65   D $50
F $55   OB $50
C $55   CT $45

Comments: 1983; Original Retail $18.00/$21.00
In my opinion, frames were not collected as the figurines in the early days of collecting. I now see a search has begun on these "sleepers."
See #8, page XII.

Personal Data: _____
____Want Mark ____ Mark _____ Purch. 19__ Pd $ _____

E-0522 BELL - Boy with Wreath
"Surrounded With Joy"

DATED 1983   MM $75
F $70

Comments: 1983; Original Retail $18.00
If the date is missing from the ribbon add $50 to secondary market value. Anytime a decal is used on a piece, it is not uncommon for a collector to report that it is missing. Attractive bell! Collect them all! The last dated bell with this style (figurine was handle of bell) was produced in '93. A dated '94 bell (different look) was also produced.

Personal Data: _____
____Want Mark ____ Mark _____ Purch. 19__ Pd $ _____

E-0523 Soldier
"Onward Christian Soldiers"

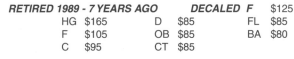

				DECALED F	$120
MM	$120	CT	$40	GC	$40
F	$65	FL	$40	B	$40
C	$45	BA	$40	TRP	$37.50
D	$45	FLM	$40	S	$37.50
OB	$45	V	$40	H	$37.50

Comments: 1983; Original Retail $24.00/$37.50
Very popular piece. Scarce in 1983. Has been found with MM (an error). RARE! Also found with Decaled F. Precious Collectibles™ alerted collectors first about "decaled" marks, "erasable" marks, etc., around 1983. Very little demand except for MM and F. Good suspension candidate.
See #24, page XIV.

Personal Data: _____
____Want Mark ____ Mark _____ Purch. 19__ Pd $ _____

E-0525 Boy and Dog Running Away
"You Can't Run Away From God"

RETIRED 1989 - 7 YEARS AGO   DECALED F $125
HG $165   D $85   FL $85
F $105   OB $85   BA $80
C $95   CT $85

Comments: 1983; Original Retail $28.50/$38.50
Color and dot differences have been found on knapsack; also "no eyebrows" found. Several HG marks have been reported to us! Decaled F - exciting to find! ***See #3 & 4, page XI.***

Personal Data: _____
____Want Mark ____ Mark _____ Purch. 19__ Pd $ _____

E-0526   Angel Catching Boy on Skates
"He Upholdeth Those Who Call"
"He Upholdeth Those Who Fall"

SUSP. 1985 - 11 YEARS AGO

	DECALED	F	$145
MM $140		C	$85
F $90		D	$80

Comments: 1983; Original Retail $28.50/$35.00
Has been found w/MM and Decaled Fish. This piece was originally produced with the name *"He Upholdeth Those Who Call."* It has been changed to *"He Upholdeth Those Who Fall."* To date, we have heard of no one having the changed inspiration, *"Fall."* Do you have *"Fall?"*

Personal Data: _____
____Want Mark ____ Mark _____ Purch. 19__ Pd $ _____

E-0530   Girl with Bird in Hand
"His Eye Is On The Sparrow"

RETIRED 1987 - 9 YEARS AGO

MM $135		D	$100
F $130		OB	$100
C $110		CT	$95

Comments: 1983; Original Retail $28.50/$32.50
Nice piece.

Personal Data: _____
____Want Mark ____ Mark _____ Purch. 19__ Pd $ _____

E-0531   *ORNAMENT* - Boy Caroling
"O Come All Ye Faithful"

SUSP. 1986 -10 YEARS AGO   F $65   D $55
                                    C $55   OB $50

Comments: 1983; Original Retail $9.00/$10.00
Caroler from 1983 Christmas piece E-2353.

Personal Data: _____
____Want Mark ____ Mark _____ Purch. 19__ Pd $ _____

E-0532   *ORNAMENT* - Angel w/Songbook & Bird
"Let Heaven And Nature Sing"

RETIRED 1986 - 10 YEARS AGO

	F	$50	D	$45
	C	$50	OB	$35

Comments: 1983; Original Retail $9.00/$10.00

Personal Data: _____
____Want Mark ____ Mark _____ Purch. 19__ Pd $ _____

E-0533   *ORNAMENT* - Girl Reading Book to Doll
"Tell Me The Story Of Jesus"

SUSP. 1988 - 8 YEARS AGO   F $70   OB $50
                                      C $60   CT $50
                                      D $55   FL $60

Comments: 1983; Original Retail $9.00/$12.50
One report of a FL mark. Any others? The scarcity of suspended ornaments depends upon the time of year the suspension took place.

Personal Data: _____
____Want Mark ____ Mark _____ Purch. 19__ Pd $ _____

E-0534   *ORNAMENT* - Girl with Kittens
"To Thee With Love"

RETIRED 1989 - 7 YEARS AGO

F	$60	CT	$45
C	$55	FL	$40
D	$55	BA	$35
OB	$50		

Comments: 1983; Original Retail $9.00/$13.50
Most scarce of 1989 retired pieces.

Personal Data: _____
____Want Mark ____ Mark _____ Purch. 19__ Pd $ _____

E-0535   *ORNAMENT* - Boy with Slate
"Love Is Patient"

SUSP. 1986 - 10 YEARS AGO   F $70   D $60
                                          C $65   OB $60

Comments: 1983; Original Retail $9.00/$10.00
Becoming very hard to find! One report and photo came to our office of an upside down "Merry Christmas" decal on the slate. Insure for $125.

Personal Data: _____
____Want Mark ____ Mark _____ Purch. 19__ Pd $ _____

E-0536   *ORNAMENT* - Girl with Slate
"Love Is Patient"

SUSP. 1986 - 10 YEARS AGO   F $80   D $60
                                          C $70   OB $60

Comments: 1983; Original Retail $9.00/$10.00
Not easy to find.

Personal Data: _____
____Want Mark ____ Mark _____ Purch. 19__ Pd $ _____

E-0537 **ORNAMENT** - Boy in Nightcap/Candle
"Jesus Is The Light That Shines"

SUSP. 1985 - 11 YEARS AGO F $80
C $85
D $80

Comments: 1983; Original Retail $9.00/$10.00
Only a three year production on this ornament.

Personal Data: _____
____Want Mark ____ Mark _____ Purch. 19__ Pd $ _____

E-0538 **PLATE** - "Wee Three Kings"

LE 1983 - 13 YEARS OLD MM $55
F $50
OB $45

Comments: 1983; Original Retail $40.00/$45.00
1983 Limited Edition 15,000. Third issue in *Christmas Collection Series.*
MM means missing mark.

Personal Data: _____
____Want Mark ____ Mark _____ Purch. 19__ Pd $ _____

E-0539 **DOLL** - "Katie Lynne"

SUSP. 1988 - 8 YEARS AGO MM $185   OB $180
F $185   CT $180
C $180   FL $180
D $180

Comments: 1983; Original Retail $150.00/$175.00
Interest seems less now than earlier.

Personal Data: _____
____Want Mark ____ Mark _____ Purch. 19__ Pd $ _____

E-1372B through E-2013 were the FIRST TWENTY-ONE pieces to appear on retailers' shelves. These "No Mark" pieces are considered by many avid collectors the most desired to own and enjoy. Those that remain in production and have not come back from suspension still carry the J&D Licensee trade name.

E-1372B **Boy with Teddy** *One of the "Original 21"*
"Jesus Loves Me"

NM	$110	D	$35	FLM	$28	S	$27.50
T	$115	OB	$35	V	$28	H	$27.50
HG	$50	CT	$35	GC	$28		
F	$40	FL	$35	B	$27.50		
C	$40	BA	$35	TRP	$27.50		

Comments: 1977; Original Retail $7.00/$27.50
Next to the Angels on Cloud (E-3115), this piece and E-1372G have become the "logo" figures of the Precious Moments® Collection. A nine inch version of this figurine is on display at the Chapel. Retail price increased in 1995. (Fewer T than NM.) *See #10, page XII.*

Personal Data: _____
____Want Mark ____ Mark _____ Purch. 19__ Pd $ _____

E-1372G **Girl with Bunny** *One of the "Original 21"*
"Jesus Loves Me"

NM	$110	D	$35	FLM	$30	S	$27.50
T	$115	OB	$35	V	$30	H	$27.50
HG	$55	CT	$35	GC	$27.50		
F	$45	FL	$30	B	$27.50		
C	$40	BA	$30	TRP	$27.50		

Comments: 1977; Original Retail $7.00/$27.50
Has been found with 1978 license date which is an error. Still has the Jonathan & David trademark as this piece has not been suspended and production has continued on the artwork licensed by J&D. Collectors do not realize there are fewer T than NM for this piece. May find for less if you look. Retail price increased in 1995. *See #18, page XIII.*

Personal Data: _____
____Want Mark ____ Mark _____ Purch. 19__ Pd $ _____

E-1373B **Boy with Black Eye** *One of the "Original 21"*
"Smile, God Loves You"

RETIRED 1984 - 12 YEARS AGO

		NM	$115	F	$45
Brown Eye -- no significant		T	$90	C	$45
difference.		HG	$70		

Comments: 1977; Original Retail $7.00/$17.00
1982 pieces have very pale "black eye." This figurine is not sought after.
See #11, page XII.

Personal Data: _____
____Want Mark ____ Mark _____ Purch. 19__ Pd $ _____

E-1373G**Girl with Candle***One of the "Original 21"*
"Jesus Is The Light"

RETIRED 1988 - 8 YEARS AGO

NM	$135	F	$60	OB	$60
T	$95	C	$60	CT	$55
HG	$75	D	$60	FL	$55

Comments: 1977; Original Retail $7.00/$21.00
Older marks are more sought after on Original 21 as collectors want to own pieces with the darker colors.

Personal Data: _____
____Want Mark ____ Mark _____ Purch. 19__ Pd $ _____

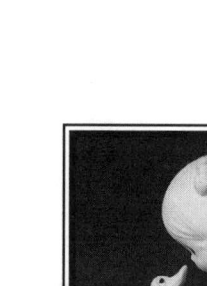

E-1374B**Ice Cream Cone Boy***One of the "Original 21"*
"Praise The Lord Anyhow"

RETIRED 1982 - 14 YEARS AGO

	NM	$125
	T	$100
	HG	$90
Brown Nose	HG	$95

Comments: 1976; Original Retail $8.00/$17.00
Dog found with brown nose. "Overproduced" after retirement announcement. (My first piece – that started it all for me.)

Personal Data: _____
____Want Mark ____ Mark _____ Purch. 19__ Pd $ _____

Shrinking in the mold during firing has created several variations of the
"Goose Girl" (E-1374G) above right There is no significant secondary market value
difference as to touching or not touching.

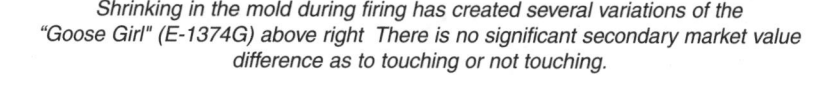

E-1374G**Girl with Goose***One of the "Original 21"*
"Make A Joyful Noise"

NM	$130	D	$40	FLM	$35	S	$32.50
T	$90	OB	$40	V	$35	H	$32.50
HG	$60	CT	$40	GC	$35		
F	$50	FL	$40	B	$35		
C	$40	BA	$40	TRP	$32.50		

Comments: 1978; Original Retail $8.00/32.50
Mold shrinkage problems. Goose sometimes touches girl's face. No secondary market difference. Still has J&D on base. ***Probably the most popular piece in collection.*** The Goose Girl almost could be considered the Precious Moments® logo. Only the old marks are sought after on pieces that have been produced as long as this one.

Personal Data: _____
____Want Mark ____ Mark _____ Purch. 19__ Pd $ _____

E-1375A**Boy & Girl on Seesaw***One of the "Original 21"*
"Love Lifted Me"

RETIRED 1993 - 3 YEARS AGO

NM	$175	D	$80	FLM	$75
T	$145	OB	$80	V	$75
HG	$95	CT	$80	GC	$70
F	$90	FL	$80	B	$60
C	$80	BA	$75		

Comments: 1977; Original Retail $11.00/$37.50
Part of "Original 21." NM very dark in color! Nice! Produced after retirement announcement. NM seems to be the most sought after mark on the secondary market. This piece has been found with a 1978 license date on it; no significant secondary price increase.

Personal Data: _____
____Want Mark ____ Mark _____ Purch. 19__ Pd $ _____

E-1375B**Boy and Girl Praying***One of the "Original 21"*
"Prayer Changes Things"

SUSP. 1984 - 12 YEARS AGO

NM	$230	F	$165
T	$175	C	$160
HG	$170		

Comments: 1976; Original Retail $11.00/$22.50
Very hard to find on secondary market for several years.   NM is the piece to have! Earlier pieces were more colorful! *See #36, page XV.*

Personal Data: _____
____Want Mark ____ Mark _____ Purch. 19__ Pd $ _____

E-1376   Boy and Girl Sitting on Stump
"Love One Another"   ***One of the "Original 21"***

NM	$130	D	$50	FLM	$45	S	$40
T	$95	OB	$50	V	$45	H	$40
HG	$70	CT	$50	GC	$45		
F	$65	FL	$50	B	$40		
C	$60	BA	$50	TRP	$40		

Comments: 1976; Original Retail $10.00/$40.00
Considered ***"First Piece"*** in the Precious Moments art collection. 1978 has been found on some pieces. NM would be the avid collector's choice. The original artwork of this piece was stolen from the Grand Rapids Showroom. Original 21 figurines **still in production** usually do not increase significantly in secondary market value after the T mark. Reported w/no eyebrows. Retail price increased in 1996.

Personal Data: _____
____Want Mark _____ Mark _____ Purch. 19__ Pd $ _____

E-1377A   Boy Leading Lamb   *One of the "Original 21"*
"He Leadeth Me"

SUSP. 1984 - 12 YEARS AGO

NM	$130	HG	$100	C	$90
T	$115	F	$90		

Comments: 1977; Original Retail $9.00/$20.00
Not as hard to find with the NM as others in the Original 21 group. NMs are very colorful. Easy to find at listed prices. E-1377A and E-1377B have been found in NMs several times with switched inspirations.

Personal Data: _____
____Want Mark _____ Mark _____ Purch. 19__ Pd $ _____

E-1377B   Boy Helping Lamb   *One of the "Original 21"*
"He Careth For You"

SUSP. 1984 - 12 YEARS AGO

NM	$140	F	$98
T	$120	C	$90
HG	$110		

Comments: 1976; Original Retail $9.00/$20.00
NM becoming hard to find. Popular piece! E-1377B and E-1377A have been found several times with switched inspirations on them in NMs.

Personal Data: _____
____Want Mark _____ Mark _____ Purch. 19__ Pd $ _____

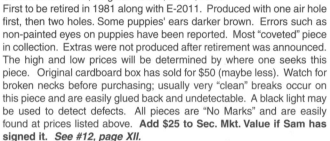

E-1378   Girl with Puppies in Cart
"God Loveth A Cheerful Giver"
    One of the "Original 21"

RETIRED 1981 - 15 YEARS AGO	NM	$750-800
	No Box	$700-750

Comments: 1977; Original Retail $9.50/ $15.00
First to be retired in 1981 along with E-2011. Produced with one air hole first, then two holes. Some puppies' ears darker brown. Errors such as non-painted eyes on puppies have been reported. Most "coveted" piece in collection. Extras were not produced after retirement was announced. The high and low prices will be determined by where one seeks this piece. Original cardboard box has sold for $50 (maybe less). Watch for broken necks before purchasing; usually very "clean" breaks occur on this piece and are easily glued back and undetectable. A black light may be used to detect defects. All pieces are "No Marks" and are easily found at prices listed above. **Add $25 to Sec. Mkt. Value if Sam has signed it. See #12, page XII.**

Personal Data: _____
____Want Mark _____ Mark _____ Purch. 19__ Pd $ _____

E-1379A   Boy with Turtle   *One of the "Original 21"*
"Love Is Kind"

SUSP. 1984 - 12 YEARS AGO

No Hole in Base	NM	$135		
	NM	$130	F	$95
	T	$120	C	$90
	HG	$100		

Comments: 1977; Original Retail $8.00/$19.00
First produced with no hole in base; higher on secondary market. This is a very popular piece! Watch that butterfly when dusting! NMs are becoming harder to locate on these 1300 series of figurines.

Personal Data: _____
____Want Mark _____ Mark _____ Purch. 19__ Pd $ _____

E-1379B   Boy with Report Card
"God Understands"   ***One of the "Original 21"***

SUSP. 1984 - 12 YEARS AGO

NM	$125	F	$85
T	$110	C	$85
HG	$90		

Comments: 1978; Original Retail $8.00/$19.00
In 1983 the "eyes" were changed in the molds to be larger. Not as popular as others in the Original 21 group.

Personal Data: _____
____Want Mark _____ Mark _____ Purch. 19__ Pd $ _____

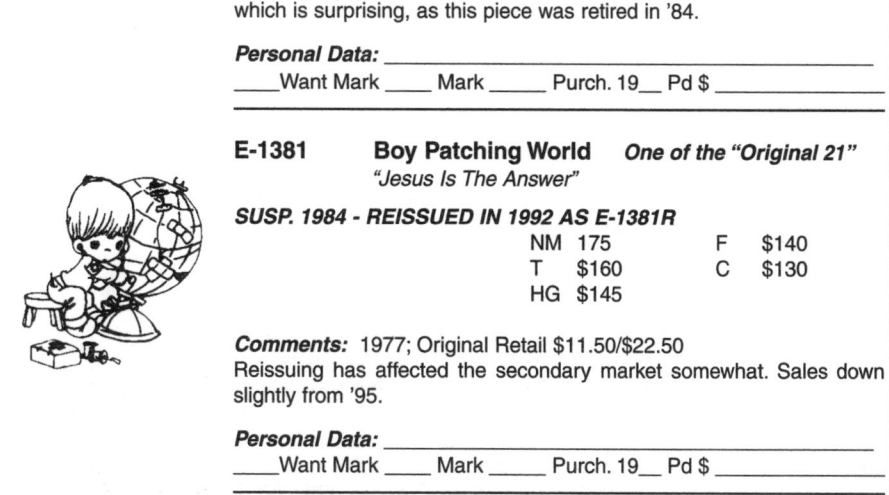

E-1380B Indian Boy *One of the "Original 21"*
"O, How I Love Jesus"

RETIRED 1984 - 12 YEARS AGO

NM	$135	F	$90
T	$120	C	$65
HG	$100		

Comments: 1977; Original Retail $8.00/$19.00
Scarce until late 1982. A collector reported having this with the D mark which was a surprise to me as it was retired in '84. Also heard report of dog having red nose.

Personal Data: _____
____Want Mark ____ Mark _____ Purch. 19__ Pd $ _____

E-1380G Indian Girl *One of the "Original 21"*
"His Burden Is Light"

RETIRED 1984 - 12 YEARS AGO

NM	$135	F	$95
T	$125	C	$75
HG	$110		

Comments: 1977; Original Retail $8.00/$19.00
Scarce until late 1982. A collector reported having this with the D mark which is surprising, as this piece was retired in '84.

Personal Data: _____
____Want Mark ____ Mark _____ Purch. 19__ Pd $ _____

E-1381 Boy Patching World *One of the "Original 21"*
"Jesus Is The Answer"

SUSP. 1984 - REISSUED IN 1992 AS E-1381R

NM	175	F	$140
T	$160	C	$130
HG	$145		

Comments: 1977; Original Retail $11.50/$22.50
Reissuing has affected the secondary market somewhat. Sales down slightly from '95.

Personal Data: _____
____Want Mark ____ Mark _____ Purch. 19__ Pd $ _____

Missing marks (MM) occurring before 1983 are considered more significant than missing marks in recent years. We previously called these No Marks. Many of the older pieces with Missing Marks should have been Triangle marks. Also in 1982, many Hourglass marks were left off pieces. These older MM pieces could be more colorful than later pieces missing their marks.

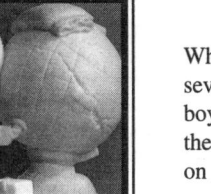

E-1381R
When this li'l fellow was returned from suspension, several changes from the original were evident: the boy is leaning over the globe more, the ribbon is off the base of the globe and there is a hot water bottle on the top of the globe.

E-1381R Boy Patching World
"Jesus Is The Answer"

RETURNED FROM SUSPENSION 1992

GC	$65	TRP	$58	H	$55
B	$58	S	$55		

Comments: 1977; Original Retail $55.00
This piece was returned from suspension in summer/fall of 1992. Several changes were made to the piece, including: the boy is leaning over the globe more and the ribbon is off the base of the globe. Also, the figurine came back larger with a hot water bottle on the globe. Word had it, with the second production in late '92 or '93, the mold would have a "changed" hot water bottle. No change was seen. E-1381R first debuted with the GC mark. It was reported that it would debut in '93 without a hot water bottle, but this was not the case. This piece has really been a confusing issue – almost as confusing as E-7156R *I Believe In Miracles*. This could be a candidate for suspension or retirement, in my opinion. **See #22, page XIII.**

Personal Data: _____
____Want Mark ____ Mark _____ Purch. 19__ Pd $ _____

E-2010 Boy Carrying Lamb *One of the "Original 21"*
"We Have Seen His Star"

SUSP. 1984 - 12 YEARS AGO

	NM	$115	F	$75
SCARCE!	T	$145	C	$75
	HG	$90		

Comments: 1978; Original Retail $8.00/$19.00
First pieces painted very dark. Most were produced in 1979-1980 through mid 1981, then 1982 on with the HG being the first "embossed" mark, not the T as thought. After researching and asking many collectors, we have received reports of collectors having E-2010, E-2012 and E-2013 with the T mark.

Personal Data: _____
____Want Mark ____ Mark _____ Purch. 19__ Pd $ _____

E-2011 Boy at Manger — One of the "Original 21"
"Come Let Us Adore Him"

RETIRED 1981 - 15 YEARS AGO

NM $250-260

Comments: 1978; Original Retail $10.00/$14.00
Has not risen on the secondary market compared to "Free Puppies" retired the same year. Price dropped on this piece!!! From $295-315 in '93 to $250-260 in '95 and many sales found to obtain the above secondary market price which has dropped to early '90s value. Prices found for "No Box" were as low as $200! Has been found with one air hole instead of two. For unpainted patch, add $50 to the above value.

Personal Data: _____
____Want Mark ____ Mark _____ Purch. 19__ Pd $ _____

E-2012 Boy/Girl School Play — One of the "Original 21"
"Jesus Is Born"

SUSP. 1984 - 12 YEARS AGO

	NM	$138	F	$100
SCARCE!	T	$170	C	$100
	HG	$115		

Comments: 1978; Original Retail $12.00/$25.00
Easily found.

Personal Data: _____
____Want Mark ____ Mark _____ Purch. 19__ Pd $ _____

E-2013 Boy/Girl with Book — One of the "Original 21"
"Unto Us A Child Is Born"

SUSP. 1984 - 12 YEARS AGO

	NM	$130	F	$105
SCARCE!	T	$150	C	$95
	HG	$110		

A	Is
Child	Born

Correct

Is	A
Born	Child

Incorrect

Comments: 1978; Original Retail $12.00/$25.00
License date appeared on figurine in 1982. Words placed incorrectly on book's pages in 1979 on a limited amount, but only have seen a photo from the company on this. We know of no actual piece with this error in anyone's collection. After researching and asking many collectors, we received a report from one collector who had this piece with a T mark. One collector's piece says "Is Born Is Born" instead of saying "A Child Is Born." **See #36, page XV.**

Personal Data: _____
____Want Mark ____ Mark _____ Purch. 19__ Pd $ _____

E-2343 ORNAMENT - Angel with Trumpet
"Joy To The World"

SUSP. 1988 - 8 YEARS AGO

NM	$65	F	$45	OB	$45
T	$55	C	$45	CT	$40
HG	$50	D	$45	FL	$40

Comments: 1981; Original Retail $9.00/$12.50
Featured on J&D Christmas wrapping paper, as was E-0513.
Personal Data: _____
____Want Mark ____ Mark _____ Purch. 19__ Pd $ _____

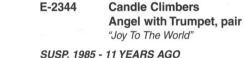

E-2344 Candle Climbers
Angel with Trumpet, pair
"Joy To The World"

SUSP. 1985 - 11 YEARS AGO

NM	$120	HG	$95	C	$95
T	$100	F	$95	D	$95

Comments: 1981; Original Retail $20.00/$22.50
Candle Climbers are no longer in production; only two styles were produced (E-2344, E-6118). Not easy to find.
Personal Data: _____
____Want Mark ____ Mark _____ Purch. 19__ Pd $ _____

E-2345 Boy in Pajamas with Teddy
"May Your Christmas Be Cozy"

SUSP. 1984 - 12 YEARS AGO

HG	$90
F	$80
C	$75

Comments: 1982; Original Retail $23.00/$30.00
Collector wrote to say her piece had an OB mark! Unusual! Only produced for three years. Somewhat scarce!
Personal Data: _____
____Want Mark ____ Mark _____ Purch. 19__ Pd $ _____

E-2346 ♪ MUSICAL - Angel with Animals Caroling
"Let Heaven And Nature Sing"

SUSP. 1989 - 7 YEARS AGO

MM	$175	D	$135	BA	$125
HG	$160	OB	$135		
F	$140	CT	$130		
C	$140	FL	$125		

Comments: 1982; Original Retail $50.00/$75.00
Quite limited, especially in 1982; HG mark. Plays *Joy To The World*. Becoming hard to find.
Personal Data: _____
____Want Mark ____ Mark _____ Purch. 19__ Pd $ _____

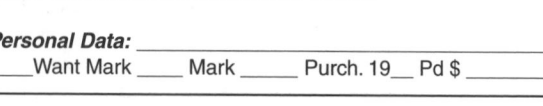

E-2347 **PLATE - Angel with Animals Caroling**
"Let Heaven And Nature Sing"

LE 15,000 MM $50 D $45
C $45 OB $40

Comments: 1982; Original Retail $40.00/$45.00
Second issue of the *Christmas Collection Series.* An edition of 4,000 would have been considered more limited.

Personal Data: _____
____Want Mark _____ Mark _____ Purch. 19__ Pd $ _____

E-2348 **Boy by Pot Belly Stove**
"May Your Christmas Be Warm"

SUSP. 1988 - 8 YEARS AGO HG $130 OB $110
F $125 CT $110
C $115 FL $110
D $110

Comments: 1982; Original Retail $30.00/$38.50
HG scarce, first production year. HG seems to be the coveted piece. Popular piece! Becoming hard to find.

Personal Data: _____
____Want Mark _____ Mark _____ Purch. 19__ Pd $ _____

E-2349 **Girl by Christmas Tree/Doll and Book**
"Tell Me The Story Of Jesus"

SUSP. 1985 - 11 YEARS AGO
HG $115 C $110
F $110 D $105

Comments: 1982; Original Retail $30.00/$33.00
Produced as an Ornament in 1983 (E-0533). Figurine was scarce in 1982; first production year. Very attractive piece! Not easily found.

Personal Data: _____
____Want Mark _____ Mark _____ Purch. 19__ Pd $ _____

E-2350 **Boy Ice Skating**
"Dropping In For Christmas"

SUSP. 1984 - 11 YEARS AGO
HG $75
F $70
C $65

Comments: 1982; Original Retail $18.00

Personal Data: _____
____Want Mark _____ Mark _____ Purch. 19__ Pd $ _____

E-2351 **Two Angels with Candles**
"Holy Smokes"

RETIRED 1987 - 9 YEARS AGO
MM $150 D $110
HG $135 OB $100
F $125 CT $100
C $115

Comments: 1982; Original Retail $27.00/$33.50
Several found w/MM error.

Personal Data: _____
____Want Mark _____ Mark _____ Purch. 19__ Pd $ _____

E-2352 ♪ **MUSICAL -Boy Caroling/Lamp Post**
"O Come All Ye Faithful"

SUSP. 1984 - 12 YEARS AGO MM $155 F $125
HG $135 C $125

Comments: 1982; Original Retail $45.00/$50.00
Plays *O Come All Ye Faithful.*

Personal Data: _____
____Want Mark _____ Mark _____ Purch. 19__ Pd $ _____

E-2353 **Boy Caroling/Lamp Post**
"O Come All Ye Faithful"

RETIRED 1986 - 10 YEARS AGO
HG $110 D $70
F $90 OB $65
C $85

Comments: 1982; Original Retail $27.50/$30.00
Attractive piece! HG mark is somewhat hard to find on the secondary market.

Personal Data: _____
____Want Mark _____ Mark _____ Purch. 19__ Pd $ _____

E-2355 ♪ **MUSICAL - Drummer Boy at Manger**
"I'll Play My Drum For Him"

SUSP. 1984 - 12 YEARS AGO
HG $185 C $165
F $175

Comments: 1982; Original Retail $45.00/$50.00
Plays *Little Drummer Boy.* Scarce in 1982 as was the figurine E-2356. Scarce because it was only produced 2½ years! Attractive and nice to own!

Personal Data: _____
____Want Mark _____ Mark _____ Purch. 19__ Pd $ _____

E-2356　Drummer Boy at Manger
"I'll Play My Drum For Him"

SUSP. 1985 - 10 YEARS AGO

HG	$125	C	$90
F	$100	D	$90

Comments: 1982; Original Retail $30.00/$33.00
HG mark is scarce. This is a beautiful piece! Produced for a short period of time. It's my opinion that this is an avid collector's "must have."

Personal Data: _____
____Want Mark ____ Mark _____ Purch. 19__ Pd $ _____

E-2357　PLATE - Drummer Boy at Manger
"I'll Play My Drum For Him"

DATED 1982　　　　　NM $60-65

Comments: 1982; Original Retail $40.00
First Issue in *Joy Of Christmas Series.* First dated plate. Seek out ads to locate, easily found. NM is correct - plate was not intended to have a mark.

Personal Data: _____
____Want Mark ____ Mark _____ Purch. 19__ Pd $ _____

E-2358　BELL - Drummer Boy
"I'll Play My Drum For Him"

DATED 1982　　　　　NM $70

Comments: 1982; Original Retail $17.00
None had the date on them as appeared in the picture on the box. The last dated bell of this style (figurine was handle of bell) was offered in '93. A dated '94 bell (different look) was also produced.

Personal Data: _____
____Want Mark ____ Mark _____ Purch. 19__ Pd $ _____

E-2359　ORNAMENT - Drummer Boy
"I'll Play My Drum For Him"

DATED 1982　　　　　HG $100

Comments: 1982; Original Retail $9.00
Closed Edition. 1982 was printed on the ornament's drum. Several "no dates" were found; add $50 above secondary market price listed. One MM has been reported.

Personal Data: _____
____Want Mark ____ Mark _____ Purch. 19__ Pd $ _____

E-2360　NATIVITY -Drummer Boy
"I'll Play My Drum For Him"

HG	$55	CT	$30	GC	$28
F	$45	FL	$30	B	$25
C	$38	BA	$30	TRP	$25
D	$35	FLM	$30	S	$25
OB	$30	V	$28	H	$25

Comments: 1982; Original Retail $16.00/$25.00
An addition to the Nativity Set. Too similar in size to the ornament and the secondary market was affected for several years because of this. Collectors complaints immediately caused future look alike productions to be changed. Excellent candidate for retirement or suspension.

Personal Data: _____
____Want Mark ____ Mark _____ Purch. 19__ Pd $ _____

E-2361　Girl with Stocking
"Christmas Joy From Head To Toe"

SUSP. 1986 - 10 YEARS AGO

HG	$90	D	$70
F	$75	OB	$65
C	$75		

Comments: 1982; Original Retail $25.00/$27.50
Somewhat scarce with HG mark. Most Christmas pieces were somewhat hard to find compared to 1983-1985 Christmas pieces. We received one report that the dog's nose was not painted. Arf!

Personal Data: _____
____Want Mark ____ Mark _____ Purch. 19__ Pd $ _____

E-2362　ORNAMENT - Baby in Stocking
"Baby's First Christmas" written on back

SUSP. 1988 - 8 YEARS AGO
Boy w/Bow - Straight hair w/caption　　　　　MM $55
Boy in Stocking - Straight hair & no caption　　MM $65
Girl in Stocking - Curly hair & no caption　　　MM $40
Girl in Stocking - Curly hair w/caption

MM	$45	D	$35	CT	$30
C	$35	OB	$30	FL	$30

Comments: 1982; Original Retail $9.00/$12.50
First pieces - no print on side. Beginning with March 1983, "Baby's First Christmas" printed on some. There are two different heads, one with straight hair, and one with curly hair. (Picture on box shows with straight hair.) Straight hair looks masculine except for bow. Appeared on earlier piece. *Original ornament looked masculine so it's been called Boy. Curly-haired pieces look feminine. Trading not as evident as back in 80s when the "change" was made and being talked about.

Personal Data: _____
____Want Mark ____ Mark _____ Purch. 19__ Pd $ _____

E-2363   Camel

MM	$50	OB	$40	V	$35	H	$32.50
HG	$50	CT	$40	GC	$35		
F	$45	FL	$40	B	$35		
C	$40	BA	$35	TRP	$35		
D	$40	FLM	$35	S	$32.50		

Comments: 1982; Original Retail $20.00/$32.50
The MM was reported in '82.

Personal Data: _____
____Want Mark ____ Mark _____ Purch. 19__ Pd $ _____

E-2364   Goat

SUSP. 1989 - 7 YEARS AGO

MM	$65	C	$40	CT	$35
HG	$60	D	$40	FL	$35
F	$55	OB	$35	BA	$35

Comments: 1982; Original Retail $10.00/$15.00
The first pieces to debut were not marked. Should have had a mark.
The MM was reported in '82.

Personal Data: _____
____Want Mark ____ Mark _____ Purch. 19__ Pd $ _____

E-2365   Boy Angel with Candle
"The First Noel"

SUSP. 1984 - 12 YEARS AGO

MM	$75	F	$65
HG	$70	C	$60

Comments: 1982; Original Retail $16.00/$17.00
MM was an error reported in '82.

Personal Data: _____
____Want Mark ____ Mark _____ Purch. 19__ Pd $ _____

E-2366   Girl Angel in Bonnet Praying
"The First Noel"

SUSP. 1984 - 12 YEARS AGO

MM	$65	F	$55
HG	$60	C	$55

Comments: 1982; Original Retail $16.00/$17.00
MM was an error reported in '82. Sales slowed on this piece…

Personal Data: _____
____Want Mark ____ Mark _____ Purch. 19__ Pd $ _____

E-2367   *ORNAMENT* - Boy Angel with Candle
"The First Noel"

SUSP. 1984 - 12 YEARS AGO

MM	$65	F	$55
HG	$60	C	$55

Comments: 1982; Original Retail $9.00/$10.00
Several MM pieces reported in '82. Sales slow in past years. Do not over insure.

Personal Data: _____
____Want Mark ____ Mark _____ Purch. 19__ Pd $ _____

E-2368   *ORNAMENT* - Girl Angel/Bonnet Praying
"The First Noel"

RETIRED 1984 - 12 YEARS AGO

HG	$65
F	$55
C	$40

Comments: 1982; Original Retail $9.00/$10.00
C marks easier to find.

Personal Data: _____
____Want Mark ____ Mark _____ Purch. 19__ Pd $ _____

E-2369   *ORNAMENT* - Boy Ice Skating
"Dropping In For Christmas"

RETIRED 1986 - 10 YEARS AGO

MM	$65	C	$50
HG	$55	D	$50
F	$50	OB	$45

Comments: 1982; Original Retail $9.00/$10.00
MM reported in '82. **See #39, page XV.**

Personal Data: _____
____Want Mark ____ Mark _____ Purch. 19__ Pd $ _____

E-2371   *ORNAMENT* - "Unicorn"

RETIRED 1988 - 8 YEARS AGO

MM	$55	D	$45
HG	$60	OB	$45
F	$55	CT	$45
C	$55	FL	$40

Comments: 1982; Original Retail $9.00/$13.00
Tended to be scarce before Retirement. Many "unicorn" collectors purchased this ornament.

Personal Data: _____
____Want Mark ____ Mark _____ Purch. 19__ Pd $ _____

E-2372 ORNAMENT - Boy with Block
"Baby's First Christmas"

SUSP. 1985 - 11 YEARS AGO

	MM	$45	C	$40
Decaled	F	$70	D	$40
	HG	$45		

Comments: 1982; Original Retail $9.00/$10.00
First pieces came with no verse on back side. As of March 1983 "Baby's First Christmas" was on the back side (same as E-2362 ornament). MM reported in '82.

Personal Data: _____
____Want Mark ____ Mark _____ Purch. 19__ Pd $ _____

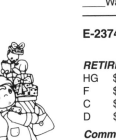

E-2374 Girl with Christmas Packages
"Bundles of Joy"

RETIRED 1993 - 3 YEARS AGO

HG	$120	OB	$75	FLM	$70
F	$95	CT	$70	V	$70
C	$90	FL	$70	GC	$65
D	$85	BA	$70	B	$65

Comments: 1982; Original Retail $27.50/$45.00
A similar ornament (525057) debuted in 11/90 as a special offering at Centers only (now called Distinguished Service Retailers).

Personal Data: _____
____Want Mark ____ Mark _____ Purch. 19__ Pd $ _____

E-2375 Girl with Pie
"Dropping Over For Christmas"

RETIRED 1991- 5 YEARS AGO

HG	$135	OB	$75	FLM	$75
F	$90	CT	$75	V	$65
C	$90	FL	$75		
D	$85	BA	$75		

Comments: 1982; Original Retail $30.00/45.00
Was not overly abundant in 1982. There is much demand for the first mark!

Personal Data: _____
____Want Mark ____ Mark _____ Purch. 19__ Pd $ _____

E-2376 ORNAMENT - Girl with Pie
"Dropping Over For Christmas"

RETIRED 1985 - 11 YEARS AGO

HG	$65	C	$50
F	$55	D	$45

Comments: 1982; Original Retail $9.00/$10.00

Personal Data: _____
____Want Mark ____ Mark _____ Purch. 19__ Pd $ _____

E-2377 Girl Knitting Tie for Boy
"Our First Christmas Together"

SUSP. 1985 - 11 YEARS AGO

HG	$110	C	$80
F	$85	D	$75

Comments: 1982; Original Retail $35.00/$37.50
Only produced for four years.

Personal Data: _____
____Want Mark ____ Mark _____ Purch. 19__ Pd $ _____

E-2378 PLATE - Girl Knitting Tie for Boy
"Our First Christmas Together"

SUSP. 1985 - 11 YEARS AGO MM $40   D $30
C $30

Comments: 1982; Original Retail $30.00
Open Edition, smaller plate. Plates are not as collectible as figurines. Dated annual plates were produced through 1993. However, in 1994 two additional plates were produced... one for Mother's Day and one to benefit Child Evangelism Fellowship. Annual plates were also produced for Mother's Day in 1995 and 1996.

Personal Data: _____
____Want Mark ____ Mark _____ Purch. 19__ Pd $ _____

E-2381 ORNAMENT - Mouse with Cheese

SUSP. 1984 - 12 YEARS AGO MM $135
HG $130
F $125
C $120

Comments: 1982; Original Retail $9.00
Scarce before Suspension. MM most sought after. Just try to find this li'l fella. He's scarce! MM reported in early '82.

Personal Data: _____
____Want Mark ____ Mark _____ Purch. 19__ Pd $ _____

By the time a person gets into greener pastures, he usually can't climb the fence!

E-2385   ORNAMENT - Bride & Groom
"Our First Christmas Together"

SUSP. 1991 - 5 YEARS AGO

HG	$55	OB	$30	FLM	$30
F	$40	CT	$30	V	$30
C	$40	FL	$30		
D	$35	BA	$30		

Comments: 1982; Original Retail $9.00/$15.00

Personal Data: _____
____Want Mark ____ Mark _____ Purch. 19__ Pd $ _____

E-2386   ORNAMENT - Set of 3 Animals

SUSP. 1984 - 12 YEARS AGO

MM	$105	F	$80
HG	$95	C	$80

Comments: 1982; Original Retail $25.00/$27.50
Camel, Donkey and Cow. Frequently sets contain different marks on different pieces (ex. HG on one, T on another). **See #38, page XV.** MM occurred in '82.

Personal Data: _____
____Want Mark ____ Mark _____ Purch. 19__ Pd $ _____

E-2387   MINI NATIVITY - 3 Houses and Palm Tree – 4 pc. Set

HG	$115	CT	$80	GC	$75
F	$90	FL	$80	B	$75
C	$85	BA	$75	TRP	$75
D	$80	FLM	$75	S	$75
OB	$80	V	$75	H	$75

Comments: 1982; Original Retail $45.00/$75.00
Very little trading found on this set. May be suspended in my opinion. Very seldom offered by retailers. Do not "over pay" on this set as it is still on the market and easily found.

Personal Data: _____
____Want Mark ____ Mark _____ Purch. 19__ Pd $ _____

When saving for old age, be sure to put away a few pleasant thoughts.

E-2395   MINI NATIVITY - 11 Piece (3-1/2")
"Come Let Us Adore Him"

TURBAN BOY ALONE   HG $90
(Several dozen were replaced by dealers and sold separately from this set. We were the first to learn and report this information to the collectors.)

NM	$175	OB	$140	V	$135	H	$130
HG	$165	CT	$140	GC	$130		
F	$150	FL	$140	B	$130		
C	$150	BA	$140	TRP	$130		
D	$140	FLM	$140	S	$130		

Comments: 1982; Original Retail $80.00/$130.00
Turban Boy figure replaced Boy Holding Lamb in approximately 5,000 sets. Identical to Ornament E-5630. There are no T marks because of very early 1981 production.

Personal Data: _____
____Want Mark ____ Mark _____ Purch. 19__ Pd $ _____

E-2800   NATIVITY Set - 9 pc. (4-3/4")
"Come Let Us Adore Him"

NM	$225	F	$155
T	$170	C	$155
HG	$165	D	$155

Comments: 1979; Original Retail $70.00/$90.00
Re-sculpted, changed to #104000 (heads larger). Retailers report popular Christmas gift from husbands to wives. NM good mark to seek out for your collection. **See #40, page XV.**

Personal Data: _____
____Want Mark ____ Mark _____ Purch. 19__ Pd $ _____

E-2801   Angels in Chariot
"Jesus Is Born"

SUSP. 1984 - 12 YEARS AGO

NM	$375	F	$320
T	$340	C	$300
HG	$325		

Comments: 1979; Original Retail $37.00/$55.00
This piece tends to be scarce. Back in 1979 we thought $37 retail was high. Many collectors didn't purchased this piece for that reason.
See #13, page XII.

Personal Data: _____
____Want Mark ____ Mark _____ Purch. 19__ Pd $ _____

E-2802   Boy Giving Toy Lamb to Jesus
"Christmas Is A Time To Share"

SUSP. 1984 - 12 YEARS AGO

NM	$115	F	$80
T	$95	C	$70
HG	$90	D	$90

Comments: 1979; Original Retail $20.00/$27.50
D mark has been reported, but this must have been an oversight at the factory, as this piece was suspended in 1984. **See #14, page XII.**

Personal Data: _____
____Want Mark ____ Mark _____ Purch. 19__ Pd $ _____

E-2803   Boy Kneeling at Manger/Crown
"Crown Him Lord Of All"

SUSP. 1984 - 12 YEARS AGO

NM	$120	F	$85
T	$100	C	$80
HG	$90	D	$90

Comments:: 1979; Original Retail $20.00/$27.50
D mark has been reported, but this must have been an oversight at the factory as this piece was suspended in 1984. Plentiful in '80.
See #14, page XII.
Personal Data: _____
____Want Mark ____ Mark _____ Purch. 19__ Pd $ _____

E-2804   Boy on Globe
"Peace On Earth"

SUSP. 1984 - 12 YEARS AGO

NM	$155	F	$135
T	$150	C	$130
HG	$135		

Comments: 1979; Original Retail $20.00/$27.50
Somewhat scarce. This figurine saw slight increase from last year.
Personal Data: _____
____Want Mark ____ Mark _____ Purch. 19__ Pd $ _____

E-2805   Boy in Santa Cap/Dog
"Wishing You A Season Filled With Joy"

RETIRED 1985 - 11 YEARS AGO

NM	$130	F	$95
T	$120	C	$85
HG	$100	D	$75

Comments: 1978; Original Retail $20.00/$27.50
Most D marks have two eyes painted on dog; all others have only one eye painted. Two eyes mainly appeared on the pieces produced for retirement in 1985.
Personal Data: _____
____Want Mark ____ Mark _____ Purch. 19__ Pd $ _____

E-2806 ♪ MUSICAL - Boy Giving Toy Lamb to Jesus
"Christmas Is A Time To Share"

RETIRED 1984 - 12 YEARS AGO

NM	$170	F	$160
T	$180	C	$150
HG	$165		

Comments: 1980; Original Retail $45.00/$50.00
Plays *Away In A Manger*. Fewer T produced than NM. A few reports of Musicals being defective. All have been quality produced. Fewer collectors of musicals than figurines. This is a popular piece, especially the T and NM. On figurine the box is closer to manger. This is just the difference between line art and actual figurine produced.
Personal Data: _____
____Want Mark ____ Mark _____ Purch. 19__ Pd $ _____

E-2807 ♪ MUSICAL - Boy Kneeling Manger/Crown
"Crown Him Lord Of All"

SUSP. 1984 - 12 YEARS AGO

NM	$140	F	$110
T	$125	C	$100
HG	$120		

Comments:: 1980; Original Retail $45.00/$50.00
Plays *O Come All Ye Faithful*. Most earlier musicals appeared as figurines also. The most sought after musical is the *Silent Knight*, mainly because there was no similar figurine produced.
Personal Data: _____
____Want Mark ____ Mark _____ Purch. 19__ Pd $ _____

E-2808 ♪ MUSICAL - Boy and Girl Reading Book
"Unto Us A Child Is Born"

SUSP. 1984 - 12 YEARS AGO

NM	$140	F	$115
T	$125	C	$115
HG	$120		

Comments: 1980; Original Retail $45.00/$50.00
Plays *Jesus Loves Me*. Very colorful the first year; not easily found anymore…
Personal Data: _____
____Want Mark ____ Mark _____ Purch. 19__ Pd $ _____

E-2809 ♪ MUSICAL - Boy and Girl in School Play
"Jesus Is Born"

SUSP. 1985 - 11 YEARS AGO

NM	$150	F	$130
T	$145	C	$130
HG	$145	D	$130

Comments: 1980; Original Retail $45.00/$50.00
Plays *Hark, The Herald Angels Sing*. The T and NM are colorful! Very little trading found, becoming scarcer.
Personal Data: _____
____Want Mark ____ Mark _____ Purch. 19__ Pd $ _____

E-2810 ♪ MUSICAL - NATIVITY
"Come Let Us Adore Him"

SUSP. 1993 - 3 YEARS AGO

NM	$175	C	$130	FL	$125	GC	$125
T	$160	D	$130	BA	$125	B	$125
HG	$150	OB	$130	FLM	$125		
F	$145	CT	$130	V	$125		

Comments: 1979; Original Retail $60.00/$100
Plays *Joy To The World*. NM and T preferred by collectors of musicals. These marks are coming into much demand. When a piece has been produced for 10-13 years, the secondary market is usually trading the first few marks only. Notice Retail went to $100.
Personal Data: _____
____Want Mark ____ Mark _____ Purch. 19__ Pd $ _____

E-2821 Girl with String of Hearts
"You Have Touched So Many Hearts"

F	$65	FL	$40	B	$40		
C	$60	BA	$40	TRP	$38		
D	$45	FLM	$40	S	$38		
OB	$45	V	$40	H	$37.50		
CT	$45	GC	$40				

Comments: 1982; Original Retail $25.00/$37.50
Reissued in 1990 for Easter Seals as 9" piece under dome (523283). She was also produced in 1992 with a set of letters to personalize the hearts which did not sell as well because the letters did not adhere to the hearts as planned. Visitors to the Factory in Nagoya have painted their own Girl with Hearts. (The eyes were painted for us. ☺) Mine is purple and yellow! See #523283.

Personal Data: _____
____Want Mark ____ Mark ____ Purch. 19___ Pd $ _____

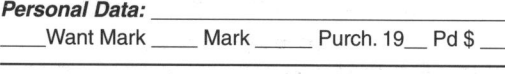

E-2822 Girl Polishing Table
"This Is Your Day To Shine"

RETIRED 1988 - 8 YEARS AGO

C	$120	CT	$95
D	$110	FL	$95
OB	$100		

Comments:: 1983; Original Retail $37.50/$40.00
Has been found with the word "Polish" missing from the bottle. Add $50 for this error. Only one report of F mark; seller had it priced at $155 several years ago. Add $100 to the C mark if you have an F mark. **See #15, page XIII**.

Personal Data: _____
____Want Mark ____ Mark ____ Purch. 19___ Pd $ _____

E-2823 Boy Holding Empty Frame
"To God Be The Glory"

SUSP. 1987 - 9 YEARS AGO

F	$130	OB	$95
C	$100	CT	$90
D	$95		

Comments:: 1983; Original Retail $40.00/$45.00
Was to be produced in 1983 but production problems occurred. Style number was originally E-0529 with retail price $23. Sam's favorite piece. Sam designed this piece in his recognition to the Lord for his "gift" of creating Precious Moments®. He acknowledges his works cannot be compared to God's. God receives the glory for Sam's gift. A very unusual and delicate piece. See front cover. This is a very special piece to have in your collection. Reported with Decaled C; add $100 to the secondary market value if you have a Decaled C.
See #37, page XV.

Personal Data: _____
____Want Mark ____ Mark ____ Purch. 19___ Pd $ _____

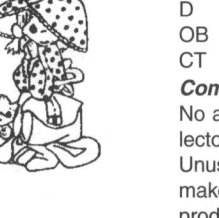

E-2824 Girl Dressing in Mom's Clothes
"To A Very Special Mom"

C	$65	FL	$50	GC	$45	H	$40
D	$60	BA	$50	B	$45		
OB	$55	FLM	$45	TRP	$40		
CT	$55	V	$45	S	$40		

Comments: 1983; Original Retail $27.50/$40.00
No air hole in base (air hole is under the hat). Hat added. Several collectors have informed us that their pieces have two holes in the base. Unusual! This is a very attractive piece! With all the colors, this would make a good candidate for suspension or retirement. Time consuming to produce. Retail price increased in '96.

Personal Data: _____
____Want Mark ____ Mark ____ Purch. 19___ Pd $ _____

E-2825 Girl Fixing Sister's Hair
"To A Very Special Sister"

C	$80	FL	$60	GC	$55	H	$50
D	$65	BA	$60	B	$50		
OB	$65	FLM	$60	TRP	$50		
CT	$60	V	$55	S	$50		

Comments: 1983; Original Retail $37.50/$50.00
Excellent "gift" item. Produced for 13 years, good suspension candidate.

Personal Data: _____
____Want Mark ____ Mark ____ Purch. 19___ Pd $ _____

E-2826 Girl at Table with Dolls
"May Your Birthday Be A Blessing"

SUSP. 1986 - 10 YEARS AGO

F	$125	D	$95
C	$105	OB	$90

Comments:: 1983; Original Retail $37.50
Has been found with brown eyes. Cute piece! Only produced for four years; note the difference in prices compared to one produced 8 or 10 years. Supply and demand! Retail would be approx. $40-45 if still in production. C mark most traded. **See #4, page XI.**

Personal Data: _____
____Want Mark ____ Mark ____ Purch. 19___ Pd $ _____

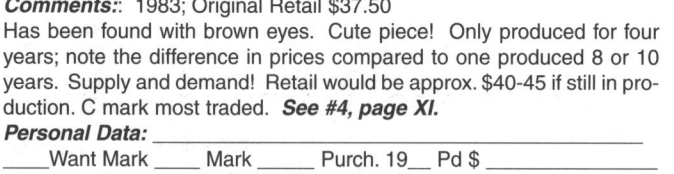

E-2827 Girl with Bucket on Head with Cow
"I Get A Kick Out Of You"

SUSP. 1986 - 10 YEARS AGO

F	$190	D	$165
C	$180	OB	$165

Comments: 1983; Original Retail $50.00
Classified as humor category but believe me, it's not funny when the ole' cow kicks over the bucket... I know! Becoming more scarce on secondary market as it has been ten years since it was produced.

Personal Data: _____
____Want Mark ____ Mark ____ Purch. 19___ Pd $ _____

E-2828   Girl at Trunk with Wedding Gown
"Precious Memories"

F	$150	FL	$70	B	$68
C	$80	BA	$70	TRP	$68
D	$75	FLM	$70	S	$65
OB	$75	V	$68	H	$65
CT	$75	GC	$68		

Comments: 1983; Original Retail $45.00/$65.00
Very few Fish marks, but have had confirmation from several collectors that they have one or have seen one. Because of the scarcity of F marks be sure to insure at $150. May be able to purchase for a little less. Good candidate for suspension.
Personal Data: _____
____Want Mark ____ Mark _____ Purch. 19__ Pd $ _____

E-2829   Girl at Mail Box
"I'm Sending You A White Christmas"

C	$90	FL	$65	GC	$55	H	$55
D	$75	BA	$60	B	$55		
OB	$70	FLM	$60	TRP	$55		
CT	$65	V	$60	S	$55		

Comments: 1984; Original Retail $37.50/$55.00
Sam designed this piece to remember his mother wanting to "mail" snowballs to her relatives in Florida when she was a little girl. This piece is displayed separately in a special case at the Chapel with a letter from Sam to his mother upon his graduation from high school. This design appeared on the 1991 crystal ornament. Musical (112402) retired in 1993. Old enough to be suspended or retired. Production costs went up 10% in 1995. I feel Sam favors this in his collection… time will tell.
Personal Data: _____
____Want Mark ____ Mark _____ Purch. 19__ Pd $ _____

E-2831   Bridesmaid
"No Flower Is As Sweet As You"

C	$38	FL	$25	GC	$25	H	$25
D	$30	BA	$25	B	$25		
OB	$28	FLM	$25	TRP	$25		
CT	$25	V	$25	S	$25		

Comments: 1983; Original Retail $13.00/$25.00
First issue of *Bridal Party Series*. Often purchased by brides for bridesmaids' gifts.
Personal Data: _____
____Want Mark ____ Mark _____ Purch. 19__ Pd $ _____

**Have you heard Sam has designed a special piece with
Jesus and the little children? When Sam feels the facial features of Jesus
are perfected to what he wants, then this piece will go into production.
I foresee it as one of the most popular pieces in this line if it is affordable to everyone
besides the avid collector.**

E-2832   Bride with Flower Girl Holding Veil
"God Bless The Bride"

C	$65	FL	$55	GC	$50	H	$50
D	$65	BA	$55	B	$50		
OB	$58	FLM	$55	TRP	$50		
CT	$58	V	$55	S	$50		

Comments: 1983; Original Retail $35.00/$50.00
Most Wedding Party pieces are not being sought after except for first marks as they are abundant and produced for the gift market. A new bride and groom figurine debuted in '95.
Personal Data: _____
____Want Mark ____ Mark _____ Purch. 19__ Pd $ _____

E-2833   Ring Bearer

C	$30	FL	$17.50	GC	$17.50	H	$17.50
D	$25	BA	$17.50	B	$17.50		
OB	$18	FLM	$17.50	TRP	$17.50		
CT	$18	V	$17.50	S	$17.50		

Comments: 1984; Original Retail $11.00/$17.50
Fourth issue of *Bridal Party Series*.
Personal Data: _____
____Want Mark ____ Mark _____ Purch. 19__ Pd $ _____

E-2834   Bridesmaid with Kitten
"Sharing Our Joy Together"

SUSP. 1991 - 5 YEARS AGO
OB	$65	FL	$60	FLM	$50
CT	$60	BA	$55	V	$48

Comments: 1986; Original Retail $31.00/$40.00
Personal Data: _____
____Want Mark ____ Mark _____ Purch. 19__ Pd $ _____

E-2835   Flower Girl

C	$45	FL	$17.50	GC	$17.50	H	$17.50
D	$35	BA	$17.50	B	$17.50		
OB	$30	FLM	$17.50	TRP	$17.50		
CT	$25	V	$17.50	S	$17.50		

Comments: 1984; Original Retail $11.00/$17.50
Third issue of *Bridal Party Series*. Small amount of trading reported on this piece. Tends to be true for most all pieces produced seven years or more. Secondary market prices do not rise on more current pieces when in continuous production for more than 5 or 6 years. Wedding pieces are not being traded abundantly. This piece is mainly bought retail for a gift. C mark is scarce.

Personal Data: _____
____Want Mark ____ Mark _____ Purch. 19__ Pd $ _____

Precious Moments® Collectibles from the

ORIENT

to You!

Photos by: Jeannie Joseph

진리를 알찌니 진리가
너희를 자유케 하리라
요한복음 8 : 2

E-2836   Groomsman with Frog
"Best Man"

C	$40	FL	$25	GC	$25	H	$25
D	$38	BA	$25	B	$25		
OB	$35	FLM	$25	TRP	$25		
CT	$30	V	$25	S	$25		

Comments: 1983; Original Retail $13.50/$25.00
Second issue of *Bridal Party Series*. "First mark" only mark popular on secondary market for *Bridal Party Series* pieces.

Personal Data: _____
____Want Mark ____ Mark ____ Purch. 19__ Pd $ _____

E-2837   Groom

No Hands	OB	$50		CT	$45-48		
W/Hands	OB	$40	FLM	$25	TRP	$25	
	CT	$35	V	$25	S	$25	
	FL	$28	GC	$25	H	$25	
	BA	$28	B	$25			

Comments: 1986; Original Retail $15.00/$25.00
Sixth issue of *Bridal Party Series*. Groom had no hands on earlier pieces. We called Sam's office first to tell him and he said it would be changed. There were many "no hands" produced. Fewer hands in OB than other marks.

Personal Data: _____
____Want Mark ____ Mark ____ Purch. 19__ Pd $ _____

E-2838   Wedding Party
"This Is The Day Which The Lord Hath Made"

LE 1987 - 9 YEARS OLD	CT	$190

Comments: 1987; Original Retail $175.00/$185.00
1987 Limited Edition, Wedding Party Group. "Large pieces" seldom rise on secondary market as quickly as most lower-priced figurines. Sad to report, but research found selling prices below original retail in 1994 and 1995. A beautiful piece!

Personal Data: _____
____Want Mark ____ Mark ____ Purch. 19__ Pd $ _____

E-2840   Angel Helping Baby Walk
"Baby's First Step"

SUSP. 1988 - 8 YEARS AGO	C	$98	CT	$85
	D	$95	FL	$85
	OB	$85		

Comments: 1982; Original Retail $35.00/$40.00
First issue of *Baby's First Series*. In my opinion this series has become more popular due to the fact that the market was not flooded. Supply and demand!

Personal Data: _____
____Want Mark ____ Mark ____ Purch. 19__ Pd $ _____

E-2841   Baby Posing for Picture
"Baby's First Picture"

RETIRED 1986 - 10 YEARS AGO	C	$165	OB	$150
	D	$155		

Comments: 1983; Original Retail $45.00
Second issue of *Baby's First Series*. C mark seems to be the most traded. Has not reached the $150 mark to date, but the *Baby's First Series* figurines are very popular!

Personal Data: _____
____Want Mark ____ Mark ____ Purch. 19__ Pd $ _____

E-2845   Junior Bridesmaid

OB	$30	FLM	$22.50	TRP	$22.50
CT	$30	V	$22.50	S	$22.50
FL	$24	GC	$22.50	H	$22.50
BA	$22.50	B	$22.50		

Comments:: 1983; Original Retail $12.50/$22.50
Fifth issue in *Bridal Party Series*. Very little trading on this piece. Retail price increased in '96.

Personal Data: _____
____Want Mark ____ Mark ____ Purch. 19__ Pd $ _____

E-2846   Bride

OB	$40	FLM	$30	TRP	$25
CT	$35	V	$25	S	$25
FL	$30	GC	$25	H	$25
BA	$30	B	$25		

Comments:: 1983; Original Retail $18.00/$25.00
Seventh issue in *Bridal Party Series*. Some line art provided by Enesco occasionally differs from the figurine later produced. The figurine produced does not include a kitten as shown in line cut.

Personal Data: _____
____Want Mark ____ Mark ____ Purch. 19__ Pd $ _____

E-2847   *PLATE* - Boy/Girl on Swing
"Love Is Kind"

LE 15,000	MM	$45	C	$40
	F	$40		

Comments: 1983; Original Retail $40.00
Limited to 15,000 pieces. Fourth issue of *Inspired Thoughts Series*. Secondary market demand is very "slow" on plates. May find for much less. An ideal place for your plates is in a plate display case with a ledge; put the matching figurine next to the plate.

Personal Data: _____
____Want Mark ____ Mark ____ Purch. 19__ Pd $ _____

E-2848   *PLATE* - Mother Wrapping Bread
"Loving Thy Neighbor"

LE 15,000
      C $40

Comments: 1983; Original Retail $40.00
Limited Edition 15,000. First plate with embossed mark.
Fourth (final) issue of *Mother's Love Series*.
Personal Data: _____
____Want Mark ____ Mark _____ Purch. 19__ Pd $ _____

E-2850   *DOLL* - Mother with Needlepoint
"Mother Sew Dear"

RETIRED 1985 - 11 YEARS AGO
     MM $300   D $250
     C $250

Comments: 1983; Original Retail $350.00
Collectors felt this doll was "overpriced at retail." She was sold to retailers later for $50 if they would use her in a promotional event as a door prize, etc.
Personal Data: _____
____Want Mark ____ Mark _____ Purch. 19__ Pd $ _____

E-2851   *DOLL* - 12" Girl Doll
"Kristy"

SUSP. 1989 - 7 YEARS AGO   C $180   CT $170
                            D $175   FL $170
                            OB $170   BA $170

Comments: 1983; Original Retail $150/$170
Dolls have not increased on the secondary market as have the figurines.
Personal Data: _____
____Want Mark ____ Mark _____ Purch. 19__ Pd $ _____

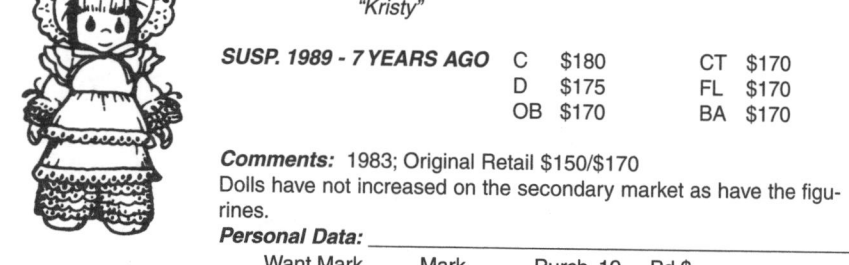

Love is not based on a person's intelligence or state in life but rather on the size of the heart.

E-2852   Baby Assortment Set (6 styles)
"Baby Figurines"

E-2852A Boy Standing	E-2852D Girl Clapping Hands
E-2852B Girl Standing	E-2852E Boy Crawling
E-2852C Boy Sitting	E-2852F Girl Lying Down

DECALED C $50

C	$30 ea.	BA	$18.50 ea.	TRP	$18.50 ea.
D	$25 ea.	FLM	$18.50 ea.	S	$18.50 ea.
OB	$22 ea.	V	$18.50 ea.	H	$18.50 ea.
CT	$20 ea.	GC	$18.50 ea.		
FL	$18.50 ea.	B	$18.50 ea.		

Comments: 1983; Original Retail $12.00/$18.50
Renumbered A-F late 1987. Usually sold in sets. Have been found with a decaled C mark! Retail price increase in '96.
Personal Data: _____
____Want Mark ____ Mark _____ Purch. 19__ Pd $ _____

E-2853   Anniversary Boy/Girl Holding Plate
*"God Blessed Our Years Together
With So Much Love And Happiness"*

C	$60	BA	$50	TRP	$50
D	$60	FLM	$50	S	$50
OB	$55	V	$50	H	$50
CT	$55	GC	$50		
FL	$50	B	$50		

Comments: 1983; Original Retail $35.00/$50.00
This piece is not traded often on the secondary market as it's still in production. Slow seller for retailers. It's time for a new anniversary figurine! And, of course, this we saw in 1996!
Personal Data: _____
____Want Mark ____ Mark _____ Purch. 19__ Pd $ _____

E-2854   1st Anniversary Figurine
*"God Blessed Our Year Together
With So Much Love And Happiness"*

1st Anniversary Fig. "Years" error	C			$72
	D			$70

1st Anniversary Fig. "Year" correction

C	$60	BA	$50	TRP	$50
D	$50	FLM	$50	S	$50
OB	$50	V	$50	H	$50
CT	$50	GC	$50		
FL	$50	B	$50		

Comments: 1984; Original Retail $35.00/$50.00
Happy Anniversary Series. First figurines changed from "Years" to "Year." Has been found with TRP having the error "Years." Unusual! Have you seen one?
Personal Data: _____
____Want Mark ____ Mark _____ Purch. 19__ Pd $ _____

E-2855   5th Anniversary Figurine
"God Blessed Our Years Together With So Much Love And Happiness"

C	$55-60	FL	$50	GC	$50	H	$50
D	$55-60	BA	$50	B	$50		
OB	$50	FLM	$50	TRP	$50		
CT	$50	V	$50	S	$50		

Comments: 1984; Original Retail $35.00/$50.00
Happy Anniversary Series. In my opinion, not many sell. Should be a candidate for suspension.
Personal Data: _____
___Want Mark ___ Mark ___ Purch. 19__ Pd $ _____

E-2856   10th Anniversary Figurine
"God Blessed Our Years Together With So Much Love And Happiness"

C	$60	FL	$50	GC	$50	H	$50
D	$60	BA	$50	B	$50		
OB	$52	FLM	$50	TRP	$50		
CT	$50	V	$50	S	$50		

Comments: 1984; Original Retail $35.00/$50.00
Happy Anniversary Series. This series not sought after on the secondary market.
Personal Data: _____
___Want Mark ___ Mark ___ Purch. 19__ Pd $ _____

E-2857   25th Anniversary Figurine
"God Blessed Our Years Together With So Much Love And Happiness"

C	$55-60	FL	$50	GC	$50	H	$50
D	$55-60	BA	$50	B	$50		
OB	$52	FLM	$50	TRP	$50		
CT	$50	V	$50	S	$50		

Comments: 1984; Original Retail $35.00/$50.00
Happy Anniversary Series. Prices for C mainly for insurance value replacement costs. Very little trading on the anniversary figurines.
Personal Data: _____
___Want Mark ___ Mark ___ Purch. 19__ Pd $ _____

E-2859   40th Anniversary Figurine
"God Blessed Our Years Together With So Much Love And Happiness"

C	$62	FL	$50	GC	$50	H	$50
D	$55	BA	$50	B	$50		
OB	$52	FLM	$50	TRP	$50		
CT	$50	V	$50	S	$50		

Comments: 1984; Original Retail $35.00/$50.00
Happy Anniversary Series.
Personal Data: _____
___Want Mark ___ Mark ___ Purch. 19__ Pd $ _____

E-2860   50th Anniversary Figurine
"God Blessed Our Years Together With So Much Love And Happiness"

C	$62-65	FL	$50	GC	$50	H	$50
D	$55-60	BA	$50	B	$50		
OB	$52	FLM	$50	TRP	$50		
CT	$50	V	$50	S	$50		

Comments: 1984; Original Retail $35.00/$50.00
Happy Anniversary Series. Not being traded frequently.
Personal Data: _____
___Want Mark ___ Mark ___ Purch. 19__ Pd $ _____

E-3104   Baby in Cradle with Bird
"Blessed Are The Pure In Heart"

SUSP. 1991 - 5 YEARS AGO

NM	$55	C	$35	FL	$30	
T	$50	D	$30	BA	$30	
HG	$48	OB	$30	FLM	$30	
F	$45	CT	$30	V	$30	

Comments: 1980; Original Retail $9.00/$19.00
Very plentiful with NM. An orginal J&D Licensee piece.
Personal Data: _____
___Want Mark ___ Mark ___ Purch. 19__ Pd $ _____

E-3105   Boy with Crutches
"He Watches Over Us All"

SUSP. 1984 - 12 YEARS AGO

NM	$100	HG	$80	D	$65	OB	$60
T	$90	F	$75	C	$60		

Comments: 1979; Original Retail $11.00/$17.00
This was an original J&D licensed figurine.
Personal Data: _____
___Want Mark ___ Mark ___ Purch. 19__ Pd $ _____

E-3106   Mother with Needlepoint
"Mother Sew Dear"

NM	$95	D	$40	FLM	$32.50	S	$32.50
T	$85	OB	$38	V	$32.50	H	$32.50
HG	$60	CT	$35	GC	$32.50		
F	$50	FL	$32.50	B	$32.50		
C	$40	BA	$32.50	TRP	$32.50		

Comments: 1979; Original Retail $13.00/$32.50
A plate has been produced with the same figure – *Mother's Love Series.* Doll with the same title was produced in 1984; retail $350. Many felt it was overpriced on retail. Retail price increased in '96. This was an orginal J&D licensed figurine.
Personal Data: _____
___Want Mark ___ Mark ___ Purch. 19__ Pd $ _____

E-3107   Boy Holding Cat/Dog
"Blessed Are The Peacemakers"

RETIRED 1985 - 11 YEARS AGO

NM	$130	F	$85
T	$110	C	$80
HG	$90	D	$75

Comments: 1979; Original Retail $13.00/$19.00
Becoming much sought after. Original J&D piece.

Personal Data: _____
____Want Mark ____ Mark ____ Purch. 19__ Pd $ _____

E-3108   Girl Rocking Cradle
"The Hand That Rocks The Future"

SUSP. 1984 -12 YEARS AGO

NM	$110	F	$75
T	$95	C	$75
HG	$80	GC	$150

Comments: 1979; Original Retail $13.00/$19.00
This piece was reportedly found with a GC mark in a Gold Crown Hallmark shop in Ohio. The collector who reported this information was aware that this piece had been suspended and said it definitely had a GC (1992) mark on it. This is not unusual – the same has been reported from time to time on other pieces.

Personal Data: _____
____Want Mark ____ Mark ____ Purch. 19__ Pd $ _____

E-3109   Grandma in Rocking Chair
"The Purr-fect Grandma"

NM	$95	D	$35	FLM	$32.50	S	$32.50
T	$85	OB	$35	V	$32.50	H	$32.50
HG	$55	CT	$32.50	GC	$32.50		
F	$40	FL	$32.50	B	$32.50		
C	$40	BA	$32.50	TRP	$32.50		

Comments: 1979; Original Retail $13.00/$32.50
NM and T are very colorful. It's time for a new Grandma! Retail price increase in '96.

Personal Data: _____
____Want Mark ____ Mark ____ Purch. 19__ Pd $ _____

E-3110B   Boy on Bench/Lollipop
"Loving Is Sharing"

RETIRED 1993 - 3 YEARS AGO

NM	$145	C	$85	FL	$80	V	$75
T	$125	D	$80	BA	$80	GC	$75
HG	$100	OB	$80	FLM	$80	B	$75
F	$85	CT	$80				

Comments: 1979; Original Retail $13.00/$30.00
Not found abundantly after retirement.

Personal Data: _____
____Want Mark ____ Mark ____ Purch. 19__ Pd $ _____

E-3110G   Girl on Bench/Lollipop
"Loving Is Sharing"

NM	$110	D	$32.50	FLM	$32.50	S	$32.50
T	$70	OB	$32.50	V	$32.50	H	$32.50
HG	$60	CT	$32.50	GC	$32.50		
F	$40	FL	$32.50	B	$32.50		
C	$35	BA	$32.50	TRP	$32.50		

Comments: 1979; Original Retail $13.00/$32.50
Because E-3110B was retired, many rushed to get this piece to "match" it. Good candidate for retirement or suspension. Error reported with no decal on book. Collector reported finding this with the dog missing and no evidence of it ever being there. Retail price up $2.50 in '96.

Personal Data: _____
____Want Mark ____ Mark ____ Purch. 19__ Pd $ _____

E-3111   Laundry Girl
"Be Not Weary In Well Doing"

RETIRED 1985 - 11 YEARS AGO

"And Well Doing" Verse Error		Error NM	$175
NM	$135	F	$90
T	$120	C	$85
HG	$105	D	$75

Comments: 1979; Original Retail $14.00/$19.00
Error on earlier pieces, "Be Not Weary 'and' Well Doing." Not many were produced.

Personal Data: _____
____Want Mark ____ Mark ____ Purch. 19__ Pd $ _____

E-3112   Boy Jogger
"God's Speed"

RETIRED 1983 - 13 YEARS AGO!

NM	$80	HG	$75
T	$75	F	$45

Comments: 1979; Original Retail $14.00/$18.00
Seems to be more plentiful than other NM Retired pieces. Much trading reported on F mark as it was plentiful. No tag is found on dog's collar. Remember, line art can be slightly different from actual piece produced. This is due to production decisions made on final piece. When this piece was retired in '83 NMs were still easily found on retailers' shelves.

Personal Data: _____
____Want Mark ____ Mark ____ Purch. 19__ Pd $ _____

E-3113   Tracing in Sand
"Thou Art Mine"

NM	$95-100	OB	$45	GC	$40
T	$80	CT	$45	B	$40
HG	$65	FL	$45	TRP	$40
F	$55	BA	$45	S	$40
C	$50	FLM	$45	H	$40
D	$50	V	$45		

Comments: 1979; Original Retail $16.00/$40.00
Sixteen years in production. Look for Suspension or Retirement of this figurine. It is an original J&D piece. Very special. Be sure to have this one. Retail price increased in 1995. The turtle has only one eye painted. This is not an error. The position of the turtle does not allow it to be seen easily, therefore no paint was needed. Suspension or Retirement candidate.

Personal Data: _____
____Want Mark ____ Mark _____ Purch. 19__ Pd $ _____

E-3114   Bride and Groom
"The Lord Bless You And Keep You"

NM	$95	OB	$50	GC	$50
T	$80	CT	$50	B	$50
HG	$70	FL	$50	TRP	$50
F	$55	BA	$50	S	$50
C	$55	FLM	$50	H	$50
D	$55	V	$50		

Comments: 1979; Original Retail $16.00/$50.00
Has been a popular wedding gift for cake toppers! Changed from original style around 1985 to larger heads. (The Samuel J. Butcher Company began in 1985.) Retail price increased in '95 and again in '96! ***See #16, page XIII.***

Personal Data: _____
____Want Mark ____ Mark _____ Purch. 19__ Pd $ _____

E-3115   Boy/Girl on Cloud
"But Love Goes On Forever"

NM	$95	OB	$40	GC	$40
T	$80	CT	$40	B	$40
HG	$60	FL	$40	TRP	$40
F	$50	BA	$40	S	$40
C	$50	FLM	$40	H	$40
D	$45	V	$40		

Comments: 1979; Original Retail $16.50/$40.00
Enesco's logo piece for the collection. Retail price increased in 1995 and 1996.

Personal Data: _____
____Want Mark ____ Mark _____ Purch. 19__ Pd $ _____

E-3116   Boy Carving Tree
"Thee I Love"

RETIRED 1994 - 2 YEARS AGO

NM	$155	OB	$65	GC	$65
T	$120	CT	$65	B	$65
HG	$85	FL	$65	TRP	$65
F	$75	BA	$65		
C	$70	FLM	$65		
D	$70	V	$65		

Comments: 1979; Original Retail $16.50/$40.00
Originals darkly colored, especially on girl's "red" patch. Long time favorite. NM hard to find! Many original J&D pieces are perfect candidates for suspension in order to relicense popular J&D sellers. NM or T is the avid collector's must.

Personal Data: _____
____Want Mark ____ Mark _____ Purch. 19__ Pd $ _____

E-3117   Boy/Girl Moving with Cart
"Walking By Faith"

NM	$140	OB	$80	GC	$75
T	$115	CT	$75	B	$75
HG	$105	FL	$75	TRP	$75
F	$95	BA	$75	S	$75
C	$85	FLM	$75	H	$75
D	$80	V	$75		

Comments: 1979; Original Retail $35.00/$75.00
"Holy Bible" omitted from Bible on some pieces. Add $75-$100 for that error on any mark. If retired or suspended, I feel NM and T will escalate in price over a three-year period after announcement. Higher priced pieces are generally suspended, not retired.

Personal Data: _____
____Want Mark ____ Mark _____ Purch. 19__ Pd $ _____

E-3118   Girl and Frying Pan
"Eggs Over Easy"

RETIRED 1983 - 13 YEARS AGO

NM	$125	HG	$95
T	$110	F	$90

Comments: 1979; Original Retail $12.00/$15.00
Cute piece!! This is one of the first J&D pieces that did not have an inspirational name. We have heard from several collectors that the egg was missing from their pieces. Add $50 to the secondary market value if the egg is missing.

Personal Data: _____
____Want Mark ____ Mark _____ Purch. 19__ Pd $ _____

E-3119   Boy/Apple/Books
"It's What's Inside That Counts"

SUSP. 1984 - 12 YEARS AGO

NM	$130	F	$110
T	$125	C	$105
HG	$115		

Comments: 1979; Original Retail $13.00/$19.00
First pieces produced were very dark in color! Especially the apple! Nice piece to own with NM or T because of their vivid color.

Personal Data: _____
____Want Mark _____ Mark _____ Purch. 19__ Pd $ _____

E-3120   Girl with Box of Kittens
"To Thee With Love"

SUSP. 1986 - 10 YEARS AGO

NM	$95	C	$70
T	$80	D	$60
HG	$75	OB	$60
F	$70		

Comments: 1979; Original Retail $13.00/$19.00
We have been told CT mark was produced and have seen ads selling the CT mark for $80-90.

Personal Data: _____
____Want Mark _____ Mark _____ Purch. 19__ Pd $ _____

E-4720   Boy Graduate
"The Lord Bless You And Keep You"

SUSP. 1987 - 9 YEARS AGO

NM	$60	F	$45	OB	$40
T	$55	C	$40	CT	$40
HG	$45	D	$40		

Comments: 1980; Original Retail $14.00/$22.50
No Marks were abundant. Still remains many collectors' favorite "graduate" compared to current pieces. This piece has been found with a misspelling on the decal, which is located on the bottom of the figurine. "Bless" is spelled B-E-L-E-S-S. This was found with the CT. Add $35-$40 for this error. Notice the present retail for E-4721 Girl Graduate.

Personal Data: _____
____Want Mark _____ Mark _____ Purch. 19__ Pd $ _____

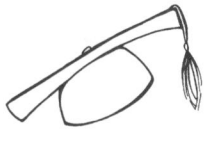

Success is to be measured not so much by the position one has reached in life as the obstacles he has overcome while trying to succeed.

E-4721   Girl Graduate
"The Lord Bless You And Keep You"

NM	$80	OB	$35	GC	$35
T	$60	CT	$35	B	$35
HG	$50	FL	$35	TRP	$35
F	$40	BA	$35	S	$35
C	$40	FLM	$35	H	$35
D	$35	V	$35		

Comments: 1979; Original Retail $14.00/$35.00
Retail price increased in 1995 and in 1996.

Personal Data: _____
____Want Mark _____ Mark _____ Purch. 19__ Pd $ _____

E-4722   Girl/Piggy Bank
"Love Cannot Break A True Friendship"

SUSP. 1985 - 10 YEARS AGO

NM	$140	F	$115
T	$135	C	$110
HG	$118	D	$105

Comments: 1980; Original Retail $22.50/$27.50
NM becoming more scarce on secondary market. T mark even more so! Most collectors do not realize there are fewer T than other marks. T mark was produced only 6 months! Not easily found!

Personal Data: _____
____Want Mark _____ Mark _____ Purch. 19__ Pd $ _____

Sam Butcher is not only known for his Precious Moments art, but other fine art as well. These pieces and more can be found in the gallery at the Precious Moments Chapel in Carthage, Missouri.

E-4723   Boy Selling Newspapers
"Peace Amid The Storm"

SUSP. 1984 - 12 YEARS AGO

NM	$110	F	$75
T	$90	C	$75
HG	$85		

Comments: 1980; Original Retail $22.50/$27.50
Sample piece had no bird on book as pictured in an earlier brochure. Remember, often illustrations are not exactly as the figurine!

Personal Data: _____
____Want Mark ____ Mark _____ Purch. 19__ Pd $ _____

E-4724   Boy/Girl/Baby Christening
"Rejoicing With You"

No "E"	NM	$110	HG	$80		
	T	$85	F	$75		

With "E"	HG	$70	CT	$55	GC	$55
	F	$60	FL	$55	B	$55
	C	$55	BA	$55	TRP	$55
	D	$55	FLM	$55	S	$55
	OB	$55	V	$55	H	$55

Comments: 1980; Original Retail $25.00/$55.00
Girl's hand covers "E" of "Bible." Some found with "E" in 1982 - most with "E" in 1983. Most found before 1983 with "Bibl" which was correct as the original art had no "E." We have received one report of this figurine being found with T mark with girl holding Holy "Byble." Often such reports are given in *Precious Collectibles*™. You do subscribe, don't you?

Personal Data: _____
____Want Mark ____ Mark _____ Purch. 19__ Pd $ _____

E-4725   Choir Boys
"Peace On Earth"

SUSP. 1984 - 12 YEARS AGO

NM	$120	F	$70
T	$85	C	$65
HG	$75		

Comments: 1980; Original Retail $25.00/$30.00
Appeared late 1981. Produced before marks began in mid 1981. "No Marks" were plentiful even in 1982 and early 1983. Suspension is bringing a rise to the secondary market since 1992. Original NM and T pieces are very colorful!

Personal Data: _____
____Want Mark ____ Mark _____ Purch. 19__ Pd $ _____

E-4726   ♪ *MUSICAL* - Choir Boys
"Peace On Earth"

SUSP. 1984 - 12 YEARS AGO	NM	$145	F	$115
	T	$125	C	$115
	HG	$120		

Comments: 1980; Original Retail $45.00/$50.00
Plays *Jesus Loves Me.* Not easily found.
Personal Data: _____
____Want Mark ____ Mark _____ Purch. 19__ Pd $ _____

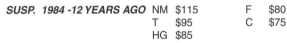

E-5200   Sad Boy/Teddy
"Bear Ye One Another's Burdens"

SUSP. 1984 -12 YEARS AGO	NM	$115	F	$80
	T	$95	C	$75
	HG	$85		

Comments: 1980; Original Retail $20.00/$25.00
Most 5200 series were produced early 1981, but with No Mark. Triangle marks appeared mid '81. Sample piece was smiling! (See Enesco's 1982/1983 brochure.) No report of collectors having a smiling piece.
See #7, page XII.
Personal Data: _____
____Want Mark ____ Mark _____ Purch. 19__ Pd $ _____

E-5201   Boy Helping Friend
"Love Lifted Me"

SUSP. 1984 - 12 YEARS AGO

NM	$115	F	$80
T	$90	C	$75
HG	$85		

Comments: 1980; Original Retail $22.50/$30.00
Personal Data: _____
____Want Mark ____ Mark _____ Purch. 19__ Pd $ _____

E-5202   Lemonade Stand
"Thank You For Coming To My Ade"

SUSP. 1984 - 12 YEARS AGO

NM	$150	F	$110
T	$125	C	$110
HG	$120		

Comments: 1980; Original Retail $22.50/$30.00
Very attractive piece. Almost a must for the avid collector to own! Seldom seen at Swap Meets…
Personal Data: _____
____Want Mark ____ Mark _____ Purch. 19__ Pd $ _____

E-5203   Angry Boy and Dog on Stairs
"Let Not The Sun Go Down Upon Your Wrath"

SUSP. 1984 - 12 YEARS AGO	NM	$175	F	$125
	T	$145	C	$125
	HG	$140		

Comments: 1980; Original Retail $22.50/$30.00
Since 1989-1990, Suspended pieces have been taking on the status of being "Retired" when one tries to locate them, especially if they have been suspended for four to five years. Seems to be plentiful at these prices. Don't insure for more!
Personal Data: _____
____Want Mark ____ Mark _____ Purch. 19__ Pd $ _____

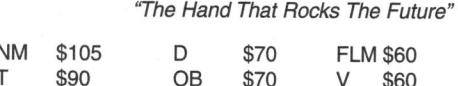

E-5204 ♪   MUSICAL - Girl/Cradle
"The Hand That Rocks The Future"

NM	$105	D	$70	FLM	$60	S	$60
T	$90	OB	$70	V	$60	H	$60
HG	$80	CT	$65	GC	$60		
F	$70	FL	$60	B	$60		
C	$70	BA	$60	TRP	$60		

Comments: 1981; OriginalRetail $30.00/$60.00
Plays *Mozart's Lullaby.* Very little trading taking place on this piece. No doubt because it's been on the shelves for seventeen years. Look for suspension maybe... ***See #21, page XIII.***
Personal Data: _____
____Want Mark ____ Mark _____ Purch. 19__ Pd $ _____

E-5205 ♪   MUSICAL - Boy Angel on Cloud
"My Guardian Angel"

SUSP. 1985 - 11 YEARS AGO	NM	$125	F	$85
	T	$105	C	$85
	HG	$90	D	$85

Comments: 1980; Original Retail $22.50/$27.50
Plays *Brahm's Lullaby.* Not easy to find. Would be excellent choice to bring back from suspension. ***See #21, page XIII.***
Personal Data: _____
____Want Mark ____ Mark _____ Purch. 19__ Pd $ _____

E-5206 ♪   MUSICAL - Girl Angel on Cloud
"My Guardian Angel"

SUSP. 1988 - 8 YEARS AGO

NM	$115	F	$85	OB	$80
T	$95	C	$85	CT	$75
HG	$85	D	$85	FL	$75

Comments: 1980; Original Retail $27.50/$33.00
Plays *Brahm's Lullaby.*
Personal Data: _____
____Want Mark ____ Mark _____ Purch. 19__ Pd $ _____

E-5207   NIGHT LIGHT - Boy/Girl Angels Cloud
"My Guardian Angel"

SUSP. 1984 - 12 YEARS AGO	NM	$225	F	$145
	T	$215	C	$145
	HG	$160		

Comments: 1980; Original Retail $30.00/$37.50
This piece without the light was placed under a dome as a special gift to Centers from Enesco in 1982-83 (E-7350) with a plaque on a wooden base. NM and T most sought after. Centers were renamed DSR or Distinguished Service Retailer.

Personal Data: _____
____Want Mark ____ Mark _____ Purch. 19__ Pd $ _____

E-5208   BELL - Boy with Teddy
"Jesus Loves Me"

SUSP. 1985 - 11 YEARS AGO	MM	$55
	C	$45
	D	$45

Comments: 1980; Original Retail $15.00/$19.00
Most bells from early 1980s through 1983 had no marks. Bells not often for sale in ads as in earlier years. Take on a challenge... collect the bisque bells! Probably more MMs than other two marks.
See #17, page XIII.

Personal Data: _____
____Want Mark ____ Mark _____ Purch. 19__ Pd $ _____

E-5209   BELL - Girl with Bunny
"Jesus Loves Me"

SUSP. 1985 - 11 YEARS AGO	MM	$55
	C	$50
	D	$48

Comments: 1980; Original Retail $15.00/$19.00
Most Bells unmarked. Production cut back on bells compared to early 1980s. ***See #17, page XIII.***

Personal Data: _____
____Want Mark ____ Mark _____ Purch. 19__ Pd $ _____

E-5210   BELL - Praying Girl
"Prayer Changes Things"

SUSP. 1984 - 12 YEARS AGO	MM	$50
	C	$45

Comments: 1980; Original Retail $15.00/$19.00
See #17, page XIII.

Personal Data: _____
____Want Mark ____ Mark _____ Purch. 19__ Pd $ _____

E-5211 *BELL* - Boy with Report Card
"God Understands"

RETIRED 1984 - 12 YEARS AGO   MM $55
                                         C $45

Comments: 1980; Original Retail $15.00/$19.00
Most Bells unmarked. Popular bell as it was Retired.
See #17, page XIII.
Personal Data: _____
____Want Mark ____ Mark _____ Purch. 19__ Pd $ _____

E-5212   Boy in Dad's Duds
"To A Special Dad"

NM	$70	D	$35	BA	$35	TRP	$35
T	$55	OB	$35	FLM	$35	S	$35
HG	$50	CT	$35	V	$35	H	$35
F	$45	CT	$35	GC	$35		
C	$40	FL	$35	B	$35		

Comments: 1980; Original Retail $20.00/$35.00
Similar to ornament in 1983. It would make an excellent piece to Retire or Suspend in '96 as it's been in production 18 years.
Personal Data: _____
____Want Mark ____ Mark _____ Purch. 19__ Pd $ _____

E-5213   Girl w/Goose in Lap
"God Is Love"

SUSP. 1989 - 7 YEARS AGO

NM	$125	C	$55	FL	$50
T	$80	D	$55	BA	$50
HG	$65	OB	$55		
F	$60	CT	$55		

Comments: 1980; Original Retail $17.00/$30.00
Mold changed to larger head in 1985. Was a J&D production... now Samuel J. Butcher Co. licensed piece. Girl's face quite chubby on original pieces. Avid collectors should look for this piece with NM, T or HG.
Personal Data: _____
____Want Mark ____ Mark _____ Purch. 19__ Pd $ _____

E-5214   Boy/Girl Praying at Table
"Prayer Changes Things"

SUSP. 1984 - 12 YEARS AGO

NM	$175	F	$100
T	$155	C	$95
HG	$125	D	$95

Comments: 1980; Original Retail $35.00/$37.50
"Holy Bible" written on 1981 and 1982 pieces on back of book; corrected in 1983. First mention of the error appeared in *Precious Collectibles™* magazine.
Personal Data: _____
____Want Mark ____ Mark _____ Purch. 19__ Pd $ _____

E-5215   *PLATE* - Boy and Girl on Stump
"Love One Another"

LE 1981 - 15 YEARS OLD   MM $55
                                            F $45

Comments: 1980; Original Retail $20.00/$40.00
1981 Limited Edition 15,000. First Edition in *Inspired Thoughts Series*. Pretty plate! ***See #1, page XI.***

Personal Data: _____
____Want Mark ____ Mark _____ Purch. 19__ Pd $ _____

E-5216   *PLATE* - Bride & Groom
"The Lord Bless You And Keep You"

SUSP. 1987 - 9 YEARS AGO

MM	$45	OB	$40
C	$40	CT	$40
D	$40		

Comments: 1981; Original Retail $30.00/$37.50
Not a lot of trading.

Personal Data: _____
____Want Mark ____ Mark _____ Purch. 19__ Pd $ _____

E-5217   *PLATE* - Mother with Needlepoint
"Mother Sew Dear"

LE 1981 - 15 YEARS OLD   MM $45

Comments: 1980; Original Retail $40.00
1981 Limited Edition 15,000. First Edition of *Mother's Love Series*. Plates still not moving on the secondary market. Deals can be found...

Personal Data: _____
____Want Mark ____ Mark _____ Purch. 19__ Pd $ _____

E-5376   Girl Opening Gift
"May Your Christmas Be Blessed"

SUSP. 1986 - 9 YEARS AGO   C $85
                                            D $65
                                            OB $60

Comments: 1984; Original Retail $37.50
"Holy Bible" written on 1984 pieces on back of book. Corrected in 1985. Very pretty piece. Not easy to locate from most dealers.

Personal Data: _____
____Want Mark ____ Mark _____ Purch. 19__ Pd $ _____

E-5377   Girl Giving Cheese to Mouse
"Love Is Kind"

RETIRED 1987 - 9 YEARS AGO

F	$115	OB	$90
C	$95	CT	$75
D	$90		

Comments: 1984; Original Retail $27.50/$30.00
Same inspiration as 1984 Plate, Girl in Swing. Readily available during the retirement announcement time. CT easy to find.

Personal Data: _____
____Want Mark ____ Mark _____ Purch. 19___ Pd $ _____

E-5378   Shepherd Playing Harp
"Joy To the World"

SUSP. 1989 - 7 YEARS AGO

C	$50	CT	$40
D	$45	FL	$40
OB	$45	BA	$40

Comments: 1984; Original Retail $18.00/$25.00
First appeared in 1984 as figurine and ornament but the print first appeared in 1981 on the first tin and on a crewel picture. There is a question as to why the license date should not be 1980 or 1981 as this drawing was used by Enesco at that time. The same question applies also to pieces E-5388, E-5385 and E-5386 as they had been produced before in a different style of figurine; same piece, so why a different license date? An error, in my opinion. It's been said this was to be a black child. In '94 African-American children debuted. ***See #18, page XIII.***

Personal Data: _____
____Want Mark ____ Mark _____ Purch. 19___ Pd $ _____

E-5379   Girl Sweeping
"Isn't He Precious"

Unpainted - $500 up/NE

C	$55	FL	$35	GC	$30	H	$30
D	$40	BA	$35	B	$30		
OB	$40	FLM	$35	TRP	$30		
CT	$40	V	$35	S	$30		

Comments: 1984; Original Retail $20.00/$30.00
Three "unpainted" pieces known to have been found in 1988. Appeared on 1983 Christmas card. Part of the Large Nativity Set. ***See #19, page XIII.***

Personal Data: _____
____Want Mark ____ Mark _____ Purch. 19___ Pd $ _____

E-5380   Shepherd at Manger/Butterfly
"A Monarch Is Born"

SUSP. 1986 - 10 YEARS AGO
PRODUCED FOR ONLY 3 YEARS

C	$100
D	$85
OB	$80

DARK MONARCH - $300   RARE!
Comments: 1984; Original Retail $33.00
A very vivid orange and black monarch butterfly was found on sample pieces. A change to produce it in pastels disappointed many collectors! I feel there were so many manger pieces that this could have been the reason for suspension. Sometimes these sample pieces get in the hands of Reps to display and they sell them later. Keep a lookout for the "dark" monarch. This piece is probably more scarce than many realize!

Personal Data: _____
____Want Mark ____ Mark _____ Purch. 19___ Pd $ _____

E-5381   Two Shepherds Whispering at Manger
"His Name Is Jesus"

SUSP. 1987 - 9 YEARS AGO

C	$125	OB	$100
D	$110	CT	$100

Comments: 1984; Original Retail $45.00/$50.00
I feel this is more scarce than collectors realize. One of my favorites!

Personal Data: _____
____Want Mark ____ Mark _____ Purch. 19___ Pd $ _____

E-5382   *NATIVITY* Set of Four   (5")
"For God So Loved The World"

SUSP. 1986 - 10 YEARS AGO

C	$130
D	$110
OB	$110

Comments: 1984; Original Retail $70.00
Has not been as collectible as the original 9-pc. Nativity Set. Many said "heads" were too large. Prices down from '94.

Personal Data: _____
____Want Mark ____ Mark _____ Purch. 19___ Pd $ _____

E-5383   Choir Girl
"Wishing You A Merry Christmas"

DATED 1984   C $42.50   D $38

Comments: 1984; Original Retail $17.00
First dated figurine produced. Surprisingly, this first dated figurine has had very little collectible significance to the avid collector to date. I have found dated ornaments more popular among collectors than the dated figurines. Reported with Dove mark. Very slow seller on the secondary market.

Personal Data: _____
____Want Mark ____ Mark _____ Purch. 19___ Pd $ _____

E-5384   Miniature Drummer Boy
"I'll Play My Drum For Him"

C	$30	FL	$18	GC	$16	H	$16
D	$28	BA	$18	B	$16		
OB	$22	FLM	$18	TRP	$16		
CT	$22	V	$16	S	$16		

Comments: 1984; Original Retail $10.00/$16.00
Many avid collectors were upset to see this piece produced as it was a reproduction of the 1982 dated ornament! All that was changed was the removal of the date and the hook from the head! This practice has been discontinued! It was recommended by collectors and retailers not to reproduce similar dated ornaments two years in a row. Secondary market values do not climb if the piece is seven or eight years old and still being produced.

Personal Data: _____
___Want Mark ____ Mark _____ Purch. 19__ Pd $ _____

E-5385   Miniature Boy Angel with Candle
"Oh Worship The Lord"

SUSP. 1986 - 10 YEARS AGO   C $55   OB $40
                                  D $45

Comments: 1984; Original Retail $10.00
Reproduction of E-2367 ornament and E-2365 figurine; made smaller previously in 1982. Why then the 1984 license date? Is it that any time the picture is reproduced in a different form, the picture has to be relicensed or has there been a misprint on the factory's part? This question has remained unanswered for several years. In my opinion, it was an error.

Personal Data: _____
___Want Mark ____ Mark _____ Purch. 19__ Pd $ _____

E-5386   Miniature Girl Angel in Bonnet Praying
"Oh Worship The Lord"

SUSP. 1986 - 10 YEARS AGO   C $60   OB $45
                                  D $50

Comments: 1984; Original Retail $10.00
A reproduction of E-2366 and retired ornament E-2368. Changes: no hook (as ornament had) and smaller than the figurine.

Personal Data: _____
___Want Mark ____ Mark _____ Purch. 19__ Pd $ _____

E-5387   *ORNAMENT* - Choir Girl
"Wishing You A Merry Christmas"

DATED 1984   C $30

Comments: 1984; Original Retail $10.00
The fourth dated ornament.

Personal Data: _____
___Want Mark ____ Mark _____ Purch. 19__ Pd $ _____

E-5388   *ORNAMENT* - Shepherd Playing Harp
"Joy To The World"

RETIRED 1987 - 9 YEARS AGO
              C $40   OB $35
              D $35   CT $35

Comments: 1984; Original Retail $10.00/$11.00
First appeared on a tin container in 1981 but the license date on the ornament is 1984. Very small amount of trading found in recent years.

Personal Data: _____
___Want Mark ____ Mark _____ Purch. 19__ Pd $ _____

E-5389   *ORNAMENT* - Choir Boy
"Peace On Earth"

SUSP. 1986 - 10 YEARS AGO   C $45
                                    D $40
                                 OB $35

Comments: 1984; Original Retail $10.00

Personal Data: _____
___Want Mark ____ Mark _____ Purch. 19__ Pd $ _____

E-5390   *ORNAMENT* - Girl /Birdhouse
"May God Bless You With A Perfect Holiday Season"

SUSP. 1989 - 7 YEARS AGO

C	$38	CT	$30
D	$35	FL	$25
OB	$30	BA	$25

Comments: 1984; Original Retail $10.00/$13.50
Same girl that was in figurine E-0503.

Personal Data: _____
___Want Mark ____ Mark _____ Purch. 19__ Pd $ _____

E-5391 ORNAMENT - Girl w/Cheese w/Bow
"Love Is Kind"

SUSP. 1989 - 7 YEARS AGO

C	$38	CT	$30
D	$35	FL	$30
OB	$35	BA	$30

Comments: 1984; Original Retail $10.00/$13.50
Several figurines and ornaments have the same inscription. E-1379A also has the same inscription as this one.

Personal Data: _____
___Want Mark ___ Mark ____ Purch. 19__ Pd $ _____

E-5392 ORNAMENT - Baby in Cradle
"Blessed Are The Pure In Heart"

DATED 1984   C $35

Comments: 1983; Original Retail $10.00
1984 Annual Edition. **See #29, page XIV.**

Personal Data: _____
___Want Mark ___ Mark ____ Purch. 19__ Pd $ _____

E-5393 BELL - Choir Girl
"Wishing You A Merry Christmas"

DATED 1984   C $45

Comments: 1984; Original Retail $19.00
Fourth dated bell. Bells not selling in abundance!

Personal Data: _____
___Want Mark ___ Mark ____ Purch. 19__ Pd $ _____

E-5394 ♪ MUSICAL - Girls with Puppy
"Wishing You A Merry Christmas"

SUSP. 1986 - 10 YEARS AGO C	$130
D	$125
OB	$115

Comments: 1984; Original Retail $55.00
Plays *We Wish You A Merry Christmas*. Also has been found to play Joy To The World. This piece has been found with NM. Not easily found.

Personal Data: _____
___Want Mark ___ Mark ____ Purch. 19__ Pd $ _____

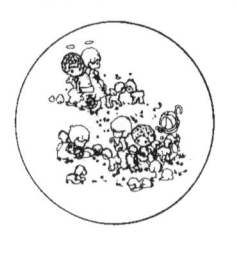

E-5395 PLATE - Angels in Chariot
"Unto Us A Child Is Born"

LE 1984 - 12 YEARS OLD

MM	$55
C	$50

Comments: 1984; Original Retail $40.00
Fourth and Final Edition of *Christmas Collection Series*; 1984 Limited Edition 15,000. Several have been found without a mark. Marks are placed in the mold, not pressed in later.

Personal Data: _____
___Want Mark ___ Mark ____ Purch. 19__ Pd $ _____

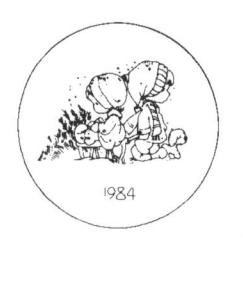

E-5396 PLATE - Boy/Girl/Sled
"The Wonder Of Christmas"

DATED 1984

MM	$45
C	$40

Comments: 1984; Original Retail $40.00
Third issue in *Joy of Christmas Series*. Plates are beautiful, but not in demand by collectors.

Personal Data: _____
___Want Mark ___ Mark ____ Purch. 19__ Pd $ _____

E-5397 DOLL - Jogger
"Timmy"

SUSP. 1991 - 5 YEARS

MM	$160	OB	$150	BA	$150
C	$155	CT	$150	FLM	$150
D	$155	FL	$150	V	$150

Comments: 1984; Original Retail $125/$150
Most dolls, if marked, are marked on the back of their necks. (Bride/Groom are hand-numbered on foot.) Notice the price differences in retail. Some collectors may be willing to sell for less because they paid the lower price.

Personal Data: _____
___Want Mark ___ Mark ____ Purch. 19__ Pd $ _____

E-5619 Baby Sleeping in Manger
"Come Let Us Adore Him"

SUSP. 1985 - 11 YEARS AGO

NM	$50	F	$30
T	$45	C	$30
HG	$35	D	$30

Comments: 1980; Original Retail $10.00/$11.00
Abundant in 1982.

Personal Data: _____
___Want Mark ___ Mark ____ Purch. 19__ Pd $ _____

E-5620   ***BELL -***   **Shepherd**

"We Have Seen His Star"

SUSP. 1985 - 11 YEARS AGO

MM	$50	C	$40
HG	$40	D	$40

Comments: 1980; Original Retail $15.00/$19.00
Most bells not marked.

Personal Data: _____
____Want Mark ____ Mark _____ Purch. 19__ Pd $ _____

E-5621   **Donkey**

MM	$32	FL	$15	B	$15
C	$18	BA	$15	TRP	$15
D	$18	FLM	$15	S	$15
OB	$16	V	$15	H	$15
CT	$15	GC	$15		

Comments: 1980; Original Retail $6.00/$15.00
Very few sales reported - easily found at retail.

Personal Data: _____
____Want Mark ____ Mark _____ Purch. 19__ Pd $ _____

Precious Moments®
Vinyl Dolls
Celebrate Christmas

Photos by Ron Graber

E-5622   *BELL* - Angel
"Let The Heavens Rejoice"

DATED 1981   NM $180

Comments: 1980; Original Retail $15.00
This is the first dated bell. This li'l angel is in stone along the path to the Chapel. Would be ideal for our outside gardens! Most sought after bell in my opinion. 1981 ornament has same li'l angel. Considered a No Mark because it was produced before mid '81, before pieces were produced with the Triangle mark. Price rose to $200 in '94/'95. Late '95 prices dropped to $150-175.

Personal Data: _____
___Want Mark _____ Mark _____ Purch. 19__ Pd $ _____

E-5623   *BELL* - Shepherd with Staff
"Jesus Is Born"

SUSP. 1984 - 12 YEARS AGO   MM $45
                                    C $40

Comments: 1980; Original Retail $15.00/$19.00

Personal Data: _____
___Want Mark _____ Mark _____ Purch. 19__ Pd $ _____

E-5624   *NATIVITY* - Camels with Wise Men (3 pc.)
"They Followed The Star"

NM	$345	D	$235	FLM	$230	S	$225
T	$280	OB	$230	V	$230	H	$225
HG	$260	CT	$230	GC	$225		
F	$250	FL	$230	B	$225		
C	$240	BA	$230	TRP	$225		

Comments: 1980; Original Retail $130.00/$225.00
It's been said some camels had no blankets. It's my opinion only sample pieces had no blankets. Large pieces usually do not rise on the secondary market as fast as smaller figurines but since 1991 we've seen several larger NM pieces begin to escalate due to demand. Very few secondary market sales reported on this set in past three years. Maybe time for suspension.

Personal Data: _____
___Want Mark _____ Mark _____ Purch. 19__ Pd $ _____

E-5627   *ORNAMENT* - Boy Angel on Cloud
"But Love Goes On Forever"

SUSP. 1985 - 11 YEARS AGO	NM	$145	F	$105
	T	$130	C	$100
	HG	$115	D	$100

Comments: 1981; Original Retail $6.00/$10.00
Scarce since 1989. Due to scarcity, prices are quite high.

Personal Data: _____
___Want Mark _____ Mark _____ Purch. 19__ Pd $ _____

E-5628   *ORNAMENT* - Girl Angel on Cloud
"But Love Goes On Forever"

SUSP. 1985 - 11 YEARS AGO	NM	$145	F	$110
	T	$140	C	$100
	HG	$120	D	$100

Comments: 1981; Original Retail $6.00/$10.00
Scarce. Tends to be more sought after than the Boy Angel, E-5627. Insure at these prices.

Personal Data: _____
___Want Mark _____ Mark _____ Purch. 19__ Pd $ _____

E-5629   *ORNAMENT* - Angel
"Let The Heavens Rejoice"

DATED 1981

	NM	$230
Most sought after ornament...	T	$215
No patch on gown........... Rare!	NM	$275
	T	$265
Patch w/no paint..... Very Rare!	NM	$310
	T	$300

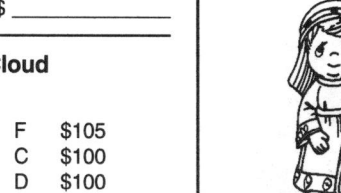

Comments: 1981; Original Retail $6.00
Patch missing on limited amount – sought after on secondary market. Significant piece for the avid collector. The patch with no paint is very rare. I have seen both errors. ***See #29, page XIV.***

Personal Data: _____
___Want Mark _____ Mark _____ Purch. 19__ Pd $ _____

E-5630   *ORNAMENT* - Shepherd
"Unto Us A Child Is Born"

SUSP. 1985 - 11 YEARS AGO	NM	$75	F	$55
	T	$60	C	$50
	HG	$55	D	$50

Comments: 1981; Original Retail $6.00/$10.00
(A small figurine identical to this ornament was placed in approx. 5000 of small Nativity Set E-2395.) If the "correct one" as shown on the box from Enesco was requested, then the retailer replaced the incorrect one with the correct shepherd. This is why we are finding the "lone" Turban Boy on the secondary market. He was not necessarily being sold separately from the set. Some collectors were able to purchase the correct piece if ordered by their retailer and they kept the turban boy. Has been found with "Isn't He Wonderful" on the box.

Personal Data: _____
___Want Mark _____ Mark _____ Purch. 19__ Pd $ _____

E-5631   *ORNAMENT* - Boy with Teddy
"Baby's First Christmas"

SUSP. 1985 - 11 YEARS AGO

NM	$75	F	$50
T	$60	C	$45
HG	$50	D	$45

Comments: 1980; Original Retail $6.00/$10.00

Personal Data: _____
___Want Mark _____ Mark _____ Purch. 19__ Pd $ _____

E-5632   *ORNAMENT* - Girl with Bunny
"Baby's First Christmas"

SUSP. 1985 - 11 YEARS AGO

NM	$75	F	$50
T	$70	C	$50
HG	$52	D	$45

Comments: 1980; Original Retail $6.00/$10.00
Suspension has increased demand.

Personal Data: _____
___Want Mark _____ Mark _____ Purch. 19__ Pd $ _____

E-5633   *NATIVITY - ORNAMENT* - 4 pc. Set
"Come Let Us Adore Him"

SUSP. 1984 - 12 YEARS AGO

NM	$155	F	$130
T	$150	C	$130
HG	$140		

Comments: 1981; Original Retail $20.00/$31.50
Not easily found.

Personal Data: _____
___Want Mark _____ Mark _____ Purch. 19__ Pd $ _____

E-5634   *ORNAMENT* - Set of Three Kings
"Wee Three Kings"

SUSP. 1984 - 12 YEARS AGO

NM	$140	F	$120
T	$130	C	$120
HG	$125		

Comments: 1980; Original Retail $25.00/$27.50
Scarce.

Personal Data: _____
___Want Mark _____ Mark _____ Purch. 19__ Pd $ _____

E-5635   *NATIVITY* - Set of Three Kings
"Wee Three Kings"

NM	$150	D	$80	FLM	$75	S	$75
T	$135	OB	$75	V	$75	H	$75
HG	$95	CT	$75	GC	$75		
F	$80	FL	$75	B	$75		
C	$80	BA	$75	TRP	$75		

Comments: 1980; Original Retail $40.00/$75.00
Originals were very colorful. NMs were somewhat scarce. See the section on pewter for the Three Kings pewter prices. When a piece is still in production, as in this case, collectors feel no need to pay much more than retail on most pieces except for the first three marks (NM, T and HG). ***See #13, page XII.***

Personal Data: _____
___Want Mark _____ Mark _____ Purch. 19__ Pd $ _____

E-5636   *NATIVITY* - Angel with Trumpet
"Rejoice O Earth"

NM	$80	D	$35	FLM	$30	S	$30
T	$65	OB	$30	V	$30	H	$30
HG	$55	CT	$30	GC	$30		
F	$40	FL	$30	B	$30		
C	$35	BA	$30	TRP	$30		

Comments: 1980; Original Retail $15.00/$30.00
Abundant - good candidate for suspension or retirement! Nativity pieces market well for sets.

Personal Data: _____
___Want Mark _____ Mark _____ Purch. 19__ Pd $ _____

E-5637   *NATIVITY* - Angel with Flashlight
"The Heavenly Light"

NM	$90	D	$40	FLM	$30	S	$30
T	$70	OB	$38	V	$30	H	$30
HG	$55	CT	$38	GC	$30		
F	$50	FL	$34	B	$30		
C	$40	BA	$34	TRP	$30		

Comments: 1980; Original Retail $15.00/$30.00
Perfect for retirement, but pieces that go with the Nativity set tend to stick around.

Personal Data: _____
___Want Mark _____ Mark _____ Purch. 19__ Pd $ _____

E5638   *NATIVITY* **- Cow with Bell**

NM	$45	CT	$35	V	$32.50	S	$32.50
C	$40	FL	$32.50	GC	$32.50	H	$32.50
D	$40	BA	$32.50	B	$32.50		
OB	$35	FLM	$32.50	TRP	$32.50		

Comments: 1980; Original Retail $16.00/$32.50
Most were never marked; abundant in 1983. Originals never had license date. The longer a piece is produced (6 to 8 years or more), the less we've found an increase in price. Suspension has been an answer in helping the secondary market values rise on many. Nativity pieces not being suspended or retired as they go well with the Nativity set.

Personal Data: _____
____Want Mark _____ Mark _____ Purch. 19__ Pd $ _____

E-5639   **Angel with Harp**
   "Isn't He Wonderful"

SUSP. 1985 - 11 YEARS AGO

NM	$75	F	$55
T	$70	C	$55
HG	$65	D	$50

Comments: 1980; Original Retail $12.00/$17.00

Personal Data: _____
____Want Mark _____ Mark _____ Purch. 19__ Pd $ _____

E-5640   **Kneeling Girl Angel with Harp**
   "Isn't He Wonderful"

SUSP. 1985 - 11 YEARS AGO

NM	$75	F	$55
T	$70	C	$55
HG	$65	D	$50

Comments: 1980; Original Retail $12.00/$17.00

Personal Data: _____
____Want Mark _____ Mark _____ Purch. 19__ Pd $ _____

E-5641   **"Follow Me" Angel with Three Kings**
   "They Followed The Star"

SUSP. 1985 - 11 YEARS AGO

NM	$235	F	$190
T	$225	C	$185
HG	$200	D	$185

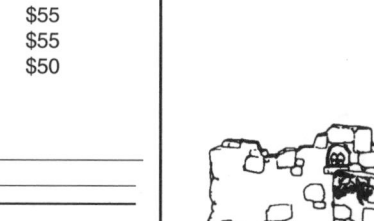

Comments: 1980; Original Retail $75/$100
Extra large and heavy piece; four figures on base. Becoming harder to find. *See #20, page XIII.*

Personal Data: _____
____Want Mark _____ Mark _____ Purch. 19__ Pd $ _____

E-5642   ♪ *MUSICAL* **- Sleeping Knight with Angel**
   "Silent Knight"

SUSP. 1985 - 11 YEARS AGO

NM	$325	F	$225
T	$265	C	$225
HG	$250	D	$225

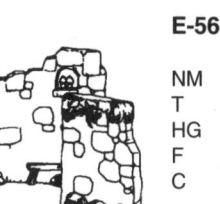

Comments: 1980; Original Retail $45.00/$60.00
Plays *Silent Night*. Hard to find, especially NM and T. Escalated in price since '93. This is probably because there is no figurine similar to this piece. Look for this if you're wanting the unusual pieces.
See #21, page XIII.

Personal Data: _____
___Want Mark _____ Mark _____ Purch. 19__ Pd $ _____

E-5644   *NATIVITY* **- Walls - 2 Sections**

NM	$170	D	$120	FLM	$120	S	$120
T	$155	OB	$120	V	$120		
HG	$145	CT	$120	GC	$120		
F	$135	FL	$120	B	$120		
C	$135	BA	$120	TRP	$120		

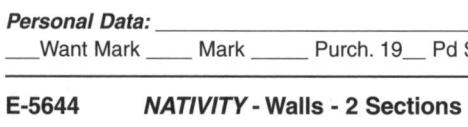

Comments: 1980; Original Retail $60.00/$120.00
It hasn't been a necessity, for some reason, to own the first marks of the buildings and walls. *See #15, page XIII.*

Personal Data: _____
___Want Mark _____ Mark _____ Purch. 19__ Pd $ _____

E-5645   ♪ *MUSICAL* **- Angel with Trumpet**
   "Rejoice O Earth"

RETIRED 1988 - 8 YEARS AGO

NM	$150	D	$100
T	$145	OB	$100
HG	$125	CT	$100
F	$100	FL	$100
C	$100		

Comments: 1980; Original Retail $35.00/$55.00
Plays *Joy To The World*.

Personal Data: _____
___Want Mark _____ Mark _____ Purch. 19__ Pd $ _____

E-5646   PLATE - Nativity
"Come Let Us Adore Him"

LE 1981 - 15 YEARS OLD

         NM $50

Comments: 1980; Original Retail $40.00
First in *Christmas Collection Series*. 1981 Limited Edition 15,000. This piece is a favorite of many.

Personal Data: _____
___Want Mark _____ Mark _____ Purch. 19__ Pd $ _____

E-6118   CANDLE CLIMBERS - Boy/Girl Angels
"But Love Goes On Forever"

SUSP. 1988 - 8 YEARS AGO

NM	$105	D	$85
T	$90	OB	$85
F	$85	CT	$85
C	$85	FL	$85

Comments: 1981; Original Retail $14.00/$25.00
Pair of Candle Climbers. Most were not marked. Only two different styles of candle climbers were produced. Adorable in a candle display. Very small number of sales found. Scarce on secondary market.

Personal Data: _____
___Want Mark _____ Mark _____ Purch. 19__ Pd $ _____

E-6120   ORNAMENT - Boy Carrying Lamb
"We Have Seen His Star"

RETIRED 1984 - 12 YEARS AGO

NM	$75	F	$60
T	$65	C	$50
HG	$60		

Comments: 1980; Original Retail $9.00/$10.00

Personal Data: _____
___Want Mark _____ Mark _____ Purch. 19__ Pd $ _____

E-6214B   DOLL – "Mikey"

SUSP. 1985 - 11 YEARS AGO

NM	$245	C	$225
HG	$240	D	$225
F	$235		

Comments: 1980; Original Retail $175.00/$200.00
This doll is usually purchased along with the Debbie doll as a set. Mark is found on neck. Very little trading on dolls in the past five years.

Personal Data: _____
___Want Mark _____ Mark _____ Purch. 19__ Pd $ _____

E-6214G   DOLL – "Debbie"

SUSP. 1985 - 11 YEARS AGO

NM	$250	F	$225	C	$225
HG	$240	D	$225		

Comments: 1980; Original Retail $175/$200
Marks began in 1983 on back of neck with HG mark. Produced in '82 but arrived for '83 sales. Very little trading on dolls the past five years.

Personal Data: _____
___Want Mark _____ Mark _____ Purch. 19__ Pd $ _____

E-6613   Girl with Present and Kitten
"God Sends The Gift Of His Love"

SUSP. 1987 - 9 YEARS AGO

F	$75	D	$65	CT	$55
C	$65	OB	$60		

Comments: 1984; Original Retail $22.50/$25.00

Personal Data: _____
___Want Mark _____ Mark _____ Purch. 19__ Pd $ _____

E-6901   PLAQUE - Oval Shaped w/Boy Angel
"Precious Moments Last Forever"

SUSP. 1986 - 10 YEARS AGO

HG	$125	C	$45	OB	$40
F	$55	D	$40	CT	$40

Comments: 1981; Original Retail $19.00/$20.00
Was available in 1982 but very few appeared on merchants' shelves due to E-6901 being left off the retailers' order blanks. Suspension may influence the secondary market in the future. Large production in '84 and '85. A new plaque debuted in 1990, #230448. Many retailers learned of this piece by reading *Precious Collectibles™*! Another reason you should subscribe!

Personal Data: _____
___Want Mark _____ Mark _____ Purch. 19__ Pd $ _____

E-7153   Boy Holding Heart
"God Is Love, Dear Valentine"

SUSP. 1986 - 10 YEARS AGO

NM	$65	F	$30	OB	$30
T	$55	C	$30		
HG	$40	D	$30		

Comments: 1981; Original Retail $16.00/$17.00
Boy was a slower seller than the girl (E-7154) at retail. Not hard to locate on the secondary market.

Personal Data: _____
___Want Mark _____ Mark _____ Purch. 19__ Pd $ _____

E-7154 Girl Holding Heart
"God Is Love, Dear Valentine"

SUSP. 1986 - 10 YEARS AGO

NM	$70	C	$30
T	$55	D	$30
HG	$40	OB	$30
F	$30		

Comments: 1981; Original Retail $16.00/$17.00
Quite abundant.

Personal Data: _____
____Want Mark ____ Mark _____ Purch. 19__ Pd $ _____

E-7155 Praying Girl
"Thanking Him For You"

SUSP. 1984 - 12 YEARS AGO

HG	$65
F	$55
C	$45

Comments: 1981; Original Retail $16.00/$17.00
Very plain figurine. Also appeared on bell. Was not a "best seller."

Personal Data: _____
____Want Mark ____ Mark _____ Purch. 19__ Pd $ _____

E-7156 Boy Holding Yellow Chick
"I Believe In Miracles"

SUSP. 1985 - 11 YEARS AGO
REISSUED IN 1987 AS E-7156R

HG	$120	D	$85
F	$110	FL	$85
C	$90	BA	$100

Comments: 1981; Original Retail $17.00/$19.00
Original piece, J&D licensee, no "Sam B." embossed on side. Boy with Yellow Chick was reissued in 1987. The only change was the color of the chick to blue. New mold later produced including large head, blue bird, etc. Order number was changed to E-7156R (see next entry). Has been found with MM – oddity! As it has been stated that no suspended piece will be retired unless it has been brought back from suspension (E-7156R), it is my opinion that this piece should also now be considered "retired" as it came back from suspension and the new piece was retired! This piece has been reported with a BA mark even though it was suspended earlier.

Personal Data: _____
____Want Mark ____ Mark _____ Purch. 19__ Pd $ _____

E-7156R Boy Holding Blue Bird
"I Believe In Miracles"

RETIRED 1992 - 4 YEARS AGO
RETURNED FROM SUSPENSION IN 1987

Large Head, Blue Chick, has "Sam B."

CT	$80	FLM	$55
FL	$70	V	$55
BA	$65		

Small Head, Blue Bird, no "Sam B."	RARE	CT	$200
Large Head, Yellow Chick, no "Sam B."	RARE	FL	$165

Comments: 1985; Original Retail $22.50/$27.50
R = Returned from Suspension.
Licensee Samuel J. Butcher Co. Made from Original Mold E-7156 with blue bird; then remolded with blue bird, large head on boy. Most avid collectors had this piece at the time of the Retirement announcement. This can be very confusing. If you want an avid collector's piece, it would be E-7156 (HG) and E-7156R with yellow chick. Very little trading in recent years for this piece. *See #5, 24, & 25, pages XI & XIV.*

Personal Data: _____
____Want Mark ____ Mark _____ Purch. 19__ Pd $ _____

E-7157 Waitress
"There Is Joy In Serving Jesus"

RETIRED 1986 - 10 YEARS AGO

HG	$65	D	$50
F	$50	OB	$40
C	$50		

Comments: 1981; Original Retail $17.00/$19.00
OB abundant! Display with *Eggs Over Easy* on a kitchen shelf!

Personal Data: _____
____Want Mark ____ Mark _____ Purch. 19__ Pd $ _____

E-7158 Nurse with Bear
"Love Beareth All Things"

HG	$70	CT	$45	GC	$45
F	$50	FL	$45	B	$45
C	$50	BA	$45	TRP	$45
D	$45	FLM	$45	S	$45
OB	$45	V	$45	H	$45

Comments: 1981; Original Retail $25.00/$45.00
Still in production; this causes a slow secondary market. Very cute piece. Popular gift item. If it sells well then it won't get retired or suspended, but it is 15 years old! Maybe 523739 will take over? Retail price raised in '96.

Personal Data: _____
____Want Mark ____ Mark _____ Purch. 19__ Pd $ _____

E-7159   Bandaged Boy by Sign
"Lord Give Me Patience"

SUSP. 1985 - 11 YEARS AGO

HG	$55	D	$45
F	$50	OB	$45
C	$45		

Comments: 1981; Original Retail $25.00/$27.50
No decal on sign, add $100 to above prices. This happens to most figurines that require similar decals; only a few are considered an error. Add $100 for decals missing from figurines (not on base).
See #15, page XIII.

Personal Data: _____
___Want Mark ____ Mark _____ Purch. 19__ Pd $ _____

E-7160   Grandpa in Rocking Chair with Dog
"The Perfect Grandpa"

SUSP. 1986 - 10 YEARS AGO

HG	$75	D	$55
F	$65	OB	$55
C	$60		

Comments: 1981; Original Retail $25.00/$27.50
The Grandpa ornament was suspended in 1990.

Personal Data: _____
___Want Mark ____ Mark _____ Purch. 19__ Pd $ _____

E-7161   Boy Painting Lamb
"His Sheep Am I"

SUSP. 1984 - 12 YEARS AGO

MM	$100	F	$70
HG	$75	C	$70

Comments: 1981; Original Retail $25.00/$27.50
Some crosses on sheep were not painted. Rare! Add $75-$100 to the above values. Another collector reported her HG marked piece was missing the word "paint" on the bucket; add $50-$75 for this error. We have had "one" report of MM; this has occurred on many recent figurines (the mark has been left off the mold).

Personal Data: _____
___Want Mark ____ Mark _____ Purch. 19__ Pd $ _____

E-7162   Girl at School Desk
"Love Is Sharing"

SUSP. 1984 - 12 YEARS AGO

HG	$165
F	$145
C	$140

Comments: 1981; Original Retail $25.00/$27.50
Was in production only three years.

Personal Data: _____
___Want Mark ____ Mark _____ Purch. 19__ Pd $ _____

E-7163   Boy with Ice Bag
"God Is Watching Over You"

SUSP. 1984 - 12 YEARS AGO

HG	$120	C	$80
F	$90		

Comments: 1981; Original Retail $27.50/$30.00
This piece is scarce - only produced three years. I purchased one that had nothing on the base, no decal - nothing!

Personal Data: _____
___Want Mark ____ Mark _____ Purch. 19__ Pd $ _____

E-7164   Boy/Girl Painting Dog House
"Bless This House"

SUSP. 1984 - 12 YEARS AGO

HG	$210	C	$170
F	$175		

Comments: 1981; Original Retail $45.00/$50.00
Not easily found on the secondary market. Only available three years. Between 1982-1984, large pieces were not ordered by retailers as often as smaller pieces. Becoming harder to find each year.

Personal Data: _____
___Want Mark ____ Mark _____ Purch. 19__ Pd $ _____

E-7165   Boy/Girl in Tub
"Let The Whole World Know"

SUSP. 1987 - 9 YEARS AGO

HG	$125	D	$90
F	$105	OB	$85
C	$95	CT	$85

Comments: 1981; Original Retail $45.00/$55.00
HG was hard to find when it debuted in '82. I drove many a mile to find it. Cute piece! ***See #23, page XIII.***

Personal Data: _____
___Want Mark ____ Mark _____ Purch. 19__ Pd $ _____

E-7166   *FRAME* - Bride & Groom
"The Lord Bless You And Keep You"

SUSP. 1993 - 2 YEARS AGO

HG	$65	OB	$50	FLM	$45
F	$58	CT	$50	V	$45
C	$55	FL	$45	GC	$40
D	$55	BA	$45	B	$40

Comments: 1982; Original Retail $22.50/$32.50
See #8, page XII

Personal Data: _____
___Want Mark ____ Mark _____ Purch. 19__ Pd $ _____

E-7167   CONTAINER - Bride and Groom
"The Lord Bless You And Keep You"

SUSP. 1985 - 11 YEARS

HG	$50	C	$45
F	$50	D	$40

Comments: 1981; Original Retail $22.50/$25.00
Container with lid. Not a popular seller when it debuted.

Personal Data: _____
____Want Mark ____ Mark _____ Purch. 19__ Pd $ _____

E-7168   FRAME - Boy Angel
"My Guardian Angel"

SUSP. 1984 - 12 YEARS AGO

HG	$75
F	$70
C	$70

Comments: 1981; Original Retail $18.00/$19.00
Here's a challenge... find all of the frames!! Very scarce.
See #8, page XII

Personal Data: _____
____Want Mark ____ Mark _____ Purch. 19__ Pd $ _____

E-7169   FRAME - Girl Angel
"My Guardian Angel"

SUSP. 1984 - 12 YEARS AGO

HG	$75
F	$70
C	$70

Comments: 1981; Original Retail $18.00/$19.00
Very scarce. *See #8, page XII*

Personal Data: _____
____Want Mark ____ Mark _____ Purch. 19__ Pd $ _____

E-7170   FRAME - Boy with Teddy
"Jesus Loves Me"

SUSP. 1985 - 11 YEARS AGO

HG	$65	C	$55
F	$55	D	$55

Comments: 1981; Original Retail $17.00/$19.00
See #8, page XII.

Personal Data: _____
____Want Mark ____ Mark _____ Purch. 19__ Pd $ _____

E-7171   FRAME - Girl with Bunny
"Jesus Loves Me"

SUSP. 1985 - 11 YEARS AGO

HG	$65	C	$50
F	$60	D	$55

Comments: 1981; Original Retail $17.00/$19.00
E-7170 and this piece are equally scarce! *See #8, page XII.*

Personal Data: _____
____Want Mark ____ Mark _____ Purch. 19__ Pd $ _____

E-7172   PLATE - Christening
"Rejoicing With You"

SUSP. 1985 - 11 YEARS AGO

MM	$40
C	$40
D	$35

Comments: 1981; Original Retail $30.00
7" Plate. Plates are beautiful and easy to find for even less than these prices. *See #1, page XI.*

Personal Data: _____
____Want Mark ____ Mark _____ Purch. 19__ Pd $ _____

E-7173   PLATE - Perfect Grandma
"The Purr-fect Grandma"

LE 1982 - 14 YEARS AGO

MM	$48
C	$45

Comments: 1981; Original Retail $40.00
8 1/2" Plate. 1982 Limited Edition 15,000. Second issue of *Mother's Love Series. See #1, page XI .*

Personal Data: _____
____Want Mark ____ Mark _____ Purch. 19__ Pd $ _____

E-7174   PLATE - Goose Girl
"Make A Joyful Noise"

LE 15,000

NM	$48
C	$40

Comments: 1981; Original Retail $40.00
8 1/2" Plate.   Limited Edition 15,000. Second issue of *Inspired Thoughts Series*. Debuted in '82. *See #1, page XI.*

Personal Data: _____
____Want Mark ____ Mark _____ Purch. 19__ Pd $ _____

E-7175 BELL - Boy Graduate
"The Lord Bless You And Keep You"

SUSP. 1985 - 11 YEARS AGO

MM	$55	D	$45
C	$50		

Comments: 1980; Original Retail $17.00/$19.00
Most bells unmarked. Debuted in '82. Seem to be more graduate bells than others. Girl is harder to locate as more bells are given to girl graduates than to boy graduates.

Personal Data: _____
___Want Mark ____ Mark _____ Purch. 19__ Pd $ _____

E-7176 BELL - Girl Graduate
"The Lord Bless You And Keep You"

SUSP. 1985 - 11 YEARS AGO

MM	$55	D	$45
C	$50		

Comments: 1980; Original Retail $17.00/$19.00
Most bells unmarked.

Personal Data: _____
___Want Mark ____ Mark _____ Purch. 19__ Pd $ _____

E-7177 FRAME - Boy Graduate
"The Lord Bless You And Keep You"

SUSP. 1987 - 9 YEARS AGO

NM	$70	F	$55	OB	$45
T	$60	C	$50	CT	$45
HG	$58	D	$50		

Comments: 1980; Original Retail $18.00/$20.00
Frames are not easily found. Have been told by several collectors that frames are now their ultimate goal to collect. ***See #8, page XII.***

Personal Data: _____
___Want Mark ____ Mark _____ Purch. 19__ Pd $ _____

E-7178 FRAME - Girl Graduate
"The Lord Bless You And Keep You"

SUSP. 1987 - 9 YEARS AGO

NM	$75	F	$55	OB	$50
T	$65	C	$55	CT	$50
HG	$60	D	$55		

Comments: 1980; Original Retail $18.00/$20.00
D through CT are more easily found than previous marks. Frames and Containers are becoming harder to find as they were not collected by the avid collector in the 70s and early 80s. ***See #8, page XII***

Personal Data: _____
___Want Mark ____ Mark _____ Purch. 19__ Pd $ _____

E-7179 BELL - Bride and Groom
"The Lord Bless You And Keep You"

SUSP. 1993 - 3 YEARS AGO

MM	$60	OB	$50	BA	$50	GC	$50
C	$60	CT	$50	FLM	$50	B	$50
D	$50	FL	$50	V	$50		

Comments: 1982; Original Retail $22.50/$35.00
MM favorite for avid collectors. Pretty bell! Easy to find.

Personal Data: _____
___Want Mark ____ Mark _____ Purch. 19__ Pd $ _____

E-7180 ♪ MUSICAL - Bride and Groom/Cake
"The Lord Bless You And Keep You"

MM	$140	D	$95	BA	$85	B	$85
HG	$115	OB	$90	FLM	$85	TRP	$85
F	$100	CT	$90	V	$85	S	$85
C	$100	FL	$90	GC	$85	H	$85

Comments: 1979; Original Retail $55.00/$85.00
Plays *Wedding March* by Mendelssohn. MM and HG are the avid collectors' favorites! Time to retire or be suspended. ***See #16, page XIII.***

Personal Data: _____
___Want Mark ____ Mark _____ Purch. 19__ Pd $ _____

E-7181 BELL - Mother Needlepointing
"Mother Sew Dear"

SUSP. 1988 - 8 YEARS AGO

		MM	$55	OB	$50
		C	$55	CT	$45
		D	$50	FL	$45

Comments: 1981; Original Retail $17.00/$22.50
We don't see many bells at collectible swap 'n sells or in ads as in earlier days. This is a pretty bell!

Personal Data: _____
___Want Mark ____ Mark _____ Purch. 19__ Pd $ _____

E-7182 ♪ MUSICAL - Mother Needlepointing
"Mother Sew Dear"

MM	$100	D	$80	BA	$65	B	$65
HG	$130	OB	$70	FLM	$65	TRP	$65
F	$85	CT	$65	V	$65	S	$65
C	$80	FL	$65	GC	$65	H	$65

Comments: 1979; Original Retail $35.00/$65.00
Plays *You Light Up My Life*. MM's are very colorful.

Personal Data: _____
___Want Mark ____ Mark _____ Purch. 19__ Pd $ _____

E-7183   *BELL* - Grandma in Rocker
"The Purr-fect Grandma"

SUSP. 1988 - 8 YEARS AGO   Inked C $40

C	$90	C	$55	OB	$50	FL	$45
MM	$60	D	$50	CT	$45		

Comments: 1981; Original Retail $17.00/22.50
Found with an inked C mark. Nice bell!

Personal Data: _____
___Want Mark ____ Mark _____ Purch. 19___ Pd $ _____

E-7184   ♪ *MUSICAL* - Grandma in Rocker
"The Purr-fect Grandma"

SUSP. 1993 - 3 YEARS AGO

MM	$110	D	$80	BA	$65	B	$60
HG	$95	OB	$75	FLM	$65		
F	$80	CT	$70	V	$65		
C	$80	FL	$75	GC	$60		

Comments: 1979; Original Retail $35.00/$60.00
Plays *Always In My Heart*. Great gift for Grandma on Mother's Day! Easy to find; do not over insure.

Personal Data: _____
___Want Mark ____ Mark _____ Purch. 19___ Pd $ _____

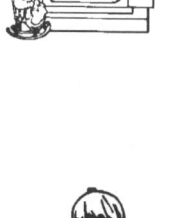

E-7185   ♪ *MUSICAL* - Girl at School Desk
"Love Is Sharing"

RETIRED 1985 - 11 YEARS AGO

		HG	$175	C	$160
		F	$165	D	$150

Comments: 1981; Original Retail $40.00/$45.00
Plays *School Days*. This piece is hard to find, mainly because it was produced only four years before retirement.

Personal Data: _____
___Want Mark ____ Mark _____ Purch. 19___ Pd $ _____

E-7186   ♪ *MUSICAL* - Boy/Girl in Tub
"Let the Whole World Know"

SUSP. 1986 - 10 YEARS AGO

		MM	$165	C	$130
		HG	$155	D	$130
		F	$135	OB	$120

Comments: 1981; Original Retail $60.00/$65.00
Plays *What A Friend We Have In Jesus*. Not plentiful. MM and HG most coveted by avid collectors.

Personal Data: _____
___Want Mark ____ Mark _____ Purch. 19___ Pd $ _____

E-7241   *FRAME* - Mother Needlepointing
"Mother Sew Dear"

SUSP. 1986 - 10 YEARS AGO

HG	$60	C	$55	OB	$50
F	$55	D	$50		

Comments: 1981; Original Retail $18.00/$19.00

Personal Data: _____
___Want Mark ____ Mark _____ Purch. 19___ Pd $ _____

E-7242   *FRAME* - Grandma in Rocker
"The Purr-fect Grandma"

SUSP. 1988 - 8 YEARS AGO

HG	$55	C	$50	OB	$50	FL	$48
F	$50	D	$50	CT	$50		

Comments: 1981; Original Retail $18.00/$22.50
Suspended eight years ago... not easily found!

Personal Data: _____
___Want Mark ____ Mark _____ Purch. 19___ Pd $ _____

E-7267B   *DOLL* - Groom
"Cubby"

LE 1981- 15 YEARS OLD

Usually sold as set only	NM Set	$750
Individual DOLL	NM	$425

Comments: 1981; Original Retail $200.00
Hand-numbered on foot. Has certificate. Limited Edition 5,000. A few sets are signed on the foot by Sam's daughter and son-in-law, "Tammy and Cubby Bearinger." They attended our Precious Collectibles Convention in '84 and signed several sets as well as cards, posters, figurines, ornaments, etc. Very few sets have been signed by them. Add $85 per set to these signed dolls. Price down from '95.

Personal Data: _____
___Want Mark ____ Mark _____ Purch. 19___ Pd $ _____

E-7267G   *DOLL* - Bride
"Tammy"

LE 1981 - 15 YEARS OLD

Usually sold as set only	NM Set	$750
Individual DOLL	NM	$500

Comments: 1981; Original Retail $300.00
Hand-numbered on foot. Has certificate. Limited Edition 5,000. Most popular PM "Collectible DOLL" set to date. See comments for E-7267B above.

Personal Data: _____
___Want Mark ____ Mark _____ Purch. 19___ Pd $ _____

E-7350 Dome with Kids on Cloud Figurine

MM $825-850 C $750-800

Comments: Gift to Centers by Enesco.
Appears to be same as E-5207 night light. Has gold plaque on dome's base. Ask your local retailer. He or she may have one and just might sell! A collector commented that this was the same size as the night light with no cord cutout. The second dome for retailers debuted in '93 with the 15-year piece ($150-$160).

Personal Data: _____
____Want Mark ____ Mark _____ Purch. 19__ Pd $ _____

E-9251 Boy with Teacher
"Love Is Patient"

SUSP. 1985 - 11 YEARS AGO

*Decaled	C	$100		
	HG	$95	C	$75
	F	$85	D	$70

Comments: 1982; Original Retail $35.00
*Inked decal C has been found. The F marked piece has been the most available piece traded. We need a $30 teacher figurine, an affordable piece for some to give to teachers. *See #24, page XIV.*

Personal Data: _____
____Want Mark ____ Mark _____ Purch. 19__ Pd $ _____

E-9252 Boy/Girl Making Up
"Forgiving Is Forgetting"

SUSP. 1989 - 7 YEARS AGO

Decaled	F	$125	D	$70
	MM	$105	OB	$70
	HG	$95	CT	$70
	F	$85	FL	$70
	C	$75	A	$65

Comments: 1981; Original Retail $37.50/$47.50
See #24, page XIV.

Personal Data: _____
____Want Mark ____ Mark _____ Purch. 19__ Pd $ _____

E-9253 Boy with Dog Ripping Britches
"The End Is In Sight"

SUSP. 1985 - 11 YEARS AGO

Decaled	F	$115	F	$65
	MM	$100	C	$60
	HG	$75	D	$60

Comments: 1982; Original Retail $25.00
Many reported sales. *See #40, page XV.*

Personal Data: _____
____Want Mark ____ Mark _____ Purch. 19__ Pd $ _____

E-9254 Secretary
"Praise The Lord Anyhow"

RETIRED 1994 - 2 YEARS AGO

"Erasable" Decaled Mark (Inked)	Very Rare	F	$195
	Decaled	F	$150

MM	$110				
HG	$145	CT	$85	GC	$80
F	$115	FL	$85	B	$75
C	$105	BA	$85	TRP	$70
D	$100	FLM	$85		
OB	$90	V	$85		

Comments: 1982; Original Retail $35.00/$55.00
Out in early '83 with HG, later in '83 with F mark. Approx. 200 pieces appeared stamped with "inked" F mark in late '83. *Precious Collectibles™* magazine was the first to report decal marks and erasable marks to collectors. Our subscribers alert us to many rarities so that we can share them with you. We have been informed of this piece having two marks — a CT and FL — one on top of the other and of having an unpainted dress. Errors such as this have a value of $200 up. This piece has been found with a MM. Finding MM ore often on new pieces than in the past since 1993.

Personal Data: _____
____Want Mark ____ Mark _____ Purch. 19__ Pd $ _____

E-9255 Groom Carrying Bride
"Bless You Two"

F	$55	CT	$45	V	$45	S	$45
C	$45	FL	$45	GC	$45	H	$45
D	$45	BA	$45	B	$45		
OB	$45	FLM	$45	TRP	$45		

Comments: 1982; Original Retail $21.00/$45.00
Not a lot of trading on this piece. This piece is not as popular as the original Bride 'n Groom couple. This is a good candidate for suspension or retirement because of the new piece that debuted in 1995. *See #16, page XIII.*

Personal Data: _____
____Want Mark ____ Mark _____ Purch. 19__ Pd $ _____

E-9256 PLATE - Mother at Cradle
"The Hand That Rocks The Future"

LE 15,000

MM	$40
C	$40

Comments: 1983; Original Retail $40.00
Third issue of *Mother's Love Series*. Limited Edition 15,000.

Personal Data: _____
____Want Mark ____ Mark _____ Purch. 19__ Pd $ _____

E-9257   **PLATE - Boy Holding Chick**
"I Believe In Miracles"

LE 15,000

MM	$40
C	$40

Comments: 1982; Original Retail $40.00
Third issue of *Inspired Thoughts Series*; Limited Edition 15,000.

Personal Data: _____
___Want Mark _____ Mark _____ Purch. 19__ Pd $ _____

E-9258   **Girl with Butterfly**
"We Are God's Workmanship"

HG	$65	OB	$35	FLM	$35	TRP	$35
F	$45	CT	$35	V	$35	S	$35
C	$35	FL	$35	GC	$35	H	$35
D	$35	BA	$35	B	$35		

Comments: 1982; Original Retail $19.00/$35.00
This was the same design used for the 1991 9" Easter Seals piece. Easily found in all marks! Good candidate for suspension. This piece was introduced thirteen years ago. Retail price increased in 1995 and again in 1996. ***See #25, page XIV.***

Personal Data: _____
___Want Mark _____ Mark _____ Purch. 19__ Pd $ _____

E-9259   **Boy and Pig in Mud**
"We're In It Together"

SUSP. 1990 - 6 YEARS AGO

HG	$80	D	$60	FL	$55
F	$65	OB	$55	BA	$55
C	$60	CT	$55	FLM	$55

Comments: 1982; Original Retail $24.00/$35.00
1983 piece came out early with HG mark which is the most difficult to find. Price dropped twenty dollars from '95 on the HG mark, many sales found.

Personal Data: _____
___Want Mark _____ Mark _____ Purch. 19__ Pd $ _____

E-9260   **Angel/Rainbow**
"God's Promises Are Sure"

SUSP. 1987 - 9 YEARS AGO

Decaled	F	$100	HG	$100	D	$70
			F	$85	OB	$70
			C	$80	CT	$70

Comments: 1983; Original Retail $30.00/$33.50
Part of *Angels on a Cloud Series*. I always thought the inscription for E-9288 would have been great on this piece. Angel pieces are a favorite for many to collect.

Personal Data: _____
___Want Mark _____ Mark _____ Purch. 19__ Pd $ _____

E-9261   **Boy Graduate with Scroll**
"Seek Ye The Lord"

SUSP. 1986 - 10 YEARS AGO

"No Capital letters" error	F	$60		
	C	$55		
	D	$55		

Corrected to capital letters	F	$50	D	$45
	C	$50	OB	$45

Comments: 1982; Original Retail $21.00
"Him" not capitalized in verse on scroll. (Actually, it isn't capitalized in the Holy Bible.) ***See #9, page XII.***

Personal Data: _____
___Want Mark _____ Mark _____ Purch. 19__ Pd $ _____

E-9262   **Girl Graduate with Scroll**
"Seek Ye The Lord"

SUSP. 1986 - 10 YEARS AGO

"No Capital letters" error	F	$70		
	C	$60		

Corrected to capital letters	F	$50	D	$45
	C	$50	OB	$40

Comments: 1982; Original Retail $21.00
Same as E-9261. "He" not capitalized in verse on scroll. (Actually, it isn't capitalized in the Holy Bible.) ***See #9, page XII.***

Personal Data: _____
___Want Mark _____ Mark _____ Purch. 19__ Pd $ _____

E-9263   **Boy/Girl in Horse Costume**
"How Can Two Walk Together Except They Agree"

SUSP. 1985 - 11 YEARS AGO

HG	$180	C	$140
F	$145	D	$140

Comments: 1982; Original Retail $35.00
Debuted in early 1983 with HG - scarce! The F mark began to appear about four weeks later. No question mark after the verse. Precious Collectibles™ was first to picture the 1983 pieces with the 1982 mark. This was the first "notice" by Precious Collectibles™ to collectors that last year's mark would be on the new year's pieces. Very hard to find! ***See #26, page XIV.***

Personal Data: _____
___Want Mark _____ Mark _____ Purch. 19__ Pd $ _____

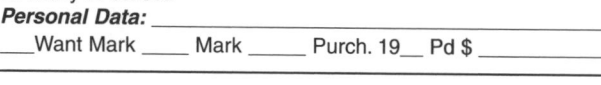

E-9265   Girl Ironing
"Press On"

HG	$120	OB	$65	FLM	$65	TRP	$65
F	$80	CT	$65	V	$65	S	$65
C	$75	FL	$65	GC	$65	H	$65
D	$70	BA	$65	B	$65		

Comments: 1982; Original Retail $40.00/$65.00
Debuted early 1983 with HG - later with F.

Personal Data: _____
____Want Mark _____ Mark _____ Purch. 19__ Pd $ _____

E-9266   *CONTAINER* w/Lid - 2 styles
(1) Lamb/Skunk and (2) Lamb/Bunny
(1) Our Love Is Heaven-Scent
(2) I'm Falling for Some Bunny and It Happens To Be You

SUSP. 1988 - 10 YEARS AGO

	Decaled F	$85	
MM	$50	D	$45
HG	$50	OB	$45
F	$45	CT	$35
C	$45	FL	$35

Comments: 1983 Original Retail $18.50/$25.00
Heart-shaped Container. Several reports of the base saying "Some Bunny Cares." Add $50 to the secondary market value for this error. Price is for each.

Personal Data: _____
____Want Mark _____ Mark _____ Purch. 19__ Pd $ _____

E-9267   Animal Figurines - Set of Six

E-9267A	Teddy Bear	E-9267D	Cat
E-9267B	Dog with Slipper	E-9267E	Lamb
E-9267C	Bunny with Carrot	E-9267F	Pig

SUSP. 1991 - 5 YEARS AGO

MM set	$160-170				
MM	$30 ea.	OB	$20 ea.	FLM	$20 ea.
F	$25 ea.	CT	$20 ea.	V	$20 ea.
C	$25 ea.	FL	$20 ea.		
D	$23 ea.	BA	$20 ea.		

Comments: 1982; Original Retail $6.50/$11.00
Originally a set of six - renumbered A-F in 1987. Different errors with the "DAD" decals on E-9267B have been reported (decals upside down or backwards). Teddy Bear is smiling, not frowning as shown in line art.
See #15, page XIII.

Personal Data: _____
____Want Mark _____ Mark _____ Purch. 19__ Pd $ _____

E-9268   Dunce Boy
"Nobody's Perfect"

RETIRED 1990 - 6 YEARS AGO

Error — "Smilie the Dunce" with smiling mouth						HG	$400 up
Corrected	HG	$75	D	$70		FL	$65
	F	$70	OB	$70		BA	$65
	C	$70	CT	$70		FLM	$55

Comments: 1982; Original Retail $21.00/$30.00
Out in late 1982 with HG, then F later in 1983. Error on approx. first 5,000 pieces; had smile instead of circle mouth. Secondary market as high as $675 by mid 1983; down to $350 in mid 1987. Just because the Dunce Boy was retired, this should not have affected "Smilie" very much as he was rare (changed in 1982 after 5,000 were produced) and was considered to have had "retired" status from day one. Price fell in '95 to $395. Price may return to $500 on "Smiley."

Personal Data: _____
____Want Mark _____ Mark _____ Purch. 19__ Pd $ _____

E-9273   Girl with Umbrella
"Let Love Reign"

RETIRED 1987 - 9 YEARS AGO

HG	$95	D	$75
F	$80	OB	$65
C	$80	CT	$60

Comments: 1982; Original Retail $22.50/$30.00
Chicks have been found with unpainted eyes... Add $50 to the secondary market value.

Personal Data: _____
____Want Mark _____ Mark _____ Purch. 19__ Pd $ _____

E-9274   Girl Making Angel Food
"Taste And See That The Lord Is Good"

RETIRED 1986 - 10 YEARS AGO

F	$75	D	$60
C	$60	OB	$55

Comments: 1982; Original Retail $22.50
Part of *Angels on a Cloud Series*.

Personal Data: _____
____Want Mark _____ Mark _____ Purch. 19__ Pd $ _____

E-9275   *PLATE* - Boy with Teddy
"Jesus Loves Me"

SUSP. 1985 - 11 YEARS AGO

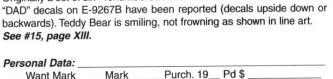

MM	$45
F	$35
C	$35

Comments: 1982; Original Retail $30.00
Trading slow on this plate.

Personal Data: _____
____Want Mark _____ Mark _____ Purch. 19__ Pd $ _____

E-9276   *PLATE* - Girl with Bunny
"Jesus Loves Me"

SUSP. 1985 - 10 YEARS AGO

MM	$42.50
F	$35
C	$35

Comments: 1982; Original Retail $30.00
Trading slow on this plate.

Personal Data: _____
____Want Mark ____ Mark _____ Purch. 19__ Pd $ _____

E-9278   *MINI FIGURINE* - Boy Holding Teddy
"Jesus Loves Me"

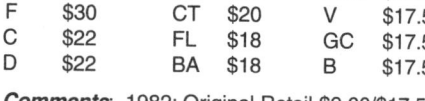

HG	$45	OB	$20	FLM	$17.50	TRP	$17.50
F	$30	CT	$20	V	$17.50	S	$17.50
C	$22	FL	$18	GC	$17.50	H	$17.50
D	$22	BA	$18	B	$17.50		

Comments: 1982; Original Retail $9.00/$17.50
HG limited in production. He's 13 years old this year! MM has been reported on this piece. Retail price increased in 1995 and 1996.

Personal Data: _____
____Want Mark ____ Mark _____ Purch. 19__ Pd $ _____

E-9279   *MINI FIGURINE* - Girl Holding Bunny
"Jesus Loves Me"

HG	$45	OB	$20	FLM	$18	TRP	$17.50
F	$30	CT	$20	V	$18	S	$17.50
C	$25	FL	$20	GC	$17.50	H	$17.50
D	$25	BA	$18	B	$17.50		

Comments: 1982; Original Retail $9.00/$17.50
HG limited in first shipment – more F. Has been found with J&D 1977 licensee and T mark; insure for $300 up. Retail price increased in 1995 and 1996.

Personal Data: _____
____Want Mark ____ Mark _____ Purch. 19__ Pd $ _____

E-9280   *CONTAINER* - Boy with Teddy
"Jesus Loves Me"

SUSP. 1985 - 11 YEARS AGO

HG	$60	C	$50
F	$55	D	$50

Comments: 1982; Original Retail $17.50/$19.00

Personal Data: _____
____Want Mark ____ Mark _____ Purch. 19__ Pd $ _____

E-9281   *CONTAINER* - Girl with Bunny
"Jesus Loves Me"

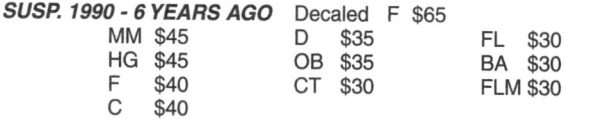

SUSP. 1985 - 11 YEARS AGO

HG	$65	C	$55
F	$55	D	$50

Comments: 1982; Original Retail $17.50/$19.00
Not easily found. Was not popular in the early '80s when it debuted. Containers are beginning to become more popular now.

Personal Data: _____
____Want Mark ____ Mark _____ Purch. 19__ Pd $ _____

E-9282A   **Bunny with Carrot / Heart-Shaped Base**
"To Some Bunny Special"

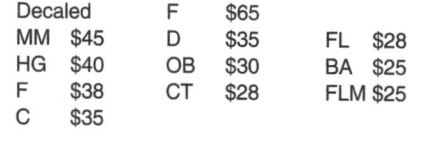

SUSP. 1990 - 6 YEARS AGO   Decaled F $65

MM	$45	D	$35	FL	$30
HG	$45	OB	$35	BA	$30
F	$40	CT	$30	FLM	$30
C	$40				

Comments: 1982; Original Retail $8.00/$13.50
Comes in a set of three, *Especially For Ewe, You're Worth Your Weight In Gold,* and *To Some Bunny Special.* Has been found with decaled F. More trading on earlier marks than later... Heart-shaped base not shown on line drawing at left.

Personal Data: _____
___Want Mark ____ Mark _____ Purch. 19__ Pd $ _____

E-9282B   **Pig on Heart-Shaped Base**
"You're Worth Your Weight In Gold"

SUSP. 1990 - 6 YEARS AGO

Decaled		F	$65		
MM	$45	D	$35	FL	$28
HG	$40	OB	$30	BA	$25
F	$38	CT	$28	FLM	$25
C	$35				

Comments: 1982; Original Retail $8.00/$13.50
Set of Three. Very popular piece. Has slot in top (piggy bank). Some have been found with two or three coins. Coins tend to be losing their shine on many pieces. Has been found with decaled F mark. Heart-shaped base not shown on original line drawing at left.

Personal Data: _____
____Want Mark ____ Mark _____ Purch. 19__ Pd $ _____

E-9282C   **Lamb on Heart-Shaped Base**
"Loving Ewe" changed to
"Especially For Ewe"

SUSP. 1990 - 6 YEARS AGO

MM	$40	D	$35	BA	$25
HG	$45	OB	$30	FLM	$25
F	$38	CT	$25		
C	$35	FL	$25		

Comments: 1982; Original Retail $8.00/$13.50
Set of Three. Loving Ewe pieces, add $25 more on value. A decaled F has been reported. Heart-shaped base not shown on original line drawing at left.

Personal Data: _____
____Want Mark ____ Mark _____ Purch. 19__ Pd $ _____

E-9283   ***CONTAINERS - "Forever Friends"***
     1) Dog on Heart-Shaped Container
     2) Cat on Heart-Shaped Container

SUSP. 1984 - 12 YEARS AGO

"Cat" Container - Decaled F	$85		
MM	$70 ea.	F	$60 ea.
T	$75 ea.	C	$55 ea.
HG	$70 ea.	D	$55 ea.

Comments: 1981; Original Retail $15 ea./$17 ea.
Two styles; cat on one box and dog on other. Somewhat more popular than other "Covered Containers." Containers are becoming more sought after. They were slow sellers in early collector days. Not many out there for sale. Scarce! Very few T marks! Very little trading in past few years.

Personal Data: _____

____Want Mark ____ Mark _____ Purch. 19__ Pd $ _____

E-9285   **Boy at Pulpit**
     "If God Be For Us, Who Can Be Against Us"

SUSP. 1985 - 11 YEARS AGO

F	$90	D	$75
C	$75		

Comments: 1982; Original Retail $27.50
Remember that inscription! It's perplexing how some pieces are pulled from production so quickly. It's been said some inscriptions affect sales.

Personal Data: _____
____Want Mark ____ Mark _____ Purch. 19__ Pd $ _____

E-9287   **Girl with Lion and Lamb**
     "Peace On Earth"

SUSP. 1986 - 10 YEARS AGO

F	$150	D	$145
C	$145	OB	$145

Comments: 1982; Original Retail $37.50
Most figurines produced for only 3-4 years and then suspended tend to rise faster on the secondary market than pieces that have been produced for more years before suspension. This is not an easy piece to find! In my opinion, as scarce as this piece is, buy any mark if you want it!

Personal Data: _____
____Want Mark ____ Mark _____ Purch. 19__ Pd $ _____

E-9288   **Girl Angel with Sprinkling Can**
     "Sending You A Rainbow"

SUSP. 1986 - 10 YEARS AGO

F	$90-95	D	$85
C	$85	OB	$80

Comments: 1982; Original Retail $22.50
Becoming scarce on the secondary market.

Personal Data: _____
____Want Mark ____ Mark _____ Purch. 19__ Pd $ _____

E-9289   **Boy Pilot Angel**
     "Trust In The Lord"

SUSP. 1987 - 9 YEARS AGO

F	$80	OB	$60
C	$70	CT	$60
D	$60		

Comments: 1982; Original Retail $20.00/$23.00
Title written on back of book; not an error. The original art was produced this way so the book could be under that arm.

Personal Data: _____
____Want Mark ____ Mark _____ Purch. 19__ Pd $ _____

12009   Girl with Quilt - Valentine Piece
"Love Covers All"

SUSP. 1991 - 5 YEARS AGO

C	$80	FL	$55
D	$65	BA	$55
OB	$60	FLM	$55
CT	$60	V	$55

Comments: 1984; Original Retail $27.50/$37.50
Valentine pieces tend to be more available than others. A similar Club Membership piece debuted in 1990 (PM-902), a girl sewing a patch on a teddy bear. Nice piece!

Personal Data: _____
___Want Mark _____ Mark _____ Purch. 19__ Pd $ _____

12017   *FRAME* - Boy Holding Heart
"Loving You"

SUSP. 1987 - 9 YEARS AGO

C	$60	OB	$55
D	$60	CT	$55

Comments: 1984; Original Retail $19.00/$20.00
Frames not easily attainable as in earlier years. ***See #8, page XII.***

Personal Data: _____
___Want Mark _____ Mark _____ Purch. 19__ Pd $ _____

12025   *FRAME* - Girl Holding Heart
"Loving You"

SUSP. 1987 - 9 YEARS AGO

C	$60	OB	$55
D	$60	CT	$55

Comments: 1984; Original Retail $19.00/$20.00
See #8, page XII.

Personal Data: _____
___Want Mark _____ Mark _____ Purch. 19__ Pd $ _____

12033   *FRAME* - Baby Boy
"God's Precious Gift"

SUSP. 1987 - 9 YEARS AGO

C	$50	OB	$40
D	$45	CT	$35

Comments: 1984; Original Retail $19.00/$20.00
Frames, as well as plates, dolls and bells, were not as popular as the figurines when they debuted. ***See #8, page XII.***

Personal Data: _____
___Want Mark _____ Mark _____ Purch. 19__ Pd $ _____

12041   *FRAME* - Baby Girl
"God's Precious Gift"

SUSP. 1992 - 4 YEARS AGO

C	$50	CT	$40	FLM	$40
D	$45	FL	$40	V	$40
OB	$40	BA	$40	GC	$40

Comments: 1984; Original Retail $19.00/$27.50
Produced longer than 12033 Baby Boy frame. ***See #8, page XII.***

Personal Data: _____
___Want Mark _____ Mark _____ Purch. 19__ Pd $ _____

12068   Girl Holding Bible
"The Voice of Spring"

LE 1985 - 11 YEARS OLD   C $250-275   D $275

Comments: 1984; Original Retail $30.00
First issue of *Four Seasons Series.* Limited Edition (one year only); coordinating plate, 12106. (All Four Seasons figurines are larger in height than regular pieces.) *Spring* and *Summer* figurines were produced in 1985 and were not difficult to locate as this new size was hard for collectors to accept. The size is now more accepted. It now appears that hindsight is better than foresight (should have bought many for future trading). The original artwork shown at left is the design for the plate; the figurine has a partial fence, shorter than the one shown, and the thimble has no fence.

Personal Data: _____
___Want Mark _____ Mark _____ Purch. 19__ Pd $ _____

12076   Girl Holding Rose
"Summer's Joy"

LE 1985 - 11 YEARS OLD   C $105   D $95

Comments: 1984; Original Retail $30.00
Second issue of *Four Seasons Series.* Limited Edition figurine. The coordinating plate is 12114.

Personal Data: _____
___Want Mark _____ Mark _____ Purch. 19__ Pd $ _____

12084   Girl with Hair Blowing
"Autumn's Praise"

LE 1986 - 10 YEARS OLD   D $80   OB $70

Comments: 1984; Original Retail $30.00
Third Issue of *Four Seasons Series.* No total production figures were ever released. The coordinating plate for this figurine is 12122.

Personal Data: _____
___Want Mark _____ Mark _____ Purch. 19__ Pd $ _____

●●●

12092 **Girl with Birds**
"Winter's Song"

LE 1986 - 10 YEARS OLD

FL	$175	OB	$110
D	$120		

Comments: 1984; Original Retail $30.00
Fourth Issue of *Four Seasons Series*. Refer to 12084 comments; same comments apply here. This piece has been found with the FL mark, which is very unusual as it is a 1986 Limited Edition piece. Insure the FL piece for $175 up.

Personal Data: _____
___Want Mark _____ Mark _____ Purch. 19__ Pd $ _____

12106 **PLATE - Girl Holding Bible**
"The Voice of Spring"

LE 1985 - 11 YEARS OLD

C	$100	OB	$65
D	$85		

Comments: 1984; Original Retail $40.00
1985 Limited Edition - First Edition in *Four Seasons Series*. Limited Edition Figurine 12068 also produced in 1985.

Personal Data: _____
___Want Mark _____ Mark _____ Purch. 19__ Pd $ _____

12114 **PLATE - Girl Holding Rose**
"Summer's Joy"

LE 1985 - 11 YEARS OLD C $75 D $60

Comments: 1984; Original Retail $40.00
1985 Limited Edition - Second Edition in *Four Seasons Series*. Limited Edition figurine also produced in 1985.

Personal Data: _____
___Want Mark _____ Mark _____ Purch. 19__ Pd $ _____

12122 **PLATE - Girl with Hair Blowing**
"Autumn's Praise"

LE 1986 - 10 YEARS OLD OB $50

Comments: 1984; Original Retail $40.00
1986 Limited Edition - Third Edition in *Four Seasons Series*.

Personal Data: _____
___Want Mark _____ Mark _____ Purch. 19__ Pd $ _____

12130 **PLATE - Girl with Birds**
"Winter's Song"

LE 1986 - 10 YEARS OLD

D	$65
OB	$60

Comments: 1984; Original Retail $40.00
1986 Limited Edition - Fourth Edition in *Four Seasons Series*.

Personal Data: _____
___Want Mark _____ Mark _____ Purch. 19__ Pd $ _____

12149 **Angel in Devil's Suit – Valentine Piece**
"Part Of Me Wants To Be Good"

SUSP. 1989 - 7 YEARS AGO

C	$90	CT	$72
D	$75	FL	$70
OB	$65	BA	$65

Comments: 1984; Original Retail $19.00/$25.00
Sam spoke to a group of collectors in 1984 concerning this piece. He painted the original drawing, remembering a special employee of his who always seemed to try to do what was right but still seemed not to get the job done! Debuted with C, then D later in 1985. Very little trading found on this piece.

Personal Data: _____
___Want Mark _____ Mark _____ Purch. 19__ Pd $ _____

12157 **Birthday Boy**
"This Is The Day The Lord Has Made"

SUSP. 1990 - 6 YEARS AGO
Error: "...Which The Lord Has Made"

OB	$65	BA	$45
CT	$60	FLM	$45
FL	$50		

Corrected:			
OB	$40	BA	$35
CT	$40	FLM	$35
FL	$35		

Comments: 1986; Original Retail $20.00/$30.00
First pieces were produced with error "Which The Lord Has Made" then changed to omit the word "Which." Unlike other error pieces which were corrected, this piece continued to be produced both with the error and with the correction for several years. Slow seller on the secondary market.

Personal Data: _____
___Want Mark _____ Mark _____ Purch. 19__ Pd $ _____

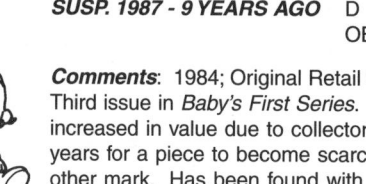

12165 ♪ **MUSICAL - Boy/Piano (2 pc. set)**
"Lord, Keep My Life In Tune"

SUSP. 1989 - 7 YEARS AGO

D	$135	CT	$115	BA	$110
OB	$120	FL	$110		

Comments: 1984; Original Retail $37.50/$50.00
Rejoice In The Lord Band Series. Plays *Amazing Grace.*

Personal Data: _____
____Want Mark ____ Mark _____ Purch. 19__ Pd $ _____

12173 **Girl Playing Triangle**
"There's A Song In My Heart"

SUSP. 1990 - 6 YEARS AGO

D	$50	CT	$40	BA	$30
OB	$40	FL	$35	FLM	$30

Comments: 1984; Original Retail $11.00/$16.50
Rejoice In The Lord Band Series.

Personal Data: _____
____Want Mark ____ Mark _____ Purch. 19__ Pd $ _____

12203 **Nun Figurine**
"Get Into The Habit Of Prayer"

SUSP. 1986 - 10 YEARS AGO C $55 OB $40
D $40

Comments: 1984; Original Retail $19.00
This piece did not sell well. Scarce now due to low production, but not being sought after. It's my opinion this piece will be considered scarce in a few years due to only a 3 year production, then value could probably increase.

Personal Data: _____
____Want Mark ____ Mark _____ Purch. 19__ Pd $ _____

12211 **Baby Getting Haircut**
"Baby's First Haircut"

SUSP. 1987 - 9 YEARS AGO D $145 CT $125
OB $125

Comments: 1984; Original Retail $32.50/$37.00
Third issue in *Baby's First Series.* This series in the last two years has increased in value due to collector demand. It sometimes takes 6 to 8 years for a piece to become scarce. More trading found on D than any other mark. Has been found with wrong inspiration on bottom, reportedly "God Bless Our Home."

Personal Data: _____
____Want Mark ____ Mark _____ Purch. 19__ Pd $ _____

12238 **Four Assorted Clowns (Mini pieces)**
12238 **A Boy Balancing Ball**
12238C **Boy Handing Ball**
12238B **Girl w/Balloon**
12238D **Girl w/Flower Pot**

Error "Crowns" instead of "Clowns" on Base D $70 ea.

Corrected D	$30 ea.	BA	$20 ea.	B	$20 ea.
OB	$30 ea.	FLM	$20 ea.	TRP	$20 ea.
CT	$22 ea.	V	$20 ea.	S	$20 ea.
FL	$22 ea.	GC	$20 ea.		

Comments: 1984; Original Retail $13.50/$20.00
Set of Four. Smaller than regular figurines. Two girls and two boys. Some retailers sell sets only; others sell individually. Renumbered A-D in late 1987. **See #9, page XII.**

Personal Data: _____
____Want Mark ____ Mark _____ Purch. 19__ Pd $ _____

12246 **MEDALLION - 1984**
"Precious Moments Last Forever"

C $110

Comments: 1984
Gift from Enesco to a member for signing up a new member to the Club. Price down last two years. Medallion not that collectible to date.

Personal Data: _____
____Want Mark ____ Mark _____ Purch. 19__ Pd $ _____

12254 **THIMBLE - Girl Stitching Quilt**
"Love Covers All"

SUSP. 1990 - 6 YEARS AGO

D	$20	CT	$15	BA	$12
OB	$18	FL	$12	FLM	$12

Comments: 1984; Original Retail $5.50/$8.00

Personal Data: _____
____Want Mark ____ Mark _____ Purch. 19__ Pd $ _____

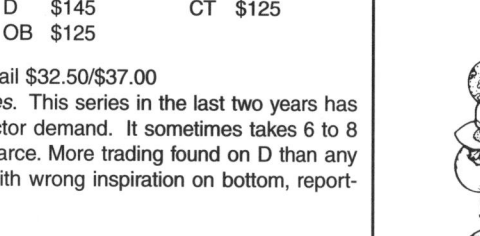

12262 **Clown Holding Balloons**
"I Get A Bang Out Of You"

D	$70	BA	$55	B	$45
OB	$60	FLM	$55	TRP	$45
CT	$55	V	$50	S	$45
FL	$55	GC	$45	H	$45

Comments: 1985; Original Retail $35.00/$45.00
First issue in *Clown Series.* Several clown figurines have been retired. Colorful! This is a very popular piece. Many report underline on "Bang."

Personal Data: _____
____Want Mark ____ Mark _____ Purch. 19__ Pd $ _____

12270   **Clown on Ball**
"Lord Keep Me On The Ball"

OB $70	FLM $50	TRP $45
CT $50	V $45	S $45
FL $50	GC $45	H $45
BA $50	B $45	

Comments: 1985; Original Retail $35.00/$45.00
Fourth issue in *Clown Series*.

Personal Data: _____
____Want Mark ____ Mark _____ Purch. 19__ Pd $ _____

12297   **Policeman**
"It Is Better To Give Than To Receive"

SUSP. 1987 - 9 YEARS AGO   D $165   CT $145
                              OB $145

Comments: 1984; Original Retail $19.00/$21.00
Popular piece!

Personal Data: _____
____Want Mark ____ Mark _____ Purch. 19__ Pd $ _____

12300   **Teacher with Report Card**
"Love Never Fails"

D $60	BA $45	B $40
OB $50	FLM $40	TRP $40
CT $50	V $40	S $40
FL $45	GC $40	H $40

Comments: 1984; Original Retail $25.00/$40.00
Teacher misspelled "Faithfulness." Probably a misspelling on "original" drawing. It's spelled "Faithfullness" with two "l's" instead of one "l." Not corrected to date. Very little trading reported on this piece for the past several years. It's time for suspension or retirement.

Personal Data: _____
____Want Mark ____ Mark _____ Purch. 19__ Pd $ _____

12319   **Boy and Girl/Sandcastle**
"God Bless Our Home"

D $80	BA $65	B $65
OB $75	FLM $65	TRP $65
CT $70	V $65	S $65
FL $70	GC $65	H $65

Comments: 1984; Original Retail $40.00/$65.00
One report received of decal "HOWSE" in the D mark. It's time to see this one retired or suspended.

Personal Data: _____
____Want Mark ____ Mark _____ Purch. 19__ Pd $ _____

12335   **Boy Angel on Cloud**
"You Can Fly"

SUSP. 1988 - 8 YEARS AGO   OB $70   FL $65
                                  CT $65

Comments: 1985; Original Retail $25.00/$30.00
Display the angels on "clouds" together. This makes a great theme display in "cotton" or angel hair.

Personal Data: _____
____Want Mark ____ Mark _____ Purch. 19__ Pd $ _____

"Send In The Clowns." How many clowns have been retired or suspended?

109584 Retired '92	104396 Susp. '90	101850 Retired '92	520632 Retired '95	101842 Retired '91
15504 Retired '89	113964 Susp.'93	106216 Susp. '90	12467 Retired'88	12459 Retired '89
15822 Susp. '89	100668 Susp. '88	15830 Susp. '89	113972 Susp. '91	

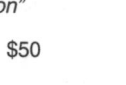

12343   Mary Knitting Booties
"Jesus Is Coming Soon"

SUSP. 1986 - 10 YEARS AGO   D $50   OB $45

Comments: 1985; Original Retail $19.00/$22.50
Reaction to this piece "varied" among collectors. It was probably the reason for suspension. This piece is hard to find! It was only in production two years! I feel it's a very pretty piece and I'd suggest you add it to your collection!

Personal Data: _____
___Want Mark _____ Mark _____ Purch. 19__ Pd $ _____

12351   Two Angels Making Snowman
"Halo, and Merry Christmas"

SUSP. 1988 - 8 YEARS AGO

D	$160	CT	$120
OB	$130	FL	$120

Comments: 1985; Original Retail $40.00/$47.50
This is a gorgeous piece! Another snowman piece (524913) debuted in 1990.

Personal Data: _____
___Want Mark _____ Mark _____ Purch. 19__ Pd $ _____

12378   Boy Banjo Player
"Happiness Is The Lord"

SUSP. 1990 - 6 YEARS AGO

C	$45	OB	$40	FL	$35	BA	$35
D	$40	CT	$35	BA	$35		

Comments: 1984; Original Retail $15.00/$22.50
Rejoice In The Lord Band Series. The Band Series was a "slow seller."

Personal Data: _____
___Want Mark _____ Mark _____ Purch. 19__ Pd $ _____

12386   Girl/Harmonica
"Lord Give Me A Song"

SUSP. 1990 - 6 YEARS AGO

D	$45	FL	$35
OB	$40	BA	$35
CT	$35	FLM	$35

Comments: 1984; Original Retail $15.00/$22.50
Rejoice In The Lord Band Series. First marks on this series are becoming harder to find.

Personal Data: _____
___Want Mark _____ Mark _____ Purch. 19__ Pd $ _____

12394   Boy/Trumpet/Dog (2 pc.)
"He Is My Song"

SUSP. 1990 - 6 YEARS AGO

F	$50	D	$45	CT	$40	BA	$35
C	$45	OB	$45	FL	$35	FLM	$35

Comments: 1984; Original Retail $17.50/$27.50
Rejoice In The Lord Band Series. Very little trading found; may be awhile before value increases.

Personal Data: _____
___Want Mark _____ Mark _____ Purch. 19__ Pd $ _____

12408   ♪ MUSICAL - Angels Making Star (3-pc. set)
"We Saw A Star"

SUSP. 1987 - 9 YEARS AGO

F	$115	D	$100	CT	$95
C	$105	OB	$100		

Comments: 1984; Original Retail $50.00/$55.00
Plays *Joy To The World*. Collectors voiced their opinion that the star was "too plain" for display. Was very slow seller at retail.

Personal Data: _____
___Want Mark _____ Mark _____ Purch. 19__ Pd $ _____

12416   ORNAMENT - Boy in Airplane
"Have A Heavenly Christmas"

Upside down error....$125-135

MM	$45	FL	$20	GC	$18.50	H	$18.50
D	$35	BA	$18.50	B	$18.50		
OB	$25	FLM	$18.50	TRP	$18.50		
CT	$22	V	$18.50	S	$18.50		

Comments: 1984; Original Retail $12.00/$18.50
Some of these appeared with decaled words "Heaven Bound" upside down on the plane. Also found with MM. Would be a great retirement piece.

Personal Data: _____
___Want Mark _____ Mark _____ Purch. 19__ Pd $ _____

12424   DOLL - Boy Angel
"Aaron"

SUSP. 1986 - 10 YEARS AGO   D $145   OB $140

Comments: 1984; Original Retail $135.00
12" Boy Angel. The embossed mark is on the neck. Dolls have been in less demand than the figurines.

Personal Data: _____
___Want Mark _____ Mark _____ Purch. 19__ Pd $ _____

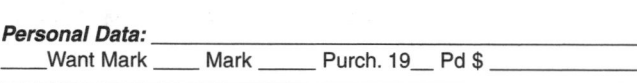

12432   *DOLL* - Girl Angel
"Bethany"

SUSP. 1986 - 10 YEARS AGO   D $145   B $140

Comments: 1985; Original Retail $135.00
12" Girl Angel. The embossed D is on the neck. Dolls have been in less demand than the figurines. Reports of sales below retail for several years! Insure at these prices.

Personal Data: _____
___Want Mark _____ Mark _____ Purch. 19__ Pd $ _____

12440   **Commemorative Ed. 5th Anniversary**
"God Bless Our Years Together"

         D $260

Comments: 1984; Original Retail $175.00
Approx. 10-12 were shipped to retailers' shelves unpainted. Value $800 up.

Personal Data: _____
___Want Mark _____ Mark _____ Purch. 19__ Pd $ _____

12459   **Girl Clown with Goose**
"Waddle I Do Without You"

RETIRED 1989 - 7 YEARS AGO

C $115	OB $95	FL $90
D $105	CT $90	BA $90

Comments: 1985; Original Retail $30.00/$40.00
Second issue in *Clown Series*. (The first was 12262. It did not say "First of Series" on it.) A very colorful piece.

Personal Data: _____
___Want Mark _____ Mark _____ Purch. 19__ Pd $ _____

12467   **Clown with Dog and Hoop**
"The Lord Will Carry You Through"

RETIRED 1988 - 8 YEARS AGO

D $110	CT $90
OB $98	FL $90

Comments: 1985; Original Retail $30.00/$35.00
Third issue in *Clown Series*. Tends to be more OB marks for sale than any other mark in recent years. Price up from '95.

Personal Data: _____
___Want Mark _____ Mark _____ Purch. 19__ Pd $ _____

12475   *DOLL* - Baby Boy
"P. D."

SUSP. 1986 - 10 YEARS AGO   MM $85   OB $75
         D $80

Comments: 1985; Original Retail $50.00
P.D. is for Philip Dale Jr., Philip Butcher's son and Sam's grandson. (Philip Sr. was killed Sept. 1990 in a car accident in Joplin, Missouri.) MM has been reported.

Personal Data: _____
___Want Mark _____ Mark _____ Purch. 19__ Pd $ _____

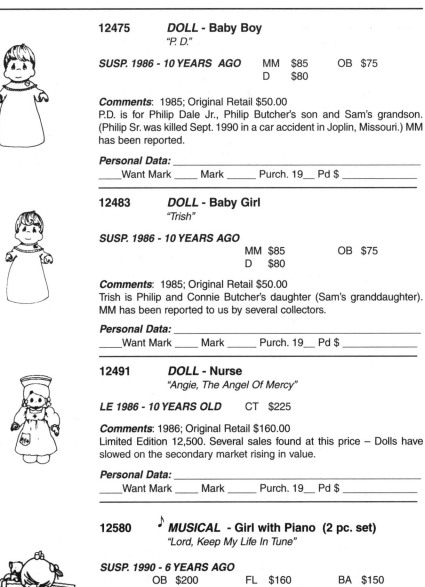

12483   *DOLL* - Baby Girl
"Trish"

SUSP. 1986 - 10 YEARS AGO
         MM $85   OB $75
         D $80

Comments: 1985; Original Retail $50.00
Trish is Philip and Connie Butcher's daughter (Sam's granddaughter). MM has been reported to us by several collectors.

Personal Data: _____
___Want Mark _____ Mark _____ Purch. 19__ Pd $ _____

12491   *DOLL* - Nurse
"Angie, The Angel Of Mercy"

LE 1986 - 10 YEARS OLD   CT $225

Comments: 1986; Original Retail $160.00
Limited Edition 12,500. Several sales found at this price – Dolls have slowed on the secondary market rising in value.

Personal Data: _____
___Want Mark _____ Mark _____ Purch. 19__ Pd $ _____

12580   ♪ *MUSICAL* - Girl with Piano (2 pc. set)
"Lord, Keep My Life In Tune"

SUSP. 1990 - 6 YEARS AGO

OB $200	FL $160	BA $150
CT $175	BA $150	FLM $150

Comments: 1986; Original Retail $37.50/$55.00
Plays *I'd Like To Teach The World To Sing*. It seems she has been more sought after the last two years than the Boy (12165) but he's popular too!

Personal Data: _____
___Want Mark _____ Mark _____ Purch. 19__ Pd $ _____

13293   *THIMBLE* - Mother with Needlepoint
"Mother Sew Dear"

D	$20	FL	$12	V	$12	TRP	$10
OB	$15	BA	$1	GC	$12	S	$8
CT	$15	FLM	$12	B	$10	H	$8

Comments: 1984; Original Retail $5.50/$8.00
See #27, page XIV.

Personal Data: _____
___Want Mark _____ Mark _____ Purch. 19__ Pd $ _____

13307   *THIMBLE* - Grandma in Rocking Chair
"The Purr-fect Grandma"

D	$20	FL	$12	V	$12	TRP	$10
OB	$15	BA	$12	GC	$10	S	$10
CT	$15	FLM	$12	B	$10	H	$8

Comments: 1984; Original Retail $5.50/$8.00

Personal Data: _____
___Want Mark _____ Mark _____ Purch. 19__ Pd $ _____

15237   *PLATE* - Girl Story Teller
"Tell Me The Story Of Jesus"

DATED 1985   D $80

Comments: 1984; Original Retail $40.00
Fourth issue in *Joy of Christmas Series*. More scarce than other dated plates. Easily found at $75-$80. Advertise for it in Precious Collectibles™ or attend one of our Midwest Fest Shows to find your sought after piece. ***See #1, page XI.***

Personal Data: _____
___Want Mark _____ Mark _____ Purch. 19__ Pd $ _____

15482   Boy Tangled in Lights
"May Your Christmas Be Delightful"

SUSP. 1994 - 2 YEARS AGO

D	$65	FL	$55	V	$50	TRP	$40
OB	$60	BA	$50	GC	$50		
CT	$55	FLM	$50	B	$40		

Comments: 1985; Original Retail $25.00/$35.00
Also an ornament (#15849). MM reported, insure for $75. Plenty on the market. Only suspended two years. Can still be easily found with TRP and B marks

Personal Data: _____
___Want Mark _____ Mark _____ Purch. 19__ Pd $ _____

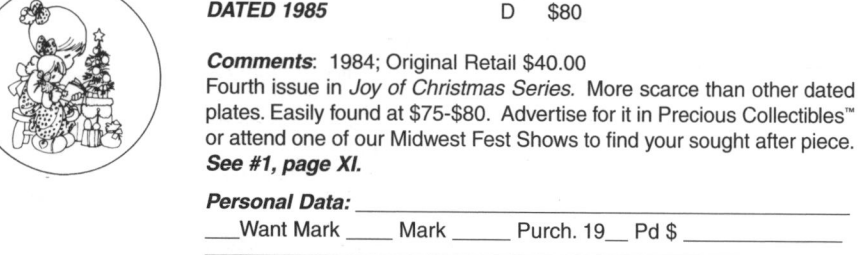

15490   Goose in Bonnet with Babies (2 pc. set)
"Honk If You Love Jesus"

D	$35	BA	$22	B	$20
OB	$32.50	FLM	$22	TRP	$20
CT	$25	V	$22	S	$20
FL	$22	GC	$20	H	$20

Comments: 1985; Original Retail $13.00/$20.00
Delicate! Be careful when dusting! Many goose necks have been broken, including my goose! Ha!

Personal Data: _____
___Want Mark _____ Mark _____ Purch. 19__ Pd $ _____

15504 ♪ *MUSICAL* - Jack in the Box
"God Sent You Just In Time"

RETIRED 1989 - 7 YEARS AGO

		D	$115	FL	$100
		OB	$105	BA	$95
		CT	$100		

Comments: 1985; Original Retail $45.00/$60.00
Plays *We Wish You A Merry Christmas*.

Personal Data: _____
___Want Mark _____ Mark _____ Purch. 19__ Pd $ _____

15539   Baby Boy Holding Bottle
"Baby's First Christmas"

DATED 1985 - 11 YEARS AGO   D $35

Comments: 1985; Original Retail $13.00
The first marked *Baby's First Christmas* dated pieces (cradle) debuted in 1983. Secondary market dealers report dated *Baby's First* is not traded as often as in years past. ***See #29, page XIV.***

Personal Data: _____
___Want Mark _____ Mark _____ Purch. 19__ Pd $ _____

15547   Baby Girl Holding Bottle
"Baby's First Christmas"

DATED 1985   D $37.50

Comments: 1985; Original Retail $13.00
See #29, page XIV.

Personal Data: _____
___Want Mark _____ Mark _____ Purch. 19__ Pd $ _____

15768   ***ORNAMENT* - Angel with Holly Wreath**
"God Sent His Love"

DATED 1985   D $37.50

Comments: 1985; Original Retail $10.00
This ornament is the fifth in the dated ornament series (not including *Baby's First Christmas* dated ornaments). **See #29, page XIV.**

Personal Data: _____
____Want Mark _____ Mark _____ Purch. 19__ Pd $ _____

15776   **Mother with Cookies**
"May You Have The Sweetest Christmas"

SUSP. 1992 - 4 YEARS AGO

	D $50	FL $35	V $32
	OB $40	BA $35	GC $30
	CT $38	FLM $35	

Comments: 1985; Original Retail $17.00/$25.00
First issue in the *Family Christmas Scene Series*. This series was also produced in "painted pewter" in 1990. Painted pewter is not as collectible as some thought it would become. The eyes were not painted well and paint chipped on first years' production. It will be interesting to watch the collectibility of the Goebel miniatures.

Personal Data: _____
____Want Mark _____ Mark _____ Purch. 19__ Pd $ _____

15784   **Father in Chair Reading Bible**
"The Story Of God's Love"

SUSP. 1992 - 4 YEARS AGO

	D $65	FL $50	V $45
	OB $55	BA $45	GC $45
	CT $50	FLM $45	

Comments: 1985; Original Retail $22.50/$35.00
Second issue in the *Family Christmas Scene Series* D mark only one being sought on secondary market. **See 15776, pewter.**

Personal Data: _____
____Want Mark _____ Mark _____ Purch. 19__ Pd $ _____

  *The best thing to do with the Bible is to **know** it in the head, **stow** it in the heart, **sow** it in the world, and **show** it in the life.*

15792   **Little Boy Sitting**
"Tell Me A Story"

SUSP. 1992 - 4 YEARS AGO

	D $37.50	FL $27.50	V $25
	OB $28	BA $25	GC $22
	CT $27.50	FLM $25	

Comments: 1985; Original Retail $10.00/$15.00
Third issue in the *Family Christmas Scene Series*. Only piece in demand to date is D mark. **See 15776, pewter.**

Personal Data: _____
____Want Mark _____ Mark _____ Purch. 19__ Pd $ _____

15806   **Girl Hanging an *Ornament***
"God Gave His Best"

SUSP. 1992 - 4 YEARS AGO

	D $40	FL $30	V $25
	OB $35	BA $30	GC $25
	CT $35	FLM $30	

Comments: 1985; Original Retail $13.00/$19.00
Fourth issue in the *Family Christmas Scene Series*. Do not over inflate prices as seen in other guides! **See 15776, pewter.**

Personal Data: _____
____Want Mark _____ Mark _____ Purch. 19__ Pd $ _____

15814   ♪ ***MUSICAL* - Tree**
"Silent Night"

SUSP. 1992 - 4 YEARS AGO

	D $100	FL $65	V $65
	OB $80	BA $65	GC $65
	CT $70	FLM $65	

Comments: 1985; Original Retail $37.50/$55.00
Plays *Silent Night*. Fifth issue in *Family Christmas Scene Series*. This has been a "slow seller." Not being sought after heavily to date. **See 15776, pewter.**

Personal Data: _____
____Want Mark _____ Mark _____ Purch. 19__ Pd $ _____

15822   *ORNAMENT -* **Clown with Balloon**
"May Your Christmas Be Happy"

SUSP. 1989 - 7 YEARS AGO

D $45	CT $35	FL $35
OB $35	FL $35	BA $35

Comments: 1985; Original Retail $10.00/$13.50

Personal Data: _____
____Want Mark ____ Mark _____ Purch. 19__ Pd $ _____

15830   *ORNAMENT -* **Boy Clown with Ball**
"Happiness Is The Lord"

SUSP. 1989 - 7 YEARS AGO

D $35	CT $30	BA $25
OB $32	FL $28	

Comments: 1985; Original Retail $10.00/$13.50

Personal Data: _____
____Want Mark ____ Mark _____ Purch. 19__ Pd $ _____

15849   *ORNAMENT -* **Boy Tangled in Lights**
"May Your Christmas Be Delightful"

SUSP. 1993 - 3 YEARS AGO

D $37.50	FL $30	V $25
OB $32	BA $28	GC $25
CT $30	FLM $28	B $25

Comments: 1985; Original Retail $10.00/$15.00
Cute ornament, still easily found. ***See #39, page XV.***

Personal Data: _____
____Want Mark ____ Mark _____ Purch. 19__ Pd $ _____

15857   *ORNAMENT -* **Mother Goose**
"Honk If You Love Jesus"

SUSP. 1993 - 3 YEARS AGO

MM $40	CT $25	FLM $22	B $20
D $30	FL $222	V $20	
OB $28	BA $22	GC $20	

Comments: 1985; Original Retail $10.00/$15.00
Easily found for these prices!   ***See #39, page XV.***

Personal Data: _____
____Want Mark ____ Mark _____ Purch. 19__ Pd $ _____

15865   *THIMBLE -* Angel/Wreath
"God Sent His Love"

DATED 1985

   D $40-45

Comments: 1985; Original Retail $5.50
Only scarce thimble to date, but trading slow in past year with lower prices. Embossed D mark, not decaled as on first three thimbles which debuted in 1985 (12254, 13293, and 13307).

Personal Data: _____
____Want Mark ____ Mark _____ Purch. 19__ Pd $ _____

15873   *BELL -* **Angel with Holly Wreath**
"God Sent His Love"

DATED 1985

   D $30

Comments: 1985; Original Retail $19.00
1993 was the last year for dated bells of this design.

Personal Data: _____
____Want Mark ____ Mark _____ Purch. 19__ Pd $ _____

15881   **Angel with Holly Wreath Figurine**
"God Sent His Love"

DATED 1985   D $40

Comments: 1985; Original Retail $17.00

Personal Data: _____
____Want Mark ____ Mark _____ Purch. 19__ Pd $ _____

15903   *ORNAMENT -* **Boy Holding Bottle**
"Baby's First Christmas"

DATED 1985   D $38

Comments: 1985; Original Retail $10.00

Personal Data: _____
____Want Mark ____ Mark _____ Purch. 19__ Pd $ _____

15911   ***ORNAMENT* - Girl Holding Bottle**
"Baby's First Christmas"

DATED 1985   D $38

Comments: 1985; Original Retail $10.00
There were more girls "for sale" in '93 and '94 than boys.

Personal Data: _____
____Want Mark ____ Mark _____ Purch. 19__ Pd $ _____

15938   **Baby - Teddy/Caboose**
"May Your Birthday Be Warm"

D	$35	BA	$20	B	$15
OB	$25	FLM	$18	TRP	$15
CT	$22	V	$15	S	$15
FL	$20	GC	$15	H	$15

Comments: 1985; Original Retail $10.00/$15.00
Part of *Birthday Train Series*. *See #30, page XIV.*

Personal Data: _____
____Want Mark ____ Mark _____ Purch. 19__ Pd $ _____

15946   **Age 1 - Lamb**
"Happy Birthday Little Lamb"

D	$40	BA	$20	B	$15
OB	$25	FLM	$18	TRP	$15
CT	$20	V	$15	S	$15
FL	$20	GC	$15	H	$15

Comments: 1985; Original Retail $10.00/$15.00
Part of *Birthday Train Serie*s. Many of the Birthday Train animals have been found with the numeral decals missing. Very limited. Add $75 on such an error. *See #30, page XIV.*

Personal Data: _____
____Want Mark ____ Mark _____ Purch. 19__ Pd $ _____

15954   **Age 3 - Pig**
"Heaven Bless Your Special Day"

D	$40	BA	$20	B	$17.50
OB	$25	FLM	$20	TRP	$17.50
CT	$22	V	$17.50	S	$17.50
FL	$20	GC	$17.50	H	$17.50

Comments: 1985; Original Retail $11.00/$17.50
Part of *Birthday Train Series*. Retail price increased in 1995.
See #30, page XIV.

Personal Data: _____
____Want Mark ____ Mark _____ Purch. 19__ Pd $ _____

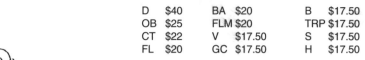

15962   **Age 2 - Seal**
"God Bless You On Your Birthday"

D	$40	BA	$20	B	$17.50
OB	$25	FLM	$20	TRP	$17.50
CT	$22	V	$17.50	S	$17.50
FL	$20	GC	$17.50	H	$17.50

Comments: 1985; Original Retail $11.00/$17.50
Part of *Birthday Train Series*. Retail price increased in 1995. Children's "age" pieces usually are traded most on ages Baby through #2
See #30, page XIV.

Personal Data: _____
____Want Mark ____ Mark _____ Purch. 19__ Pd $ _____

15970   **Age 4 - Elephant**
"May Your Birthday Be Gigantic"

D	$40	BA	$22	B	$20
OB	$28	FLM	$20	TRP	$20
CT	$25	V	$20	S	$20
FL	$22	GC	$20	H	$20

Comments: 1985; Original Retail $12.50/$20.00
Part of *Birthday Train Series*. Retail price increased in 1995. Retail rising faster than secondary market. *See #30, page XIV.*

Personal Data: _____
____Want Mark ____ Mark _____ Purch. 19__ Pd $ _____

Collecting From The Heart!

Lena stands next to her Precious Moments Nativity display. Precious Moments ornaments, mauve ribbons and balls adorn Lena Fisher's tree. Her husband, Cecil, is Precious Collectibles™ "Famous Auctioneer"!

15989 **Age 5 - Lion**
"This Day Is Something To Roar About"

D	$38	BA	$25	B	$22.50
OB	$25	FLM	$25	TRP	$22.50
CT	$25	V	$22.50	S	$22.50
FL	$25	GC	$22.50	H	$22.50

Comments: 1985; Original Retail $13.50/$22.50
Part of *Birthday Train Series*. Retail price increased in 1995 by nine dollars. Most collectors are not seeking these pieces after their child reaches ages five or more. **See #30, page XIV.**

Personal Data: _____
____Want Mark _____ Mark _____ Purch. 19__ Pd $ _____

15997 **Age 6 - Giraffe**
"Keep Looking Up"

D	$35	BA	$23	B	$22.50
OB	$27.50	FLM	$22.50	TRP	$22.50
CT	$25	V	$22.50	S	$22.50
FL	$25	GC	$22.50	H	$22.50

Comments: 1985; Original Retail $13.50/$22.50
Part of *Birthday Train Series*. Giraffe collectors enjoy this piece! Retail price increased in 1995 by nine dollars! **See #30, page XIV.**

Personal Data: _____
____Want Mark _____ Mark _____ Purch. 19__ Pd $ _____

16004 **Clown Pulling Train**
"Bless The Days Of Our Youth"

D	$36	FL	$25	V	$22.50	TRP	$22.50
OB	$28	BA	$23	GC	$22.50	S	$22.50
CT	$25	FLM	$22	B	$22.50	H	$22.50

Comments: 1985; Original Retail $15.00/$22.50
Part of *Birthday Train Series*. Retail price increased $7.50. **See #30, page XIV.**

Personal Data: _____
____Want Mark _____ Mark _____ Purch. 19__ Pd $ _____

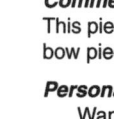

16012 **Angel Pushing Buggy**
"Baby's First Trip"

SUSP. 1989 - 7 YEARS AGO

D	$275	CT	$250	BA	$250
OB	$250	FL	$250		

Comments: 1985; Original Retail $32.50/$45.00
Fourth in *Baby's First Series*. This series is very popular and this is a great piece! Not easy to find. Predicted in '94 for price increase. Bingo! Very much sought after in '94. Look for this piece to "level off" at these prices in '96.

Personal Data: _____
____Want Mark _____ Mark _____ Purch. 19__ Pd $ _____

16020 **NIGHT LIGHT - Angel Behind Rainbow**
"God Bless You With Rainbows"

SUSP. 1989 -7 YEARS AGO

D	$125	FL	$100	
OB	$115	BA	$90	
CT	$105			

Comments: 1985; Original Retail $45.00/$57.50
This piece has not been easy to find since 1989. Very pretty. Three rainbow pieces have been produced.

Personal Data: _____
____Want Mark _____ Mark _____ Purch. 19__ Pd $ _____

Michael Belofsky holds the attention of his audience while demonstrating the benefits of the computer inventory program he designed especially for Precious Moments collectors by using this guide's price values. See page 92 for his advertisement.

100021   Boy Sitting with Teddy
"To My Favorite Paw"

SUSP. 1988 - 8 YEARS AGO

D	$60	CT	$55
OB	$55	FL	$50

Comments: 1985; Original Retail $22.50/$27.00
Figurines for "Dad" are not top retail sellers as those for "Mom."

Personal Data: _____
____Want Mark ____ Mark _____ Purch. 19__ Pd $ _____

100048   Girl with Fawn
"To My Deer Friend"

OB	$100	FLM	$50	TRP	$50
CT	$60	V	$50	S	$50
FL	$55	GC	$50	H	$50
BA	$55	B	$50		

Comments: 1986; Original Retail $33.00/$50.00
Suspension coming soon, in my opinion, as demand is decreasing after eleven years; prices have been found below retail on several ads recently.

Personal Data: _____
____Want Mark ____ Mark _____ Purch. 19__ Pd $ _____

Subscribe to the Collectors' Bulletin™
to find your wanted figurines
in the Classified Ads!
Call! 1-800-445-8745

100056   Boy on Cloud with Bow and Arrow
"Sending My Love"

SUSP. 1991 - 5 YEARS AGO

D	$60	BA	$45
OB	$52	FLM	$45
CT	$50	V	$45
FL	$45		

Comments: 1985; Original Retail $22.50/$32.50
First appeared on a Halo Card, H039-B. May be considered a part of the *Halo Series* produced previously (Cloud as the base). First appeared on dealers' shelves in late Nov. 1985 for early 1986 Valentine's sales; had 1985 mark. This is the "norm" for Valentine pieces. (100250 also reached shelves at the same time.) **See #31, page XIV.**

Personal Data: _____
____Want Mark ____ Mark _____ Purch. 19__ Pd $ _____

100064   Girl Kneeling at Church Window
"O Worship The Lord"

D	$55	BA	$40	B	$40
OB	$45	FLM	$40	TRP	$40
CT	$40	V	$40	S	$40
FL	$40	GC	$40	H	$40

Comments: 1985; Original Retail $24.00/$40.00
Appeared on J&D Card, A197-B. I feel this would be a good one to suspend or retire as it is a large piece that does not display as well with others due to its size. (Same for the Boy at Church Window, 102229.) Has been found with and without the "O" in title. No significant difference in secondary market. Perfect candidate for suspension or possible retirement. Collector wrote commenting that these figurines (100064 and 102229) were bookends!

Personal Data: _____
____Want Mark ____ Mark _____ Purch. 19__ Pd $ _____

100072   Two Girls Holding Flowers
"To My Forever Friend"

D	$100	BA	$55	B	$55
OB	$70	FLM	$55	TRP	$55
CT	$65	V	$55	S	$55
FL	$55	GC	$55	H	$55

Comments: 1985; Original Retail $33.00/$55.00
There have not been many double-figured pieces with two girls. This is an attractive piece! More colorful than most. (So colorful and time consuming to produce; it may be a good candidate for retirement.) The 1995 Easter Seals piece resembles this piece with flowers, etc. Retail price up in '96.

Personal Data: _____
____Want Mark ____ Mark _____ Purch. 19__ Pd $ _____

100080 Girl/Boy Mending Broken Heart
"He's The Healer Of Broken Hearts"

OB $65	FLM $50	TRP $50
CT $62	V $50	S $50
FL $60	GC $50	H $50
BA $60	B $50	

Comments: 1986; Original Retail $33.00/$50.00
Candidate for suspension?

Personal Data: _____
____Want Mark ____ Mark _____ Purch. 19__ Pd $ _____

100102 Girl with Sick Bear
"Make Me A Blessing"

RETIRED 1990 – 6 YEARS AGO

OB $135	FL $85	FLM $75
CT $85	BA $80	

Comments: 1986; Original Retail $35.00/$50.00
Most available of the 1990 retirement pieces after retirement announcement... but not for long.

Personal Data: _____
____Want Mark ____ Mark _____ Purch. 19__ Pd $ _____

100110 Baseball Player with Bat
"Lord, I'm Coming Home"

D $60	BA $35	B $35
OB $48	FLM $35	TRP $35
CT $45	V $35	S $35
FL $40	GC $35	H $35

Comments: 1985; Original Retail $22.50/$35.00
Sports themes began in 1986. Slow secondary market seller. Good potential for retirement or suspension because of that.

Personal Data: _____
____Want Mark ____ Mark _____ Purch. 19__ Pd $ _____

100129 Ballerina
"Lord, Keep Me On My Toes"

RETIRED 1988 - 8 YEARS AGO

D $100	CT $80
OB $80	FL $75

Comments: 1985; Original Retail $22.50/$27.00

Personal Data: _____
____Want Mark ____ Mark _____ Purch. 19__ Pd $ _____

100137 Mom with Babies
"The Joy Of The Lord Is My Strength"

D $110	BA $55	B $55
OB $75	FLM $55	TRP $55
CT $60	V $55	S $55
FL $55	GC $55	H $55

Comments: 1985; Original Retail $35.00/$55.00
Cute piece, much detail. Easy to find. Retail up $5 in '96. This piece was reported with a C Mark. Very Rare!

Personal Data: _____
____Want Mark ____ Mark _____ Purch. 19__ Pd $ _____

100145 Mom/Dad/Girl Adoption
"God Bless The Day We Found You"

SUSP. 1990 - 6 YEARS AGO
RETURNED FROM SUSPENSION 1995

OB $100	BA $95
CT $95	FLM $95
FL $95	

Comments: 1985; Original Retail $40.00/$55.00
Very slow seller on the secondary market. New piece has color changes so expect this piece to be most popular on sec. mkt. sales. A collector called to report that her *God Bless The Day We Found You* had a C Mark. She didn't say whether or not it was the girl or boy figurine. Very rare either way.

Personal Data: _____
____Want Mark ____ Mark _____ Purch. 19__ Pd $ _____

100145R Mom/Dad/Girl Adoption
"God Bless The Day We Found You"

RETURNED FROM SUSPENSION IN EARLY 1995

TRP $68	H $60
S $65	

Comments: 1985; Original Retail $60.00
Returned from suspension with color changes.

Personal Data: _____
____Want Mark ____ Mark _____ Purch. 19__ Pd $ _____

100153 Mom/Dad/Boy Adoption
"God Bless The Day We Found You"

SUSP. 1990 - 6 YEARS AGO
RETURNED FROM SUSPENSION 1995

OB	$100	BA	$95
CT	$95	FLM	$95
FL	$95		

Comments: 1985; Original Retail $40.00/$55.00
Secondary market prices were up but dropped somewhat with reintroduction. Prices dropped in '95. Look for less demand now due to reintroduction of 100153 R.

Personal Data: _____
____Want Mark ____ Mark _____ Purch. 19__ Pd $ _____

100153R Mom/Dad/Boy Adoption
"God Bless The Day We Found You"

RETURNED FROM SUSPENSION IN 1995

TRP	$62.50
S	$60.00
H	$60.00

Comments: 1985; Original Retail $60.00
Returned from suspension.

Personal Data: _____
____Want Mark ____ Mark _____ Purch. 19__ Pd $ _____

100161 Girl Tennis Player
"Serving The Lord"

SUSP. 1990 - 6 YEARS AGO	D	$70	FL	$45
	OB	$55	BA	$40
	CT	$50	FLM	$40

Comments: 1985; Original Retail $19.00/$27.50
See #32, page XIV.

Personal Data: _____
____Want Mark ____ Mark _____ Purch. 19__ Pd $ _____

100188 Boy with Football
"I'm A Possibility"

RETIRED 1993 - 3 YEARS AGO

OB	$80	BA	$60	GC	$55
CT	$70	FLM	$60	B	$55
FL	$70	V	$60		

Comments: 1985; Original Retail $22.00/$35.00

Personal Data: _____
____Want Mark ____ Mark _____ Purch. 19__ Pd $ _____

100196 Girl on Scales
"The Spirit Is Willing But The Flesh Is Weak"

RETIRED 1991 - 5 YEARS AGO

OB	$100	BA	$65
CT	$80	FLM	$60
FL	$65	V	$55

Comments: 1986; Original Retail $19.00/$30.00
From letters I've received, this piece slowed the demand to purchase the only other Curler Girl piece. Collectors wanted the Curler Girl, thus this piece made a good substitute. Figurine actually shows one hand holding candy box and one hand taking piece of candy, unlike line cut... often line cuts are different than the figurines.

Personal Data: _____
____Want Mark ____ Mark _____ Purch. 19__ Pd $ _____

100226 Girl/Cat and Bird Cage
"The Lord Giveth And The Lord Taketh Away"

RETIRED 1995 - 1 YEAR AGO

CT	$85	FLM	$68	B	$60
FL	$75	V	$65	TRP	$55
BA	$70	GC	$65	S	$50

Comments: 1986; Original Retail $33.50/$40.00
Sam relates this piece to when Katy lost her bird to a feline! I know how she felt!!!

Personal Data: _____
____Want Mark ____ Mark _____ Purch. 19__ Pd $ _____

100250 Boy and Girl in Boat
"Friends Never Drift Apart"

D	$80	BA	$60	B	$60
OB	$65	FLM	$60	TRP	$60
CT	$65	V	$60	S	$60
FL	$60	GC	$60	H	$60

Comments: 1985; Original Retail $35.00/$60.00
1986 Valentine piece. Produced in late months of 1985, thus first pieces had D mark. Some heads touch due to mold shrinkage. Have had one report of missing oars. This would be a good retirement piece. Lots of work in production but suspension more likely. Price increase in '96. Similar style ornament (522937) retired in 1995.

Personal Data: _____
____Want Mark ____ Mark _____ Purch. 19__ Pd $ _____

100269 Boy/Ink Spot
"Help, Lord I'm In A Spot"

RETIRED 1989 - 7 YEARS AGO

OB	$70	FL	$60
CT	$65	BA	$55

Comments: 1985; Original Retail $18.50/$25.00
Definitely did not sell well, not even on the secondary market after being retired. The ink spot was "too light" in color to be effective! BA still easily found for under $50 at collectible shows. One collector reported the ink bottle sitting straight up instead of on its side. Add $100 to the secondary market value for this error.

Personal Data: _____
____Want Mark ____ Mark _____ Purch. 19__ Pd $ _____

100277 Girl In Bathtub
"He Cleansed My Soul"

D	$65	BA	$40	B	$40
OB	$50	FLM	$40	TRP	$40
CT	$45	V	$40	S	$40
FL	$45	GC	$40	H	$40

Comments: 1985; Original Retail $24.00/$40.00
Has been found without "Holy Bible" decal on Bible. This increases the value by $75 on the secondary market. Place iridescent beads around this piece. It makes a delightful display in the bathroom!

Personal Data: _____
____Want Mark ____ Mark _____ Purch. 19__ Pd $ _____

100285 ♪ MUSICAL - Baby with Toys
"Heaven Bless You"

SUSP. 1993 - 3 YEARS AGO

D	$90	FL	$65	V	$70
OB	$75	BA	$65	GC	$70
CT	$70	FLM	$70	B	$65

Comments: 1984; Original Retail $45.00/$60.00
Plays *Brahm's Lullaby*. May go higher due to suspension, but not to date! Not being sought after.

Personal Data: _____
____Want Mark ____ Mark _____ Purch. 19__ Pd $ _____

Miracles often happen when we're at the end of our rope!

100293 Boy Tennis Player
"Serving The Lord"

SUSP. 1990 - 6 YEARS AGO

D	$50	FL	$45		
OB	$45	BA	$45		
CT	$45	FLM	$40		

Comments: 1985; Original Retail $19.00/$27.50
See #32, page XIV.

Personal Data: _____
____Want Mark ____ Mark _____ Purch. 19__ Pd $ _____

100455 DOLL - Boy Clown
"Bong Bong"

LE 1985 - 11 YEARS OLD   OB $265

Comments: 1985; Original Retail $150.00
Limited Ed. 12,000. Very colorful – nice. Secondary market prices affecting slow sales. Insure at $265, but to sell quickly price may have to be reduced.

Personal Data: _____
____Want Mark ____ Mark _____ Purch. 19__ Pd $ _____

100463 DOLL - Girl Clown
"Candy"

LE 1985 - 11 YEARS OLD   OB $265

Comments: 1985; Original Retail $150.00
Limited Ed. 12,000. Pretty! Scarce. Not easily found - very colorful! See 100455 for same comments.

Personal Data: _____
____Want Mark ____ Mark _____ Purch. 19__ Pd $ _____

100498 Parents of the Groom
"God Bless Our Family"

CT	$65	FLM	$55	B	$50	H	$50
FL	$55	V	$50	TRP	$50		
BA	$55	GC	$50	S	$50		

Comments: 1986; Original Retail $35.00/$50.00
Not easily found. Slow seller; retailers don't order in volume. Cute piece. Potential for suspension, in my opinion, as $50 for a wedding gift usually isn't affordable for most.

Personal Data: _____
____Want Mark ____ Mark _____ Purch. 19__ Pd $ _____

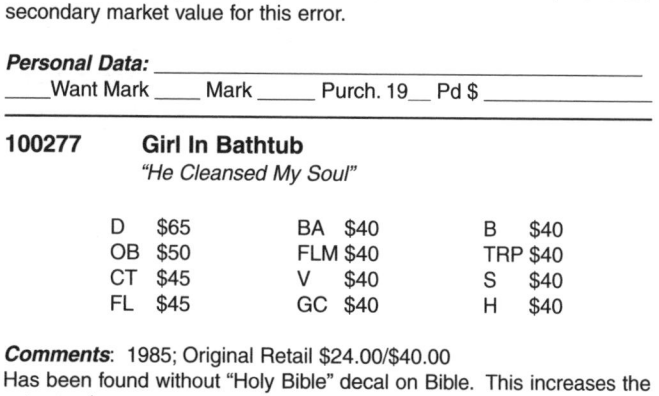

100501   Parents of the Bride
"God Bless Our Family"

CT	$65	FLM	$50	B	$50	H	$50
FL	$55	V	$50	TRP	$50		
BA	$55	GC	$50	S	$50		

Comments: 1986; Original Retail $35.00/$50.00
Not easily found. Slow seller; retailers don't order in volume. (I feel these would sell faster if the price could have been held lower. See 100498; same opinion.) This is probably a suspension candidate.

Personal Data: _____
____Want Mark ____ Mark _____ Purch. 19__ Pd $ _____

100528   Girl with Skunk
"Scent From Above"

RETIRED 1991 - 5 YEARS AGO

OB	$70	BA	$55
CT	$65	FLM	$50
FL	$60	V	$45

Comments: 1986; Original Retail $19.00/$27.50
Is this Diane and Beau K?

Personal Data: _____
____Want Mark ____ Mark _____ Purch. 19__ Pd $ _____

100536   Boy with Flower and Mom
"I Picked A Very Special Mom"

LE 1987 - 9 YEARS OLD   OB $80
                      CT $70

Error *"I Picked A Special Mom"* OB $90
                                CT $75

Comments: 1986; Original Retail $37.50/$40.00
1987 Limited Edition piece. Mainly CT pieces being sold... OB not as abundant.

Personal Data: _____
____Want Mark ____ Mark _____ Purch. 19__ Pd $ _____

100544   Pilgrim/Indian/Turkey
"Brotherly Love"

SUSP. 1989 - 7 YEARS AGO   OB $95   FL $75
                                 CT $78   BA $75

Comments: 1985; Original Retail $37.00/$47.50
Ideal for "Thanksgiving Theme." I was quite surprised when this was suspended! This is an unusual piece, different than the "norm."

Personal Data: _____
____Want Mark ____ Mark _____ Purch. 19__ Pd $ _____

100625   THIMBLE - Girl Holding Heart
"God Is Love, Dear Valentine"

SUSP. 1989 - 7 YEARS AGO   D $20   FL $12
                                 OB $18   BA $12
                                   CT $15

Comments: 1985; Original Retail $5.50/$8.00

Personal Data: _____
____Want Mark ____ Mark _____ Purch. 19__ Pd $ _____

100633   THIMBLE - Bride
"The Lord Bless You And Keep You"

SUSP. 1991 - 5 YEARS AGO   D $18   BA $12
                                 OB $15   FLM $12
                                   CT $14   V $12
                                 FL $14

Comments: 1979; Original Retail $5.50/$8.00
As the original artwork of the Bride/Groom was sold to Enesco in 1979, I'm assuming the thimble would carry the same license date. Research found very little trading in thimbles.

Personal Data: _____
____Want Mark ____ Mark _____ Purch. 19__ Pd $ _____

100641   THIMBLES - "Four Seasons" (Set of 4)
"Worship The Lord"

LE 1985 - 11 YEARS OLD   OB $80 set
                                   $20 ea.

Comments: 1985; Original Retail $20.00
1985 Limited Edition.

Personal Data: _____
____Want Mark ____ Mark _____ Purch. 19__ Pd $ _____

100668   THIMBLES - (Set of 2)
"Clowns"

SUSP. 1988 - 8 YEARS AGO
         CT $30 set
         FL $30 set
         OB $35 set

Comments: 1985; Original Retail $11.00/$14.00

Personal Data: _____
____Want Mark ____ Mark _____ Purch. 19__ Pd $ _____

101702 ♪ **MUSICAL - Boy and Girl in Box**
"Our First Christmas Together"

RETIRED 1992 - 4 YEARS AGO

OB	$120	FLM	$110
CT	$110	V	$100
FL	$110	GC	$100
BA	$110		

Comments: 1985; Original Retail $50.00/$70.00
Plays *We Wish You A Merry Christmas*. In the 1990 guide I predicted suspension or retirement of this Musical due to its size. Did not see many FLM marks in 1990. Judge each piece carefully and you'll soon recognize candidates for suspension or retirement, especially after 7 or 8 years of production. It's interesting to see how other guides keep raising prices on this piece and all price lists and known sales do not equal their high prices. Do they plan to keep raising prices 10-20% a year forever?!

Personal Data: _____
____Want Mark ____ Mark _____ Purch. 19__ Pd $ _____

101826 **Angel and Girl at Heaven's Gate**
"No Tears Past The Gate"

OB	$115	FLM	$70	TRP	$70
CT	$80	V	$70	S	$70
FL	$70	GC	$70	H	$70
BA	$70	B	$70		

Comments: 1986; Original Retail $40.00/$70.00
The front mural in the Precious Moments Chapel depicts a similar scene. Has been found without decal on bucket.

Personal Data: _____
____Want Mark ____ Mark _____ Purch. 19__ Pd $ _____

101834 **PLATE - Girl at Mailbox**
"I'm Sending You A White Christmas"

DATED 1986   OB $55

Comments: 1986; Original Retail $45.00
First issue in *Christmas Love Series*. A "flaw" similar to an HG mark appeared on most plates.

Personal Data: _____
____Want Mark ____ Mark _____ Purch. 19__ Pd $ _____

101842 **Clown Upside Down on Drum**
"Smile Along The Way"

RETIRED 1991 - 5 YEARS AGO

MM	$175	BA	$135
OB	$160	FLM	$130
CT	$140	V	$125
FL	$135		

Comments: 1986; Original Retail $30.00/$45.00
Extra pieces were not produced after the retirement announcement. This piece is colorful and popular. Most of the trading was found on CT mark in '93, '94 and '95. Price remained at '95 values.

Personal Data: _____
____Want Mark ____ Mark _____ Purch. 19__ Pd $ _____

101850 **Clown on Unicycle**
"Lord, Help Us Keep Our Act Together"

RETIRED 1992 - 4 YEARS AGO

D	$150	BA	$115
OB	$140	FLM	$115
CT	$125	V	$90
FL	$125		

Comments: 1986; Original Retail $35.00/$50.00
Much trading found for OB and V marks in '93 and '94! D Scarce!

Personal Data: _____
____Want Mark ____ Mark _____ Purch. 19__ Pd $ _____

102229 **Boy Kneeling at Church Window**
"O Worship The Lord"

D	$50	BA	$40	B	$40
OB	$45	FLM	$40	TRP	$40
CT	$45	V	$40	S	$40
FL	$45	GC	$40	H	$40

Comments: 1985; Original Retail $24.00/$40.00
Notice the great difference between this piece's order number and the Kneeling Girl's number (100064). Most generally "similar" pieces as these have similar order numbers. Not a best seller. Look for possible suspension. Found with and without "O" in title.

Personal Data: _____
____Want Mark ____ Mark _____ Purch. 19__ Pd $ _____

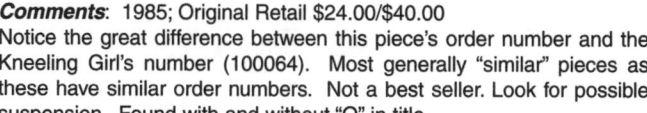

●●

102253   *DOLL*
"Connie"

OB $260

Comments: 1985; Original Retail $160.00
Limited Edition 7,500. Named after Sam's daughter-in-law
(Philip Butcher's wife). A very pretty doll.

Personal Data: _____
____Want Mark ____ Mark _____ Purch. 19__ Pd $ _____

102261   *MINI NATIVITY* - Angel with Lamb
"Shepherd Of Love"

OB	$28	BA	$17	GC	$16	S	$16
CT	$20	FLM	$16	B	$16	H	$16
FL	$17	V	$16	TRP	$16		

Comments: 1985; Original Retail $10.00/$16.00
Addition to Miniature Nativity.

Personal Data: _____
____Want Mark ____ Mark _____ Purch. 19__ Pd $ _____

102288   *ORNAMENT* - Angel with Lamb
"Shepherd Of Love"

SUSP. 1993 - 3 YEARS AGO

OB	$35	BA	$25	GC	$22
CT	$28	FLM	$25	B	$22
FL	$25	V	$22		

Comments: 1985; Original Retail $10.00/$15.00
Very popular ornament. Easily found.

Personal Data: _____
____Want Mark ____ Mark _____ Purch. 19__ Pd $ _____

Crystal Thurman's wall display was featured in the winter issue of Precious Collectibles™ as a collection of the month.

102296   *MINI NATIVITY* - Set of 3 Animals

SUSP. 1992 - 4 YEARS AGO

Black Sheep (not gray)		OB	$38		
		FL	$30		
OB	$30	BA	$25	GC	$25
CT	$28	FLM	$25		
FL	$28	V	$25		

Comments: 1985; Original Retail $13.50/$19.00
Additions to Miniature Nativity (Bunny, Turtle and Lamb). 12 sets found
in Kentucky and Wisconsin with gray lamb (OB) and black lamb (GC).
(Formerly black was OB and FL.)

Personal Data: _____
____Want Mark ____ Mark _____ Purch. 19__ Pd $ _____

102318   *BELL* - Girl with Muff
"Wishing You A Cozy Christmas"

DATED 1986   OB $25

Comments: 1985; Original Retail $20.00
Price plummeted from $35-40 in '94, and remained through '95 to now.
Bells not as collectible as figurines.

Personal Data: _____
____Want Mark ____ Mark _____ Purch. 19__ Pd $ _____

102326   *ORNAMENT* - Girl with Muff
"Wishing You A Cozy Christmas"

DATED 1986   OB $30

Comments: 1985; Original Retail $10.00
Several $20 sales were evident from research.

Personal Data: _____
____Want Mark ____ Mark _____ Purch. 19__ Pd $ _____

102334   *THIMBLE* - Girl with Muff
"Wishing You A Cozy Christmas"

DATED 1986   OB $20

Comments: 1985; Original Retail $5.50

Personal Data: _____
____Want Mark ____ Mark _____ Purch. 19__ Pd $ _____

102342   *FIGURINE* - **Girl with Muff**
"Wishing You A Cozy Christmas"

DATED 1986   OB $32

Comments: 1985; Original Retail $18.00
Dated figurines have not made "news" recently on the secondary market. Several sales of $30 reported.

Personal Data: _____
____Want Mark ____ Mark _____ Purch. 19__ Pd $ _____

102350   ***ORNAMENT*** - **Boy/Girl in Gift Box**
"Our First Christmas Together"

DATED 1986   OB $25

Comments: 1985; Original Retail $10.00
This ornament was also produced in 1987 (112399) and 1988 (520233). The only differences were the marks, style numbers and the dates.
See #29, page XIV.

Personal Data: _____
____Want Mark ____ Mark _____ Purch. 19__ Pd $ _____

102369   ***ARCH*** - **Bridal Series**
"Wedding Arch"

SUSP. 1992 - 4 YEARS AGO

OB $35	BA $30	GC $30
CT $30	FLM $30	
FL $30	V $30	

Comments: 1986; Original Retail $22.50/$30.00
Not sought after on the secondary market; not a collectible piece.

Personal Data: _____
____Want Mark ____ Mark _____ Purch. 19__ Pd $ _____

102377   ***ORNAMENT*** - **Policeman**
"Trust And Obey"

OB $28	BA $18	GC $17	S $17
CT $25	FLM $17	B $17	H $17
FL $20	V $17	TRP $17	

Comments: 1985; Original Retail $10.00/$17.00

Personal Data: _____
____Want Mark ____ Mark _____ Purch. 19__ Pd $ _____

102385   ***ORNAMENT*** - **Fireman**
"Love Rescued Me"

OB $28	BA $18	GC $17	S $17
CT $22	FLM $17	B $17	H $17
FL $20	V $17	TRP $17	

Comments: 1985; Original Retail $10.00/$17.00
The ornament does not have the water hose on his foot as shown; the similar figurine does.

Personal Data: _____
____Want Mark ____ Mark _____ Purch. 19__ Pd $ _____

102393   **Fireman**
"Love Rescued Me"

OB $50	FLM $37.50	TRP $37.50
CT $45	V $37.50	S $37.50
FL $40	GC $37.50	H $37.50
BA $38	B $37.50	

Comments: 1985; Original Retail $22.50/$37.50

Personal Data: _____
____Want Mark ____ Mark _____ Purch. 19__ Pd $ _____

102407   ***ORNAMENT*** - **Nurse**
"Angel Of Mercy"

OB $26	FLM $18	TRP $17
CT $22	V $17	S $17
FL $18	GC $17	H $17
BA $18	B $17	

Comments: 1985; Original Retail $10.00/$17.00
This is a popular gift item.

Personal Data: _____
____Want Mark ____ Mark _____ Purch. 19__ Pd $ _____

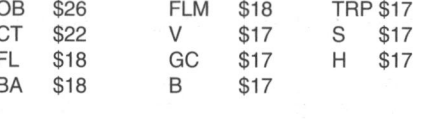

102415   ***ORNAMENT*** - **Doctor**
"It's A Perfect Boy"

SUSP. 1989 - 7 YEARS AGO   OB $35   FL $25
                                 CT $30   BA $25

Comments: 1985; Original Retail $10.00/$13.50

Personal Data: _____
____Want Mark ____ Mark _____ Purch. 19__ Pd $ _____

102423 **_ORNAMENT_ - Ballerina**
"Lord, Keep Me On My Toes"

RETIRED 1990 - 6 YEARS AGO

OB	$52	BA	$35
CT	$50	FLM	$35
FL	$40		

Comments: 1985; Original Retail $10.00/$15.00
Was a popular ornament but had to be hung in order to be displayed. Not abundant before or after retirement.

Personal Data: _____
____Want Mark ____ Mark _____ Purch. 19__ Pd $ _____

102431 **_ORNAMENT_ - Tennis Boy**
"Serve With A Smile"

SUSP. 1988 - 8 YEARS AGO

OB	$28
CT	$25
FL	$25

Comments: 1985; Original Retail $10.00/$12.50

Personal Data: _____
____Want Mark ____ Mark _____ Purch. 19__ Pd $ _____

102458 **_ORNAMENT_ - Tennis Girl**
"Serve With A Smile"

SUSP. 1988 - 8 YEARS AGO

OB	$30
CT	$25
FL	$25

Comments: 1985; Original Retail $10.00/$12.50

Personal Data: _____
____Want Mark ____ Mark _____ Purch. 19__ Pd $ _____

102466 **_ORNAMENT_ - Reindeer**

DATED 1986

MM	$195
D	$185
OB	$170

Comments: 1986; Original Retail $11.00
Scarce! First ornament for _Birthday Club Series_. D mark found on leg. Rose to $125 on the secondary market by Dec. 1987, went down to $95, and up to $150-160 in 1991; down to $145-150 in 1992 and up to $190 in 1993. This piece appeared only on a few retailers' shelves as it was not placed on order forms. _Precious Collectibles_™ was the first to alert collectors to search for this piece and several were found from our advertisers.

Personal Data: _____
____Want Mark ____ Mark _____ Purch. 19__ Pd $ _____

102474 **_ORNAMENT_ - Rocking Horse**

SUSP. 1991 - 5 YEARS AGO

OB	$30	BA	$20
CT	$25	FLM	$18
FL	$22	V	$18

Comments: 1985; Original Retail $10.00/$15.00

Personal Data: _____
____Want Mark ____ Mark _____ Purch. 19__ Pd $ _____

102482 **Nurse with Flower**
"Angel Of Mercy"

OB	$45	FLM	$32.50	TRP	$32.50
CT	$38	V	$32.50	S	$32.50
FL	$35	GC	$32.50	H	$32.50
BA	$35	B	$32.50		

Comments: 1985; Original Retail $20.00/$32.50

Personal Data: _____
____Want Mark ____ Mark _____ Purch. 19__ Pd $ _____

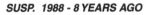

102490 **Dad/Mom/Cookies/Dog**
"Sharing Our Christmas Together"

SUSP. 1988 - 8 YEARS AGO

OB	$85
CT	$75
FL	$65

Comments: 1986; Original Retail $37.00/$45.00

Personal Data: _____
____Want Mark ____ Mark _____ Purch. 19__ Pd $ _____

102504 **_ORNAMENT_ - Girl with Candy Cane**
"Baby's First Christmas"

DATED 1986   OB $30

Comments: 1985; Original Retail $10.00

Personal Data: _____
____Want Mark ____ Mark _____ Purch. 19__ Pd $ _____

102512   ORNAMENT - Boy with Candy Cane
"Baby's First Christmas"

DATED 1986   OB $30

Comments: 1985; Original Retail $10.00
Seek and you might find below $20.

Personal Data: _____
____Want Mark ____ Mark _____ Purch. 19__ Pd $ _____

102520   ♪ MUSICAL - Clown on Elephant
"Let's Keep In Touch"

OB	$115	FLM	$95	TRP	$90
CT	$100	V	$95	S	$90
FL	$95	GC	$95	H	$90
BA	$95	B	$90		

Comments: 1985; Original Retail $65.00/$90.00
Plays *Be A Clown*. "Babe" was the name of Sam's secretary when he was a part of the J&D Co. "Babe" is written on the elephant's blanket. Retirement or suspension candidate? It's my opinion a $90 figurine is more likely to be suspended than retired because of collector reaction to the price at retirement announcement time.

Personal Data: _____
____Want Mark ____ Mark _____ Purch. 19__ Pd $ _____

102903   Girl with Pearl
"We Are All Precious In His Sight"

LE 1987 - 9 YEARS OLD   MM $75-80   CT $65

Comments: 1986; Original Retail $30.00
1987 Limited Edition. The inspiration was omitted from all pieces and the figurine was not marked "Limited." Several have been found without a mark which is an error. This piece was abundant during the issue year.

Personal Data: _____
____Want Mark ____ Mark _____ Purch. 19__ Pd $ _____

102938   Uncle Sam
"God Bless America"

LE 1986 - 10 YEARS OLD   OB $68

Comments: 1985; Original Retail $30.00
1986 Limited Edition. Very colorful and cute! Somewhat scarce starting mid-1992. This piece was abundant in 1986. Display him with the service people and a small flag, a red carnation, etc.

Personal Data: _____
____Want Mark ____ Mark _____ Purch. 19__ Pd $ _____

If you know that God's hand is in everything you can leave everything in God's hand.

102954   PLATE - Four Children
"My Peace I Give Unto Thee"

DATED 1987   CT $50

Comments: 1986; Original Retail $45.00
Second issue in *Christmas Love Series*. Many plates selling below retail. Beautiful but not as collectible as the figurines. Do not over insure!

Personal Data: _____
____Want Mark ____ Mark _____ Purch. 19__ Pd $ _____

102962   Boy Angel/Birthday Cake
"It's The Birthday Of A King"

SUSP. 1989 - 7 YEARS AGO

OB	$45	FL	$35
CT	$38	BA	$35

Comments: 1985; Original Retail $19.00/$25.00
Was a "slow" seller at retail.

Personal Data: _____
____Want Mark ____ Mark _____ Purch. 19__ Pd $ _____

102970   Baby with Tub
"I Would Be Sunk Without You"

CT	$28	V	$20	S	$20
FL	$22	GC	$20	H	$20
BA	$22	B	$20		
FLM	$20	TRP	$20		

Comments: 1986; Original Retail $15.00/$20.00

Personal Data: _____
____Want Mark ____ Mark _____ Purch. 19__ Pd $ _____

103004   Damien-Dutton Figurine and Bible
"We Belong To The Lord"

SPECIAL EDITION   **DIAMOND MARK**   Fig. $180
    Bible $35

Comments: 1986; Original Retail $50.00
Special Edition produced for and sold by Damien-Dutton Society. A leather Bible accompanied this piece. The Damien-Dutton Society for Leprosy Aid was founded in 1944 by Howard Crouch for lepers in the USA and other parts of the world. The Damien-Dutton Society celebrated their 50th anniversary in September '94. This Society operates two gift shops in Bellmore and Port Jefferson, Long Island, NY. All profits from their sales go to this charity. I was privileged to speak at a meeting for the Damien-Dutton Society and Precious Moments® collectors in November 1988. This was the first trip to New York for Dave and me – a limo and all the fancies! It was a great time! We walked 26 blocks to the Statue of Liberty! Passed the Enesco Showroom on the way.

Personal Data: _____
____Want Mark ____ Mark _____ Purch. 19__ Pd $ _____

103497   Boy with Fish
"My Love Will Never Let You Go"

OB	$50	BA	$40	GC $40	S	$37.50
CT	$45	FLM	$40	B $40	H	$37.50
FL	$40	V	$40	TRP $37.50		

Comments: 1986; Original Retail $25.00/$37.50
A great piece! Great gift for men/sportsmen. May be suspended as a new fisherman debuted in '95.

Personal Data: _____
____Want Mark ____ Mark _____ Purch. 19__ Pd $ _____

103632   Girl with Cross
"I Believe In The Old Rugged Cross"

D	$50	BA	$40	B	$35
OB	$45	FLM	$40	TRP	$35
CT	$40	V	$40	S	$35
FL	$40	GC	$35	H	$35

Comments: 1985; Original Retail $25.00/$35.00
Very popular figurine. Ideal to display with the '92-'93 Limited Edition pieces (526185 and 523593). Perfect "retirement" piece, wouldn't you say?

Personal Data: _____
____Want Mark ____ Mark _____ Purch. 19__ Pd $ _____

104000   *NATIVITY - 9 pc. with Cassette*
"Come Let Us Adore Him"

D	$145	BA	$135	B	$130
OB	$140	FLM	$135	TRP	$130
CT	$135	V	$135	S	$130
FL	$135	GC	$135	H	$130

Comments: 1986; Original Retail $95/$130
Changed from original set, E-2800. Heads now are larger. Sets produced in 1991 included a 16-page booklet featuring the Christmas story and family traditions. No demand on secondary market (E-2800 more popular). Maybe it's time for a new Nativity set?

Personal Data: _____
____Want Mark ____ Mark _____ Purch. 19__ Pd $ _____

104019   Boy Giving Girl Ring
"With This Ring I..."

CT	$68-75	FLM	$70	B	$65	H	$65
FL	$65-68	V	$65	TRP	$65		
BA	$65-68	GC	$65	S	$65		

Comments: 1986; Original Retail $40.00/$65.00
Due to price increase, retailers are reporting that this piece has "slowed" on retail sales as $40 was more affordable for a gift item. The collection could use a less expensive "engagement" figurine for a gift item.

Personal Data: _____
____Want Mark ____ Mark _____ Purch. 19__ Pd $ _____

104027   Boy/Hobby Horse
"Love Is The Glue That Mends"

SUSP. 1990 - 6 YEARS AGO

CT	$75	BA	$65
FL	$65	FLM	$60

Comments: 1986; Original Retail $33.50/$40.00
This is a nice piece! Not many out there with only four years of production.

Personal Data: _____
____Want Mark ____ Mark _____ Purch. 19__ Pd $ _____

Don't just be good. Be good for something.

"I thank my God every time I remember you."
Philippians 1:3 NIV

104035 Girl Cheerleader
"Cheers To The Leader"

CT	$45	V	$32.50	S	$32.50
FL	$40	GC	$32.50	H	$32.50
BA	$35	B	$32.50		
FLM	$32.50	TRP	$32.50		

Comments: 1986; Original Retail $22.50/$32.50
A collector found this piece with a double V mark, which is an error; add $100 to secondary market value.

Personal Data: _____
____Want Mark ____ Mark _____ Purch. 19__ Pd $ _____

104396 Clown with Books
"Happy Days Are Here Again"

SUSP. 1990 - 6 YEARS AGO

CT	$65	BA	$55
FL	$62	FLM	$50

Comments: 1986; Original Retail $25.00/$32.50
Several other clowns have been suspended or retired. May become harder to find as it was produced for only four years! No significant change form '95.

Personal Data: _____
____Want Mark ____ Mark _____ Purch. 19__ Pd $ _____

104418 Rhino with Bird
"Friends To The End"

SUSP. 1993 - 3 YEARS AGO

MM	$55	FLM	$25	B	$20
FL	$30	V	$22		
BA	$25	GC	$20		

Comments: 1988; Original Retail $15.00/$18.50
(A shiny glass Rhino night light was available on retailers' shelves; it may still available.)

Personal Data: _____
____Want Mark ____ Mark _____ Purch. 19__ Pd $ _____

104515 ORNAMENT - Bear in Tub/Skis
"Bear The Good News Of Christmas"

DATED 1987   CT $20

Comments: 1986; Original Retail $12.50
Second *Birthday Club Series* ornament. Quite abundant! Scarce at first. Secondary market dealers bought all they could find... then very large shipments arrived by mid December. Cute piece!

Personal Data: _____
____Want Mark ____ Mark _____ Purch. 19__ Pd $ _____

104523 NATIVITY - 9" Dealer
"Come Let Us Adore Him"

OB $425

Comments: 1986; Original Retail $400.00
Produced for dealers, but collectors purchased them at $400 plus tax. These would have been a very much sought-after collectible, and collectors thought so too, buying several sets. But the following year Enesco produced almost the same set for retail, diminishing demand for the Dealer Nativity Sets. If you're brave, sell these pieces individually. You'll get more! If you price them at $50 for sheep, $50 for Baby and $100 for other pieces, it would total $650! Sell this way for other sets, too; you'll get more. It may take longer, though.

Personal Data: _____
____Want Mark ____ Mark _____ Purch. 19__ Pd $ _____

104531 9" - 1988 EASTER SEALS - Girl w/Bunny
"Jesus Loves Me"

LE 1988 - 8 YEARS AGO   CT $1600-1750
                              FL $1450-1500

Comments: 1988; Original Retail $500.00
1988 - 9" Figurine. Same as E-1372G. Limited Edition 1000 pcs. Most limited of the 9" Easter Seals pieces. Most sought after. Production on current 9" pieces is now at 2000; they are not scarce. 9" Boy with Teddy to match should be produced. *See #25, page XIV.*

Personal Data: _____
____Want Mark ____ Mark _____ Purch. 19__ Pd $ _____

104817 Baby Boy/Tub
"A Tub Full Of Love"

CT	$42	FLM	$32.50	B	$32.50	H	$32.50
FL	$38	V	$32.50	TRP	$32.50		
BA	$35	GC	$32.50	S	$32.50		

Comments: 1986; Original Retail $22.50/$32.50

Personal Data: _____
____Want Mark ____ Mark _____ Purch. 19__ Pd $ _____

104825   Angel On Stool
"Sitting Pretty"

SUSP. 1990 - 6 YEARS AGO

CT	$55	FLM	$38
FL	$45	V	$35
BA	$40		

Comments: 1986; Original Retail $22.50/$30.00
Slow seller. Although suspended in 1990, collectors have reported that they have found this piece with the V (1991) mark; in my opinion, a slip-up at the factory. Not a sought – after piece.

Personal Data: _____
____Want Mark ____ Mark _____ Purch. 19__ Pd $ _____

105635   Boy with Scroll
"Have I Got News For You"

SUSP. 1991 - 5 YEARS AGO

CT	$50	FLM	$35
FL	$45	V	$30
BA	$38		

Comments: 1986; Original Retail $22.50/$30.00
Slow seller on the secondary market.

Personal Data: _____
____Want Mark ____ Mark _____ Purch. 19__ Pd $ _____

105643   Girl Holding Doll with Dog
"Something's Missing When You're Not Around"

SUSP. 1991 - 5 YEARS AGO

FL	$78	FLM	$50
BA	$60	V	$40

Comments: 1988; Original Retail $32.50/$37.50
Figurine has base.

Personal Data: _____
____Want Mark ____ Mark _____ Purch. 19__ Pd $ _____

105813   Dentist with Boy's Tooth
"To Tell The Tooth You're Special"

SUSP. 1990 - 6 YEARS AGO

CT	$150	BA	$145
FL	$145	FLM	$145

Comments: 1986; Original Retail $38.50/$50.00
Becoming scarce!

Personal Data: _____
____Want Mark ____ Mark _____ Purch. 19__ Pd $ _____

105821   Cowboy on Fence
"Hallelujah Country"

CT	$250	FLM	$50	B	$45	H	$45
FL	$60	V	$45	TRP	$45		
BA	$55	GC	$45	S	$45		

Comments: 1986; Original Retail $35.00/$45.00
CT marks are very scarce. I only know of a few collectors who have the CT mark. Do you? The little cowgirl, *Hallelujah Hoedown*, debuts this year.

Personal Data: _____
____Want Mark ____ Mark _____ Purch. 19__ Pd $ _____

105945   Elephant Showering Mouse
"Showers Of Blessing"

RETIRED 1993 - 3 YEARS AGO

CT	$50	BA	$40	V	$35	B	$35
FL	$40	FLM	$35	GC	$35		

Comments: 1986; Original Retail $16.00/$20.00
Birthday Series. Price not much higher than in '94 and '95. Smaller than the average piece. May have reached its peak for awhile.

Personal Data: _____
____Want Mark ____ Mark _____ Purch. 19__ Pd $ _____

105953   Skunk and Mouse
"Brighten Someone's Day"

SUSP. 1993 - 3 YEARS AGO

CT	$35	BA	$25	V	$22	B	$20
FL	$30	FLM	$25	GC	$22		

Comments: 1986; Original Retail $12.50/15.00
Several pieces found with decal missing from paint can. Add $50 to price. Price stabilized since 1994.

Personal Data: _____
____Want Mark ____ Mark _____ Purch. 19__ Pd $ _____

106151   Boy with Donkey
"We're Pulling For You"

SUSP. 1991 - 5 YEARS AGO

CT	$75	BA	$65	V	$65
FL	$65	FLM	$65		

Comments: 1986; Original Retail $40.00/$55.00
Different colored strings have been found but have not made a significant secondary market difference to date. Remained about the same throughout 1995.

Personal Data: _____
____Want Mark ____ Mark _____ Purch. 19__ Pd $ _____

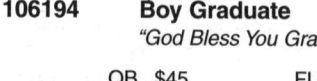

106194 Boy Graduate
"God Bless You Graduate"

OB	$45	FLM	$35	TRP	$35
CT	$38	V	$35	S	$35
FL	$35	GC	$35	H	$35
BA	$35	B	$35		

Comments: 1986; Original Retail $20.00/$35.00

Personal Data: _____
____Want Mark ____ Mark _____ Purch. 19__ Pd $ _____

106208 Girl Graduate
"Congratulations, Princess"

OB	$45	FLM	$35	TRP	$35
CT	$40	V	$35	S	$35
FL	$35	GC	$35	H	$35
BA	$35	B	$35		

Comments: 1986; Original Retail $20.00/$35.00
Not sought after to date on secondary market.

Personal Data: _____
____Want Mark ____ Mark _____ Purch. 19__ Pd $ _____

106216 Clown Going to School
"Lord, Help Me Make The Grade"

SUSP. 1990 - 6 YEARS AGO

CT	$55	BA	$50
FL	$50	FLM	$45

Comments: 1987; Original Retail $25.00/$32.50

Personal Data: _____
____Want Mark ____ Mark _____ Purch. 19__ Pd $ _____

106755 Groom Popping Out of Trunk
"Heaven Bless Your Togetherness"

CT	$110	V	$90	S	$90
FL	$90	GC	$90	H	$90
BA	$90	B	$90		
FLM	$90	TRP	$90		

Comments: 1986; Original Retail $65.00/$90.00
I look for this piece to be suspended or retired as, in my opinion, it was intended as a special gift item and a $90 retail limits many gift buyers! Not being traded often on today's secondary market; this seems to be the norm for pieces priced over $55.

Personal Data: _____
____Want Mark ____ Mark _____ Purch. 19__ Pd $ _____

106763 Couple on Couch Reading
"Precious Memories"

CT	$70	FLM	$50	B	$50	H	$50
FL	$60	V	$50	TRP	$50		
BA	$55	GC	$50	S	$50		

Comments: 1986; Original Retail $37.50/$50.00

Personal Data: _____
____Want Mark ____ Mark _____ Purch. 19__ Pd $ _____

106798 Anniversary Couple with Puppy
"Puppy Love Is From Above"

RETIRED 1995 - 1 YEAR AGO

CT	$80	FLM	$70	B	$70
FL	$78	V	$70	TRP	$70
BA	$75	GC	$70	S	$65

Comments: 1987; Original Retail $45.00/$55.00
Anniversary pieces not traded a lot on secondary market. This one is cuter than several of the others.

Personal Data: _____
____Want Mark ____ Mark _____ Purch. 19__ Pd $ _____

106836 Girl/Poppy Plant
"Happy Birthday Poppy"

SUSP. 1993 - 3 YEARS AGO

CT	$55	FLM	$45	B	$40
FL	$50	V	$45		
BA	$45	GC	$40		

Comments: 1987; Original Retail $27.50/$35.00
Inspiration eliminates many sales for birthdays as not many buy figurines for "Pop" on birthdays. Another "Poppy" figurine (604208) debuted in 1994.

Personal Data: _____
____Want Mark ____ Mark _____ Purch. 19__ Pd $ _____

106844 Girl Sewing Boy's Pants
"Sew In Love"

CT	$70	FLM	$60	B	$55	H	$55
FL	$65	V	$60	TRP	$55		
BA	$60	GC	$55	S	$55		

Comments: 1987; Original Retail $45.00/$55.00
She reminds us of the li'l girl sewing the quilt.

Personal Data: _____
____Want Mark ____ Mark _____ Purch. 19__ Pd $ _____

107999   *EASTER SEALS* **- Girl On Crutches**
"He Walks With Me"

LE 1987/88   OB $40   CT $35

Comments: 1986; Original Retail $25.00
Commemorative Easter Seals Figurine 1987 Limited Edition w/decaled Lily Mark. Easter Seals Logo on base. Produced in great abundance that year. Easily found at these prices! Collector reported this with a C mark. Very Rare indeed!

Personal Data: _____
____Want Mark ____ Mark _____ Purch. 19__ Pd $ _____

108243   *MINI NATIVITY* **- Three Kings on Camels**
"They Followed The Star"

CT	$135	FLM	$120	B	$120	H	$120
FL	$120	V	$120	TRP	$120		
BA	$120	GC	$120	S	$120		

Comments: 1986; Original Retail $75.00/$120.00
Addition to Miniature Nativity. Only CT sales reported. Not much trading on these pieces has been reported the past four years!

Personal Data: _____
____Want Mark ____ Mark _____ Purch. 19__ Pd $ _____

109231   **Baby Boy with Dog/Stocking**
"The Greatest Gift Is A Friend"

CT	$55	FLM	$37.50	B	$37.50	H	$37.50
FL	$45	V	$37.50	TRP	$37.50		
BA	$40	GC	$37.50	S	$37.50		

Comments: 1986; Original Retail $30.00/$37.50
This is a great title. It needs to have been on an everyday figurine as retailers say "Friends" figurines are great sellers for gift items.

Personal Data: _____
____Want Mark ____ Mark _____ Purch. 19__ Pd $ _____

109401   *ORNAMENT* **- Girl/Rocking Horse**
"Baby's First Christmas"

DATED 1987   CT $40

Comments: 1986; Original Retail $12.00
We received one report of OB mark.

Personal Data: _____
____Want Mark ____ Mark _____ Purch. 19__ Pd $ _____

109428   *ORNAMENT* **- Boy/Rocking Horse**
"Baby's First Christmas"

DATED 1987   CT $38

Comments: 1986; Original Retail $12.00
We have received one report of OB mark.

Personal Data: _____
____Want Mark ____ Mark _____ Purch. 19__ Pd $ _____

109460   **Age 8 - Ostrich**
"Isn't Eight Just Great"

CT	$34	FLM	$24	B	$23	H	$22.50
FL	$28	V	$24	TRP	$23		
BA	$24	GC	$24	S	$22.50		

Comments: 1985; Original Retail $18.50/$22.50
Part of the *Birthday Train Series*. Ages 7 and 8 debuted in 1988.
See #30, page XIV.

Personal Data: _____
____Want Mark ____ Mark _____ Purch. 19__ Pd $ _____

109479   **Age 7 - Leopard**
"Wishing You Grr-eatness"

CT	$34	FLM	$25	B	$23	H	$22.50
FL	$28	V	$25	TRP	$22.50		
BA	$24	GC	$23	S	$22.50		

Comments: 1985; Original Retail $18.50/$22.50
Part of the *Birthday Train Series*. Ages 7 and 8 debuted in 1988.
See #30, page XIV.

Personal Data: _____
____Want Mark ____ Mark _____ Purch. 19__ Pd $ _____

109487   **Boy with Barbells**
"Believe The Impossible"

SUSP. 1991 - 5 YEARS AGO
	CT	$100	FLM	$55
	FL	$55	V	$55
	BA	$55		

Comments: 1987; Original Retail $35.00/$45.00
CT is scarce! Retailers reported "broken" bars when received. No doubt biggest reason for suspension.

Personal Data: _____
____Want Mark ____ Mark _____ Purch. 19__ Pd $ _____

109584   Clown Angel/Bouquet
"Happiness Divine"

RETIRED 1992 - 4 YEARS AGO

FL	$80	V	$60
BA	$65	GC	$60
FLM	$60		

Comments: 1987; Original Retail $25.00/$30.00
The only figurine in the 1988 First Allotment not found with CT mark. On figurine clown is holding bouquet instead of halo (as shown at left). GC easiest to find.

Personal Data: _____
____Want Mark ____ Mark _____ Purch. 19__ Pd $ _____

109746   ♪ *MUSICAL* - Kids Caroling
"Peace On Earth"

SUSP. 1993 - 3 YEARS AGO

CT	$165	FLM	$155	B	$150
FL	$160	V	$150		
BA	$158	GC	$150		

Comments: 1988; Original Retail $100.00/$130.00
Plays *Hark The Herald Angels Sing*. Nice!

Personal Data: _____
____Want Mark ____ Mark _____ Purch. 19__ Pd $ _____

109754   Girl/Ice Cream Cone
"Wishing You A Yummy Christmas"

SUSP. 1994 - 2 YEARS AGO

CT	$75	FLM	$60	B	$55
FL	$65	V	$60	TRP	$55
BA	$60	GC	$55		

Comments: 1986; Original Retail $35.00/$50.00

Personal Data: _____
____Want Mark ____ Mark _____ Purch. 19__ Pd $ _____

Never give an excuse
that you would not be willing to accept.

109762   Family/Thanksgiving
"We Gather Together To Ask The Lord's Blessing"

RETIRED 1995 1 YEAR AGO

CT	$245-255	FLM	$225	B	$200
FL	$230	V	$215	TRP	$200
BA	$230	GC	$200	S	$200

Comments: 1986; Original Retail $130.00/$150.00
Contains several separate pieces. We've seen many figurines debut using song titles or verses from songs and hymns as the inspiration. Collectors have reported sets containing two fathers or two mothers, rather than one of each. Contact your dealer for an exchange or refund. Adorable addition to your collection! Not many on retailers' shelves. Very little trading on this piece in past four years!

Personal Data: _____
____Want Mark ____ Mark _____ Purch. 19__ Pd $ _____

109770   *ORNAMENT* - Girl with Presents
"Love Is The Best Gift Of All"

DATED 1987   CT $35

Comments: 1986; Original Retail $11.00
This piece has been found without the date decal. Add $50-60 to the secondary market value.

Personal Data: _____
____Want Mark ____ Mark _____ Purch. 19__ Pd $ _____

109800   Girl with Kitten
"Meowie Christmas"

FL	$55	V	$35	TRP	$35
BA	$42	GC	$35	S	$35
FLM	$40	B	$35	H	$35

Comments: 1988; Original Retail $30.00/$35.00

Personal Data: _____
____Want Mark ____ Mark _____ Purch. 19__ Pd $ _____

109819   Grandma in Rocking Chair "Sled"
"Oh What Fun It Is To Ride"

C	$135	FLM	$115	B	$110	H	$110
FL	$125	V	$110	TRP	$110		
BA	$120	GC	$110	S	$110		

Comments: 1986; Original Retail $85.00/$110.00
Retailers do not order this piece in large quantities due to the high price. It's a cute piece. Great for a winter display.

Personal Data: _____
____Want Mark ____ Mark _____ Purch. 19__ Pd $ _____

109835   *BELL* - Girl with Present
"Love Is The Best Gift Of All"

DATED 1987   CT $25

Comments: 1986; Original Retail $22.50
Slow seller on the secondary market.

Personal Data: _____
____Want Mark ____ Mark _____ Purch. 19__ Pd $ _____

109843   *THIMBLE* - Girl with Present
"Love Is The Best Gift Of All"

DATED 1987   CT $25

Comments: 1987; Original Retail $6.00

Personal Data: _____
____Want Mark ____ Mark _____ Purch. 19__ Pd $ _____

109886   Girl/Bunny in Hands
"Wishing You A Happy Easter"

CT	$45	FLM	$35	B	$35	H	$35
FL	$42	V	$35	TRP	$35		
BA	$35	GC	$35	S	$35		

Comments: 1987; Original Retail $23.00/$35.00
Suspension candidate – very similar to other pieces. Easter pieces do not sell well all year for retailers.

Comments: 1988; Original Retail $30.00/$35.00

Personal Data: _____
____Want Mark ____ Mark _____ Purch. 19__ Pd $ _____

109924   Boy/Basket with Chick
"Wishing You A Basket Full Of Blessings"

CT	$45	FLM	$38	B	$35	H	$35
FL	$42	V	$35	TRP	$35		
BA	$39.50	GC	$35	S	$35		

Comments: 1987; Original Retail $23.00/35.00
Pretty! Pretty!

Personal Data: _____
____Want Mark ____ Mark _____ Purch. 19__ Pd $ _____

109967   Girl on Cloud Dropping Hearts
"Sending You My Love"

CT	$65	FLM	$50	B	$45	H	$45
FL	$55	V	$50	TRP	$45		
BA	$55	GC	$45	S	$45		

Comments: 1987; Original Retail $35.00/$45.00

Personal Data: _____
____Want Mark ____ Mark _____ Purch. 19__ Pd $ _____

109975   Boy with Flower
"Mommy, I Love You"

CT	$40	FLM	$35	B	$30	H	$30
FL	$38	V	$30	TRP	$30		
BA	$38	GC	$30	S	$30		

Comments: 1987: Original Retail $22.50/$30.00
Slow seller on the secondary market. Suspension or retirement candidate.

Personal Data: _____
____Want Mark ____ Mark _____ Purch. 19__ Pd $ _____

109983   Girl Pushing Doll/Sleigh
"January"

CT	$55	FLM	$50	B	$45	H	$45
FL	$50	V	$45	TRP	$45		
BA	$50	GC	$45	S	$45		

Comments: 1987; Original Retail $37.50/$45.00
January Calendar Girl. Look for calendar pieces to phase out in a few years as retail price is increasing and may soon be out of the reach of "Birthday" gift buyers.

Personal Data: _____
____Want Mark ____ Mark _____ Purch. 19__ Pd $ _____

109991   Girl Looking at Plant in Snow
"February"

CT	$50	FLM	$38	B	$37.50	H	$37.50
FL	$40	V	$37.50	TRP	$37.50		
BA	$38	GC	$37.50	S	$37.50		

Comments: 1987; Original Retail $27.50/$37.50
February Calendar Girl. Wouldn't a birthstone be nice in a Precious Moments® figurine for birthdays?! Hint, hint, to Enesco and Sam. ☺

Personal Data: _____
____Want Mark ____ Mark _____ Purch. 19__ Pd $ _____

110019 Girl with Kite
"March"

CT	$55	FLM	$40	B	$37.50	H	$37.50
FL	$45	V	$37.50	TRP	$37.50		
BA	$45	GC	$37.50	S	$37.50		

Comments: 1987; Original Retail $27.50/$37.50
March Calendar Girl. A very popular piece. Suggested retail price increased in '95.

Personal Data: _____
____Want Mark ____ Mark _____ Purch. 19__ Pd $ _____

110027 Girl with Umbrella
"April"

CT	$130	V	$40	S	$40
FL	$50	GC	$40	H	$40
BA	$45	B	$40		
FLM	$45	TRP	$40		

Comments: 1987; Original Retail $27.50/$40.00
April Calendar Girl. CT mark harder to find. Sells at retail more quickly than other calendar pieces. Attractive piece. Suggested retail price increased in '95 and again in '96.

Personal Data: _____
____Want Mark ____ Mark _____ Purch. 19__ Pd $ _____

110035 Girl with Potted Plant
"May"

CT	$115	FLM	$42	B	$35	H	$35
FL	$45	V	$35	TRP	$35		
BA	$42	GC	$35	S	$35		

Comments: 1987; Original Retail $27.50/$35.00
May Calendar Girl.

Personal Data: _____
____Want Mark ____ Mark _____ Purch. 19__ Pd $ _____

110043 Girl Dressing Up As Bride
"June"

CT	$95	FLM	$55	B	$50	H	$50
FL	$55	V	$50	TRP	$50		
BA	$55	GC	$50	S	$50		

Comments: 1987; Original Retail $40.00/$50.00
June Calendar Girl. Several "Calendar" pieces debuted with the previous year's mark (CT) which were scarce. These were favored by the avid collector who wants "First Marks" but CT not sought after on this piece as compared to April.

Personal Data: _____
____Want Mark ____ Mark _____ Purch. 19__ Pd $ _____

110051 Girl with Puppy in Basket
"July"

FL	$55	V	$45	TRP	$45
BA	$50	GC	$45	S	$45
FLM	$50	B	$45	H	$45

Comments: 1988; Original Retail $35.00/$45.00
July Calendar Girl.

Personal Data: _____
____Want Mark ____ Mark _____ Purch. 19__ Pd $ _____

110078 Girl in Pool
"August"

FL	$65	V	$50	TRP	$50
BA	$55	GC	$50	S	$50
FLM	$55	B	$50	H	$50

Comments: 1988; Original Retail $40.00/$50.00
August Calendar Girl. Several sales reported below retail.

Personal Data: _____
____Want Mark ____ Mark _____ Purch. 19__ Pd $ _____

110086 Girl Balancing Books
"September"

FL	$50	V	$37.50	TRP	$37.50
BA	$42	GC	$37.50	S	$37.50
FLM	$40	B	$37.50	H	$37.50

Comments: 1988; Original Retail $27.50/$37.50
September Calendar Girl.

Personal Data: _____
____Want Mark ____ Mark _____ Purch. 19__ Pd $ _____

110094 Girl with Pumpkins
"October"

FL	$55	V	$45	TRP	$45
BA	$50	GC	$45	S	$45
FLM	$45	B	$45	H	$45

Comments: 1988; Original Retail $35.00/$45.00
October Calendar Girl. Pretty piece!

Personal Data: _____
____Want Mark ____ Mark _____ Purch. 19__ Pd $ _____

110108 Girl in Pilgrim Dress
"November"

FL	$50	V	$40	TRP	$37.50
BA	$45	GC	$37.50	S	$37.50
FLM	$40	B	$37.50	H	$37.50

Comments: 1988; Original Retail $32.50/$37.50
November Calendar Girl.

Personal Data: _____
____Want Mark ____ Mark _____ Purch. 19__ Pd $ _____

110116 Girl with Christmas Candle
"December"

FL	$50	V	$35	TRP	$35
BA	$40	GC	$35	S	$35
FLM	$35	B	$35	H	$35

Comments: 1988; Original Retail $27.50/$35.00
December Calendar Girl.

Personal Data: _____
____Want Mark ____ Mark _____ Purch. 19__ Pd $ _____

110930 Girl with Present
"Love Is The Best Gift Of All"

DATED 1987   CT $38

Comments: 1986; Original Retail $22.50
Dated figurines have not been as popular with the avid collector as the dated ornaments (but the 1993 dated figurine was maybe more popular than ever!!)

Personal Data: _____
____Want Mark ____ Mark _____ Purch. 19__ Pd $ _____

111120 ORNAMENT - Football Player
"I'm A Possibility"

SUSP. 1990 - 6 YEARS AGO

CT	$35	BA	$25
FL	$30	FLM	$25

Comments: 1986; Original Retail $11.00/15.00
Look for suspended ornaments to increase in value two to four years after suspension date. Similar figurine was retired in '93.

Personal Data: _____
____Want Mark ____ Mark _____ Purch. 19__ Pd $ _____

111155 Girl with Plunger
"Faith Takes The Plunge"

PUCKERED MOUTH (frown w/pucker in lip)

CT	$55	FLM	$40	B	$35	H	$35
FL	$45	V	$35	TRP	$35		
BA	$40	GC	$35	S	$35		

SMILE - Error

CT	$65
FL	$60
BA	$60

CIRCLE MOUTH   VERY RARE (Estimated value)

FL	$200
BA	$200

Comments: 1987; Original Retail $27.50/$35.00
This piece debuted with the Smile and was immediately changed to a Puckered Mouth. We have heard of a Circle Mouth from a "good source" but we have never actually seen one. Excellent candidate for suspension or retirement.

Personal Data: _____
____Want Mark ____ Mark _____ Purch. 19__ Pd $ _____

111163 Girl Adding Seasoning to Batter
"Tis The Season"

FL	$50	V	$40	TRP	$35
BA	$40	GC	$35	S	$35
FLM	$40	B	$35	H	$35

Comments: 1988; Original Retail $27.50/$35.00
Slower seller for some reason. A suspension or retirement candidate.

Personal Data: _____
____Want Mark ____ Mark _____ Purch. 19__ Pd $ _____

111333 NATIVITY (4 pc.)
"O Come Let Us Adore Him"

SUSP. 1991 - 5 YEARS AGO

CT	$250	V	$220
FLM	$230	BA	$220
FL	$225		

Comments: 1987; Original Retail $200.00/$220.00
This is the set that detracted from the Dealer Set's rise on the secondary market (104523).

Personal Data: _____
____Want Mark ____ Mark _____ Purch. 19__ Pd $ _____

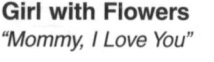

112143   Girl with Flowers
"Mommy, I Love You"

CT	$45	FLM	$30	B	$30	H	$30
FL	$40	V	$30	TRP	$30		
BA	$35	GC	$30	S	$30		

Comments: 1987; Original Retail $22.50/$30.00
Suspension or retirement candidate. Slow seller on secondary market. Retail price increased in '95.

Personal Data: _____
____Want Mark ____ Mark ____ Purch. 19__ Pd $ _____

112313   Baby Girl in Tub
"A Tub Full Of Love"

CT	$40	FLM	$32	B	$32	H	$32
FL	$35	V	$32	TRP	$32		
BA	$35	GC	$32	S	$32		

Comments: 1987; Original Retail $22.50/$32.00
I look for her and the boy in tub to be suspended in the future due to retail price increase to $30 for a smaller than normal piece. Price increased to $32 in 1996.

Personal Data: _____
____Want Mark ____ Mark ____ Purch. 19__ Pd $ _____

112356   ORNAMENT - Girl with String of Hearts
"You Have Touched So Many Hearts"

CT	$28	FLM	$18	B	$18	H	$17
FL	$22	V	$18	TRP	$17		
BA	$18	GC	$18	S	$17		

Comments: 1986; Original Retail $11.00/$17.00
Appeared as the 1990 9" Easter Seals figurine. Perfect retirement candidate.

Personal Data: _____
____Want Mark ____ Mark ____ Purch. 19__ Pd $ _____

112364   ORNAMENT - Girl Clown with Goose
"Waddle I Do Without You"

CT	$25	FLM	$18	B	$18	H	$17
FL	$22	V	$18	TRP	$17		
BA	$20	GC	$18	S	$17		

Comments: 1986; Original Retail $11.00/$17.00
Maybe a retirement candidate... Why? Because of the many colors and time consuming design; also, she's a clown.

Personal Data: _____
____Want Mark ____ Mark ____ Purch. 19__ Pd $ _____

112372   ORNAMENT - Girl Mailing Snowball
"I'm Sending You A White Christmas"

SUSP. 1992 - 4 YEARS AGO

CT	$32	FLM	$24
FL	$28	V	$22
BA	$25	GC	$20

Comments: 1986; Original Retail $11.00/15.00
Musical of similar design retired in 1993.

Personal Data: _____
____Want Mark ____ Mark ____ Purch. 19__ Pd $ _____

112380   ORNAMENT - Girl in Tub
"He Cleansed My Soul"

CT	$30	FLM	$18	B	$17	H	$17
FL	$25	V	$18	TRP	$17		
BA	$20	GC	$17	S	$17		

Comments: 1986; Original Retail $12.00/$17.00
Cute ornament, very popular!

Personal Data: _____
____Want Mark ____ Mark ____ Purch. 19__ Pd $ _____

112399   ORNAMENT - Boy/Girl in Package
"Our First Christmas Together"

DATED 1987   CT $28

Comments: 1986; Original Retail $11.00
This ornament was also produced in 1986 (102350) and 1988 (520233). The only differences were the marks, style numbers and the dates.

Personal Data: _____
____Want Mark ____ Mark ____ Purch. 19__ Pd $ _____

112402 ♪ MUSICAL - Girl Mailing Snowball
"I'm Sending You A White Christmas"

RETIRED 1993 - 3 YEARS AGO

CT	$150	FLM	$125	B	$110
FL	$130	V	$125		
BA	$125	GC	$110		

Comments: 1987; Original Retail $55.00/$75.00
Plays *White Christmas*.

Personal Data: _____
____Want Mark ____ Mark ____ Purch. 19__ Pd $ _____

112577 ♪ **MUSICAL - Girl with String of Hearts**
"You Have Touched So Many Hearts"

CT	$75	FLM	$65	B	$65	H	$65
FL	$65	V	$65	TRP	$65		
BA	$65	GC	$65	S	$65		

Comments: 1988; Original Retail $50.00/$65.00
Plays *Everybody Loves Somebody*. Musicals are becoming more popular on the secondary market. Notice retail price increase again for '96. Double FLM mark found – insure for $100 over secondary market value. Up $15 since 1994, secondary market up but so was retail!

Personal Data: _____
____Want Mark ____ Mark _____ Purch. 19__ Pd $ _____

113956 **ORNAMENT - Two Girls Holding Basket/Wreath**
"To My Forever Friend"

FL	$36	V	$20	TRP	$18.50
BA	$25	GC	$18.50	S	$18.50
FLM	$22	B	$18.50	H	$18.50

Comments: 1988; Original Retail $16.00/$18.50
Pretty! Pretty! The actual ornament is different from the original artwork shown at left. The ornament is of one girl with holly in her hair, holding a basket, and another girl holding a wreath.

Personal Data: _____
____Want Mark ____ Mark _____ Purch. 19__ Pd $ _____

113964 **ORNAMENT - Clown Doing Handstand**
"Smile Along The Way "

SUSP. 1993 - 3 YEARS AGO

FL	$35	FLM	$28	GC	$25
BA	$30	V	$25	B	$25

Comments: 1988; Original Retail $15.00/$17.50

Personal Data: _____
____Want Mark ____ Mark _____ Purch. 19__ Pd $ _____

113972 **ORNAMENT - Clown with Jack-in-Box**
"God Sent You Just In Time"

SUSP. 1991 - 5 YEARS AGO

FL	$38	FLM	$32
BA	$32	V	$30

Comments: 1988; Original Retail $13.50/$15.00
We predicted this piece would be either retired or suspended in 1991... It was suspended! Poor li'l clowns! Display with Sammy's Circus.

Personal Data: _____
____Want Mark ____ Mark _____ Purch. 19__ Pd $ _____

113980 **ORNAMENT - Angel with Trumpet**
"Rejoice O Earth"

RETIRED 1991 - 5 YEARS AGO

FL	$48	FLM	$35
BA	$45	V	$30

Comments: 1988; Original Retail $13.50/$15.00
Four years of production.

Personal Data: _____
____Want Mark ____ Mark _____ Purch. 19__ Pd $ _____

113999 **ORNAMENT - Cheerleader**
"Cheers To The Leader"

SUSP. 1991 - 5 YEARS AGO

FL	$38	FLM	$30
BA	$35	V	$28

Comments: 1988; Original Retail $13.50/$15.00
Four years of production.

Personal Data: _____
____Want Mark ____ Mark _____ Purch. 19__ Pd $ _____

114006 **ORNAMENT - Fisherman**
"My Love Will Never Let You Go"

SUSP. 1991 - 5 YEARS AGO

FL	$35	FLM	$30
BA	$30	V	$25

Comments: 1988; Original Retail $13.50/$15.00
Four years of production.

Personal Data: _____
____Want Mark ____ Mark _____ Purch. 19__ Pd $ _____

114014 **Boy with Broken Heart**
"This Too Shall Pass"

CT	$40	FLM	$30	B	$30	H	$30
FL	$35	V	$30	TRP	$30		
BA	$32	GC	$30	S	$30		

Comments: 1987; Original Retail $23.00/$30.00
This piece was designed when Sam was feeling sad... Retailers report that he's too sad for a sale. Suspension or retirement candidate?

Personal Data: _____
____Want Mark ____ Mark _____ Purch. 19__ Pd $ _____

114022   **Couple with Dog and Puppies**
"The Good Lord Has Blessed Us Tenfold"

LE 1988 - 8 YEARS OLD   CT $160
                               FL $145

Comments: 1987; Original Retail $90.00
10-Year Club Anniversary Piece. 1988 Limited Edition. Easily found at these prices. Do not overinsure! Twelve unpainted pieces were released accidentally from the factory! *See #19, page XIII.*

Personal Data: _____
____Want Mark ____ Mark _____ Purch. 19__ Pd $ _____

115231   **Girl Carrying Bag/Balloons**
"You Are My Main Event"

          Pink Strings   CT $75
          White Strings   CT $55
                     FL $50

Comments: 1987; Original Retail $30.00
1988 Special Events Piece, for Special Events only. *Precious Collectibles*™ was first to announce the "pink strings" difference to collectors. These debuted early in the year. This piece is not being traded as much on the secondary market as in 1987 and 1988.

Personal Data: _____
____Want Mark ____ Mark _____ Purch. 19__ Pd $ _____

115274   **Bunnies**
"Some Bunny's Sleeping"

FL $28	V $20	TRP $18.50
BA $25	GC $20	S $18.50
FLM $22	B $20	H $18.50

Comments: 1988; Original Retail $15.00/$18.50

Personal Data: _____
____Want Mark ____ Mark _____ Purch. 19__ Pd $ _____

115282   **ORNAMENT** - Boy with Bear in Sleigh
"Baby's First Christmas"

DATED 1988   FL $25

Comments: 1988; Original Retail $15.00
Also produced in 1989 (523194). *See #29, page XIV.*

Personal Data: _____
____Want Mark ____ Mark _____ Purch. 19__ Pd $ _____

115290   **Couple with Gifts**
"Our First Christmas Together"

SUSP. 1991 - 5 YEARS AGO
      FL $80   FLM $75
      BA $75   V $75

Comments: 1988; Original Retail $50.00/$60.00
Popular piece, very cute! Give this piece a few more years to be in demand. Easily found at these prices.

Personal Data: _____
____Want Mark ____ Mark _____ Purch. 19__ Pd $ _____

115304   **BELL** - Girl with Calendar/Clock
"Time To Wish You A Merry Christmas"

DATED 1988   FL $35

Comments: 1988; Original Retail $25.00

Personal Data: _____
____Want Mark ____ Mark _____ Purch. 19__ Pd $ _____

115312   **THIMBLE** - Girl with Calendar/Clock
"Time To Wish You A Merry Christmas"

DATED 1988   FL $28

Comments: 1988; Original Retail $7.00
Very few sales reported in past two years.

Personal Data: _____
____Want Mark ____ Mark _____ Purch. 19__ Pd $ _____

115320   **ORNAMENT** - Girl with Calendar/Clock
"Time To Wish You A Merry Christmas"

DATED 1988   FL $40

Comments: 1988; Original Retail $13.00
Has been found without the 1988 date. Add $50 to the secondary market price. Several reported sales found below $40.

Personal Data: _____
____Want Mark ____ Mark _____ Purch. 19__ Pd $ _____

115339   **FIGURINE** - Girl with Calendar/Clock
"Time To Wish You A Merry Christmas"

DATED 1988   FL $34

Comments: 1988; Original Retail $24.00

Personal Data: _____
____Want Mark ____ Mark _____ Purch. 19__ Pd $ _____

●●●

115479   **EASTER SEALS** - Boy/Arm Braces/Dog
"Blessed Are They That Overcome"

LE 1988 - 8 YEARS AGO   CT $30
                             FL $25

Comments: 1987; Original Retail $27.50
Commemorative Easter Seals Figurine. 1988 Limited Edition. Large quantity produced. None of the pieces had the normally printed "Easter Seals Lily" mark on base. An error, no doubt, but by the time it was realized, it was too late to remedy. Easter Seals pieces are produced in large quantities for this special charity. Pieces have also been done for the Damien-Dutton Society (103004), St. Jude Children's Research Hospital (E-1381R), Disaster Relief (603864), Child Evangelism Fellowship , American Legion Auxiliary (604208) and Boys and Girls Clubs of America (521701) (See descriptive index). Many prices found below original retail in our research in the past two years!
Personal Data: _____
____Want Mark _____ Mark _____ Purch. 19__ Pd $ _____

127019   **Girl Kneeling at Flowered Cross**
"Love Blooms Eternal"

DATED 1995   TRP $38
                  S $35

Comments: 1994; Original Retail $35.00
A collector reported her decal was slanted on the front. First issue of *Dated Cross Series.*

Personal Data: _____
____Want Mark _____ Mark _____ Purch. 19__ Pd $ _____

128295A   **ORNAMENT** - Girl with Umbrella
"An Event Showered With Love"

DATED 1994   TRP $50

Comments: 1994; Original Retail $30.00
Regional event piece in Wisconsin.
Personal Data: _____
____Want Mark _____ Mark _____ Purch. 19__ Pd $ _____

128295C   **ORNAMENT** - Girl with Umbrella
"An Event Showered With Love"

DATED 1994   TRP $60

Comments: 1994; Original Retail $30.00
Regional event piece in Texas. There were fewer of these made than the Wisconsin and California ball ornaments.
Personal Data: _____
____Want Mark _____ Mark _____ Purch. 19__ Pd $ _____

128295D   **ORNAMENT** - Girl with Umbrella
"An Event Showered With Love"

DATED 1994   TRP $50

Comments: 1994; Original Retail $30.00
Regional event piece in California
Personal Data: _____
____Want Mark _____ Mark _____ Purch. 19__ Pd $ _____

127809   **Two Zebras**
"Congratulations, You Earned Your Stripes"

                  S $20
                  H $15

Comments: 1994; Original Retail $15.00
Addition to *Two By Two, Noah's Ark.*

Personal Data: _____
____Want Mark _____ Mark _____ Purch. 19__ Pd $ _____

128309   **Girl on Rainbow**
"Dreams Really Do Come True"

                  TRP $45
                  S $37.50
                  H $37.50

Comments: 1994; Original Retail $37.50

Personal Data: _____
____Want Mark _____ Mark _____ Purch. 19__ Pd $ _____

128686   **Three Bunnies with Birthday Cake**
"Another Year And More Grey Hares"

                  TRP $25
                  S $20
                  H $18.50

Comments: 1994; Original Retail $17.50/$18.50
Birthday Series addition.

Personal Data: _____
____Want Mark _____ Mark _____ Purch. 19__ Pd $ _____

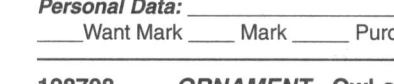

128694 **Girl in Hula Dress**
"Happy Hula Days"

S	$30
H	$30

Comments: 1994; Original Retail $30.00
Because of her black hair, I look for suspension in a year or two.

Personal Data: _____
____Want Mark ____ Mark ____ Purch. 19__ Pd $ _____

128708 **ORNAMENT - Owl on Branch**
"Owl Be Home For Christmas"

DATED 1996   H   Current

Comments: 1995; Original Retail $18.50
Birthday Series addition.

Personal Data: _____
____Want Mark ____ Mark ____ Purch. 19__ Pd $ _____

128899 **EASTER SEALS - ORNAMENT**
Girl w/ Roses
"Take Time To Smell The Roses"

DATED 1995   NM $10

Comments: 1994; Original Retail $7.50
1995 Commemorative Easter Seals two-dimensional Ornament.

Personal Data: _____
____Want Mark ____ Mark ____ Purch. 19__ Pd $ _____

129097 **Anniversary Couple**
"Love Vows To Always Bloom"

S	$70
H	Current

Comments: 1995; Original Retail $70.00
Features the more "grown-up" look.

Personal Data: _____
____Want Mark ____ Mark ____ Purch. 19__ Pd $ _____

129100 **Bride and Groom**
"I Give You My Love Forever True"

TRP	$78
S	$70
H	Current

Comments: 1994; Original Retail $70.00
This new Bride and Groom features a more "grown-up" appearance and is also more colorful.

Personal Data: _____
____Want Mark ____ Mark ____ Purch. 19__ Pd $ _____

129151 **PLATE - Girl Bending Over Flowers**
"He Hath Made Everything Beautiful In His Time"

DATED 1995   S $50

Comments: 1994; Original Retail $50.00
2nd Issue in *Mother's Day Plate Series*.

Personal Data: _____
____Want Mark ____ Mark ____ Purch. 19__ Pd $ _____

129259 **CHAPEL EXCLUSIVE - Girl with Castle**
"Grandpa's Island"

S	$110
H	Current

Comments: 1995; Original Retail $100.00

Personal Data: _____
____Want Mark ____ Mark ____ Purch. 19__ Pd $ _____

129267 **CHAPEL EXCLUSIVE**
Boy Angel w/Candle and Teddy Bear
"Lighting The Way To A Happy Holiday"

S	$35
H	Current

Comments: 1995; Original Retail $30.00

Personal Data: _____
____Want Mark ____ Mark ____ Purch. 19__ Pd $ _____

129275 **CHAPEL EXCLUSIVE - ORNAMENT**
Boy Angel w/Candle and Teddy Bear
"Lighting The Way To A Happy Holiday"

S	$25
H	Current

Comments: 1995; Original Retail $20.00

Personal Data: _____
____Want Mark ____ Mark ____ Purch. 19__ Pd $ _____

136190 **Baby Girl with Cake**
"Age 1"

S $30
H $25

Comments: 1994; Original Retail $25.00
From the *Growing In Grace Series*. Baby with cake at age 1. Has been found with a 7 on the heart.

Personal Data: _____
____Want Mark ____ Mark _____ Purch. 19__ Pd $ _____

136204 **Angel with Announcement**
"Infant Angel With Newspaper"

S $25
H $22.50

Comments: 1994; Original Retail $22.50
From the *Growing In Grace Series*. Angel with newspaper announcing "It's A Girl."

Personal Data: _____
____Want Mark ____ Mark _____ Purch. 19__ Pd $ _____

136212 **Girl with Baby Blocks**
"Age 2"

S $30
H $25

Comments: 1994; Original Retail $25.00
From the *Growing In Grace Series*. Baby girl at age 2. No doubt, missing numerals have been found on one of these pieces. Add $50 to the secondary market value for that error.

Personal Data: _____
____Want Mark ____ Mark _____ Purch. 19__ Pd $ _____

136220 **Girl with Flowers**
"Age 3"

S $30
H $25

Comments: 1994; Original Retail $25.00
From the *Growing In Grace Series*. Girl at age 3 discovering flowers.

Personal Data: _____
____Want Mark ____ Mark _____ Purch. 19__ Pd $ _____

136239 **Girl with Doll**
"Age 4"

S $32.50
H $27.50

Comments: 1994; Original Retail $27.50
From the *Growing In Grace Series*. Little girl age 4 playing with doll.

Personal Data: _____
____Want Mark ____ Mark _____ Purch. 19__ Pd $ _____

136247 **Girl with Lunch Box and Books**
"Age 5"

S $30
H $27.50

Comments: 1994; Original Retail $27.50
From the *Growing In Grace Series*. Little girl, age 5.

Personal Data: _____
____Want Mark ____ Mark _____ Purch. 19__ Pd $ _____

136255 **Girl Riding Bicycle**
"Age 6"

S $32
H $27.50

Comments: 1994; Original Retail $27.50
From the *Growing In Grace Series*. Little girl, age 6. This piece has been found without the heart and age numeral.

Personal Data: _____
____Want Mark ____ Mark _____ Purch. 19__ Pd $ _____

136263 **Girl Holding Sixteen Roses**
"Sweet Sixteen"

S $50
H $45

Comments: 1994; Original Retail $45.00
From the *Growing In Grace Series*. Sweet Sixteen with a bouquet of roses. Very similar to 1992 LE #526185.

Personal Data: _____
____Want Mark ____ Mark _____ Purch. 19__ Pd $ _____

136271   **Soldier Driving Car**
"You Will Always Be Our Hero"

LE 1995 - ONE YEAR OLD   S   **$45**

Comments: 1994; Original Retail $40.00
Limited Edition figurine commemorating the 50th Anniversary of the return to peace and the end of WW II. The first shipments of this figurine were refused by Enesco due to some production problems.

Personal Data: _____
____Want Mark ____ Mark _____ Purch. 19__ Pd $ _____

136836   **Girl with Guitar**
"Hallelujah Hoedown"

LE 1996   H   **$32.50**

Comments: 1995; Original Retail $32.50
Limited Edition figurine available for purchase only during Spring Celebration April 20, 1996. This piece could perhaps debut with the Ship mark. We'll keep you in touch in Precious Collectibles.™

Personal Data: _____
____Want Mark ____ Mark _____ Purch. 19__ Pd $ _____

139475   ***CENTURY CIRCLE***
Boy and Girl Riding Carousel
"Love Makes The World Go 'Round"

LE 15,000   S   **NE**

Comments: 1995; Original Retail $200.00
The first Century Circle Exclusive piece. These figurines were offered at only 35 retailers nationwide. Features gold accents. Still offered at retail early '96.

Personal Data: _____
____Want Mark ____ Mark _____ Purch. 19__ Pd $ _____

142654   **Girl Holding Scissors/Snowflake**
"He Covers The Earth With His Beauty"

DATED 1995   S   **$35**

Comments: 1995; Original Retail $30.00

Personal Data: _____
____Want Mark ____ Mark _____ Purch. 19__ Pd $ _____

142662   ***ORNAMENT*** - **Girl Holding Scissors/Snowflake**
"He Covers The Earth With His Beauty"

DATED 1995   S   **$20**

Comments: 1995; Original Retail $17.00

Personal Data: _____
____Want Mark ____ Mark _____ Purch. 19__ Pd $ _____

142670   ***PLATE*** - **Girl Holding Scissors and Snowflake**
"He Covers The Earth With His Beauty"

DATED 1995   S   **$50**

Comments: 1995; Original Retail $50.00

Personal Data: _____
____Want Mark ____ Mark _____ Purch. 19__ Pd $ _____

142689   ***ORNAMENT*** - **Round Porcelain Ball/Stand Girl Holding Scissors and Snowflake**
"He Covers The Earth With His Beauty"

DATED 1995   S   **$35**

Comments: 1995; Original Retail $30.00

Personal Data: _____
____Want Mark ____ Mark _____ Purch. 19__ Pd $ _____

142700   ***ORNAMENT*** - **Two Birds in Heart Wreath**
"Our First Christmas Together"

DATED 1995   S   **$22**

Comments: 1995; Original Retail $18.50

Personal Data: _____
____Want Mark ____ Mark _____ Purch. 19__ Pd $ _____

142719   ***ORNAMENT*** - **Girl Sitting on Star**
"Baby's First Christmas"

DATED 1995   S   **$22**

Comments: 1995; Original Retail $17.50

Personal Data: _____
____Want Mark ____ Mark _____ Purch. 19__ Pd $ _____

142727   *ORNAMENT* - **Boy Sitting on Star**
"Baby's First Christmas"

DATED 1995   S $22

Comments: 1995; Original Retail $17.50

Personal Data: _____
____Want Mark ____ Mark _____ Purch. 19__ Pd $ _____

142735   *NATIVITY* **(3 pc. set)**
"Come Let Us Adore Him "

                   S $55
                   H $50

Comments: 1994; Original Retail $50.00
Booklet included.

Personal Data: _____
____Want Mark ____ Mark _____ Purch. 19__ Pd $ _____

142743   *MINI NATIVITY* **(3 pc. set)**
"Making A Trail To Bethlehem"

                   S $40
                   H $35

Comments: 1994; Original Retail $35.00
Booklet included.

Personal Data: _____
____Want Mark ____ Mark _____ Purch. 19__ Pd $ _____

142751   *NATIVITY* - **Shepherd Boy on Stick Horse**
"Making A Trail To Bethlehem"

                   S $35
                   H $30

Comments: 1994; Original Retail $30.00
Large Nativity addition.

Personal Data: _____
____Want Mark ____ Mark _____ Purch. 19__ Pd $ _____

150061   **Boy on Life Preserver**
"Sailabration"

                   S $200-$300

Comments: 1995; Gift to those on the 1995 Precious Moments Cruise.

Personal Data: _____
____Want Mark ____ Mark _____ Purch. 19__ Pd $ _____

150088   **Boy Giving Heart to Baby Jesus**
"I'll Give Him My Heart"

                   S $45
                   H $40

Comments: 1994; Original Retail $40.00
This figurine included a dedication card to promise your love, faith and good will towards God.

Personal Data: _____
____Want Mark ____ Mark _____ Purch. 19__ Pd $ _____

150096   **Boy Chimney Sweep**
"Soot Yourself To A Merry Christmas"

                   S $40
                   H $35

Comments: 1994; Original Retail $35.00

Personal Data: _____
____Want Mark ____ Mark _____ Purch. 19__ Pd $ _____

150118   **Girl Holding Christmas Candle**
"Making Spirits Bright"

                   S $40
                   H $37.50

Comments: 1994; Original Retail $37.50

Personal Data: _____
____Want Mark ____ Mark _____ Purch. 19__ Pd $ _____

150126   *ORNAMENT* - **Girl Holding Holly**
"Joy From Head To Mistletoe"

                   S $22
                   H $17

Comments: 1994; Original Retail $17.00

Personal Data: _____
____Want Mark ____ Mark _____ Purch. 19__ Pd $ _____

150134   **Moose with Decorated Antlers**
"Merry Chrismoose"

DATED 1995   S $22

Comments: 1995; Original Retail $17.00
DSR Holiday Preview Event Dated ornament.
Personal Data: _____
____Want Mark ____ Mark _____ Purch. 19__ Pd $ _____

150142 ORNAMENT - Boy Holding Report Card
"You're "A" Number One In My Book, Teacher"

S $20
H $17

Comments: 1994; Original Retail $17.00

Personal Data: _____
____Want Mark ____ Mark _____ Purch. 19__ Pd $ _____

150320 ORNAMENT - Angel Blowing Trumpet
"Joy To The World"

S $22
H $20

Comments: 1994; Original Retail $20.00

Personal Data: _____
____Want Mark ____ Mark _____ Purch. 19__ Pd $ _____

151114 PLATE - Girl with String of Hearts
"You Have Touched So Many Hearts"

S $35
H Current

Comments: 1995; Original Retail $35.00
This resin plate has a 3D effect.

Personal Data: _____
____Want Mark ____ Mark _____ Purch. 19__ Pd $ _____

152277 9" EASTER SEALS – Girl with Daisy
"HE Loves Me"

LE 1996 H Current

Comments: 1995; Original Retail $500.00
1996 Commemorative Limited Edition 9" Easter Seals figurine. Matching figurine 524263.

Personal Data: _____
____Want Mark ____ Mark _____ Purch. 19__ Pd $ _____

152579 ORNAMENT - EASTER SEALS
Girl with Piggy Bank
"You Can Always Count On Me"

LE 1996 S $6.50

Comments: 1995; Original Retail $6.50
1996 Commemorative Easter Seals ornament.

Personal Data: _____
____Want Mark ____ Mark _____ Purch. 19__ Pd $ _____

153338 ORNAMENT - Angel with Flute
"Joy To The World"

H Current

Comments: 1995; Original Retail $20.00

Personal Data: _____
____Want Mark ____ Mark _____ Purch. 19__ Pd $ _____

160334D ORNAMENT - Girl with String of Sunflowers
"An Event Filled With Sunshine And Flowers"

DATED 1995

S $50

Comments: 1995; Original Retail $35.00
Porcelain Ball Ornament for Regional Event in Missouri.

Personal Data: _____
____Want Mark ____ Mark _____ Purch. 19__ Pd $ _____

160334E ORNAMENT - Girl with String of Sunflowers
"An Event Filled With Sunshine And Flowers"

DATED 1995

S $50

Comments: 1995; Original Retail $35.00
Porcelain Ball Ornament for Regional Event in Maryland.

Personal Data: _____
____Want Mark ____ Mark _____ Purch. 19__ Pd $ _____

160334F ORNAMENT - Girl with String of Sunflowers
"An Event Filled With Sunshine And Flowers"

DATED 1995

S $50

Comments: 1995; Original Retail $35.00
Ball Ornament for Regional Event in Florida.

Personal Data: _____
____Want Mark ____ Mark _____ Purch. 19__ Pd $ _____

160334G ORNAMENT - Girl with String of Sunflowers
"An Event Filled With Sunshine And Flowers"

DATED 1995

S $50

Comments: 1995; Original Retail $35.00
Porcelain Ball Ornament for Regional Event in Ohio.

Personal Data: _____
____Want Mark ____ Mark _____ Purch. 19__ Pd $ _____

163600   **Mother & Daughter**
"You Are Always There For Me"

S $55   H   Current

Comments: 1995; Original Retail $50.00
Part of the new *Family Series.*

Personal Data: _____
____Want Mark ____ Mark _____ Purch. 19__ Pd $ _____

163627   **Father & Son**
"You Are Always There For Me"

S $55   H   Current

Comments: 1995; Original Retail $50.00
Part of the new *Family Series.*

Personal Data: _____
____Want Mark ____ Mark _____ Purch. 19__ Pd $ _____

163635   **Sisters Comforting One Another**
"You Are Always There For Me"

H   Current

Comments: 1995; Original Retail $50.00
Part of *Family Series.*

Personal Data: _____
____Want Mark ____ Mark _____ Purch. 19__ Pd $ _____

Sam first drew this in 1991 as the symbol for the 25th Annual Carthage Maple Leaf Festival. Doesn't it resemble the 1996 *"Color Your World With Thanksgiving"* figurine? See page 87.

163694   **Goats**
"I'd Goat Anywhere With You"

S $12   H   Current

Comments: 1995; Original Retail $10.00
Addition to *Two By Two, Noah's Ark Series.*
Personal Data: _____
____Want Mark ____ Mark _____ Purch. 19__ Pd $ _____

163716   ***PLATE* - Girl with Spring Flowers**
"Of All The Mother's I Have Known, There's None As Precious As My Own"

DATED 1996

S $50   H   Current

Comments: 1995; Original Retail $50.00
Third issue in the *Mother's Day Plate Series.*

Personal Data: _____
____Want Mark ____ Mark _____ Purch. 19__ Pd $ _____

163732   **Girl standing at Flowered Cross**
"Standing In The Presence Of The Lord"

DATED 1996

S $37.50   H   Current

Comments: 1995; Original Retail $37.50
Second issue of *Dated Cross Series.*

Personal Data: _____
____Want Mark ____ Mark _____ Purch. 19__ Pd $ _____

163740   **Girl Nursing Sick Kitten**
"Age 7"

S $32.50   H   Current

Comments: 1995; Original Retail $32.50

Personal Data: _____
____Want Mark ____ Mark _____ Purch. 19__ Pd $ _____

163759   **Girl with Puppy/and Marbles**
"Age 8"

S $32.50   H   Current

Comments: 1995; Original Retail $32.50
Personal Data: _____
____Want Mark ____ Mark _____ Purch. 19__ Pd $ _____

163767   **Praying Girl**
"Take It To The Lord In Prayer"

S $30   H   Current

Comments: 1995; Original Retail $30.00

Personal Data: _____
____Want Mark ____ Mark _____ Purch. 19___ Pd $ _____

163775   **Girl with Umbrella**
"The Sun Is Always Shining Somewhere"

S $37.50   H   Current

Comments: 1995; Original Retail $37.50
Collectors have complained that the umbrella breaks off very easily.

Personal Data: _____
____Want Mark ____ Mark _____ Purch. 19___ Pd $ _____

163783   **Anniversary Couple with Cake**
"A Year Of Blessings"

S $75   H   Current

Comments: 1995; Original Retail $70.00
1st Anniversary.

Personal Data: _____
____Want Mark ____ Mark _____ Purch. 19___ Pd $ _____

163791   **Anniversary Couple with Clock**
"Each Hour Is Precious With You"

S $75   H   Current

Comments: 1995; Original Retail $70.00
5th Anniversary.

Personal Data: _____
____Want Mark ____ Mark _____ Purch. 19___ Pd $ _____

163805   **Anniversary Couple with Pillow**
"Ten Years Heart To Heart"

S $75   H   Current

Comments: 1995; Original Retail $70.00
10th Anniversary.

Personal Data: _____
____Want Mark ____ Mark _____ Purch. 19___ Pd $ _____

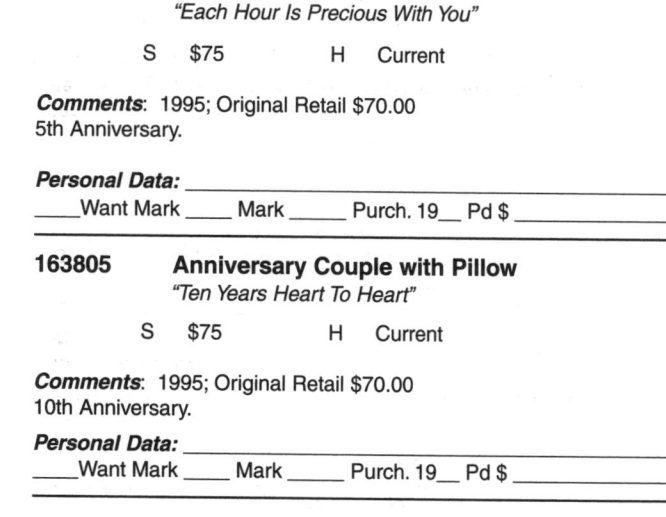

163813   **Anniversary Couple with Plate**
"A Silver Celebration To Share"

S $75   H   Current

Comments: 1995; Original Retail $70.00
25th Anniversary.

Personal Data: _____
____Want Mark ____ Mark _____ Purch. 19___ Pd $ _____

163821   **Anniversary Coulple with Gift**
"Sharing The Gift Of 40 Precious Years"

S $75   H   Current

Comments: 1995; Original Retail $70.00
40th Anniversary.

Personal Data: _____
____Want Mark ____ Mark _____ Purch. 19___ Pd $ _____

163848   **Anniversary Couple with Photo Album**
"Precious Moments To Remember"

S $75   H   Current

Comments: 1995; Original Retail $70.00
50th Anniversary.

Personal Data: _____
____Want Mark ____ Mark _____ Purch. 19___ Pd $ _____

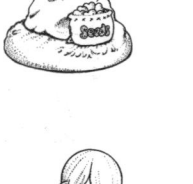

163856   **Angel Kneeling with Bag of Seeds**
"Sewing Seeds Of Kindness"

S $37.50   H   Current

Comments: 1995; Original Retail $37.50
In the brochures this was originally titled "Loving Is Hours Of Toil And Prayer."

Personal Data: _____
____Want Mark ____ Mark _____ Purch. 19___ Pd $ _____

163899   **Boy with Lawnmower/Fence**
"It May Be Greener, But It's Just As Hard To Cut"

S $37.50   H   Current

Comments: 1995; Original Retail $37.50

Personal Data: _____
____Want Mark ____ Mark _____ Purch. 19___ Pd $ _____

175277   **CENTURY CIRCLE** - Girl at Vanity
            "God's Love Is Reflected In You"
LE 15,000
                          H   Current

Comments: 1995; Original Retail $150
Special details include ral mirror, gold and pearlized accents and drop earrings on the girl.
Personal Data: _____
____Want Mark ____ Mark _____ Purch. 19__ Pd $ _____

176958   **Angel with Water Can**
            "Some Plant, Some Water,
            But God Giveth The Increase"
                          H   Current

Comments: 1995; Original Retail $37.50
Listed on original sheets as *All Things Grow With Love*.
Part of *Garden Angels Series*.

Personal Data: _____
____Want Mark ____ Mark _____ Purch. 19__ Pd $ _____

177091   **CENTURY CIRCLE ORNAMENT**
            Angel in Filigree Heart
            "Peace On Earth"
LE 15,000 DATED 1995   S $25

Comments: 1995; Original Retail $25.00
This ornament is the second Century Circle Retailers' piece.

Personal Data: _____
____Want Mark ____ Mark _____ Purch. 19__ Pd $ _____

183342   **FIGURINE** - Boy Angel with Slate
            "Peace On Earth… Anyway"
DATED 1996   H   Current

Comments: 1995; Original Retail $32.50
Personal Data: _____
____Want Mark ____ Mark _____ Purch. 19__ Pd $ _____

183350   **BALL ORNAMENT** - Boy Angel with Slate
            "Peace On Earth… Anyway"
DATED 1996   H   Current

Comments: 1995; Original Retail $30.00
Personal Data: _____
____Want Mark ____ Mark _____ Purch. 19__ Pd $ _____

183369   **ORNAMENT** - Boy Angel with Slate
            "Peace On Earth… Anyway"
DATED 1996   H   Current

Comments: 1995; Original Retail $18.50
Personal Data: _____
____Want Mark ____ Mark _____ Purch. 19__ Pd $ _____

183776   **Boy Making Snow Angel**
            "Angels On Earth"
                          H   Current

Comments: 1995; Original Retail $40
Personal Data: _____
____Want Mark ____ Mark _____ Purch. 19__ Pd $ _____

183792   **Rabbit on Snowball**
            "Snowbunny Loves You Like I Do"
                          H   Current

Comments: 1995; Original Retail $18.50
Addition to *Birthday Series*.

Personal Data: _____
____Want Mark ____ Mark _____ Purch. 19__ Pd $ _____

183830   **9" Angel with Trumpet**
            "Sing In Excelsis Deo"
                          H   Current

Comments: 1995; Original Retail $125.00

Personal Data: _____
____Want Mark ____ Mark _____ Purch. 19__ Pd $ _____

183857   **Boy as Jack Frost**
            "Color Your World With Thanksgiving"
                          H   Current

Comments: 1995; Original Retail $60
First art work done for 25th Annual Carthage Maple Festival in 1991.
See page 85.

Personal Data: _____
____Want Mark ____ Mark _____ Purch. 19__ Pd $ _____

183865 **Girl with Bird**
"Age 9"

H   Current

Comments: 1995; Original Retail $30
From the *Growing In Grace Series*.

Personal Data: _____
____Want Mark _____ Mark _____ Purch. 19___ Pd $ _____

183873 **Girl with Bowling Ball**
"Age 10"

Photo Not
Available

H   Current

Comments: 1995; Original Retail $30.50
From the *Growing In Grace Series*.

Personal Data: _____
____Want Mark _____ Mark _____ Purch. 19___ Pd $ _____

183881 ***ORNAMENT* - Mary, Joseph & Jesus**
"God's Precious Gift"

H   Current

Comments: 1995; Original Retail $20.00

Personal Data: _____
____Want Mark _____ Mark _____ Purch. 19___ Pd $ _____

183903 ***ORNAMENT* - Dog in Skate**
"When The Skating's Ruff, Try Prayer"

H   Current

Comments: 1995; Original Retail $18.50

Personal Data: _____
____Want Mark _____ Mark _____ Purch. 19___ Pd $ _____

183911 ***ORNAMENT* - Boy and Girl on Skis**
"Our First Christmas Together"

DATED 1996   H   Current

Comments: 1995; Original Retail $22.50

Personal Data: _____
____Want Mark _____ Mark _____ Purch. 19___ Pd $ _____

183938 ***ORNAMENT* - Baby Girl in Stocking**
"Baby's First Christmas"

DATED 1996   H   Current

Comments: 1995; Original Retail $17.50

Personal Data: _____
____Want Mark _____ Mark _____ Purch. 19___ Pd $ _____

183946 ***ORNAMENT* - Baby Boy in Stocking**
"Baby's First Christmas"

DATED 1996   H   Current

Comments: 1995; Original Retail $17.50

Personal Data: _____
____Want Mark _____ Mark _____ Purch. 19___ Pd $ _____

183954 ***NATIVITY* - Shepherd with Lambs (3 pc)**
"Shepherd With Lambs"

Photo Not
Available

H   Current

Comments: 1995; Original Retail $37.50
Addition to large Nativity.

Personal Data: _____
____Want Mark _____ Mark _____ Purch. 19___ Pd $ _____

184004 ***MINI NATIVITY* - Boy on Stick Horse**
"Making A Trail To Bethlehem"

H   Current

Comments: 1995; Original Retail $25.00
Mini Nativity addition.

Personal Data: _____
____Want Mark _____ Mark _____ Purch. 19___ Pd $ _____

184012 ***NATIVITY* - Girl with Bird Cage and Birds**
"All Sing His Praises"

Photo Not
Available

H   Current

Comments: 1995; Original Retail $32.50
Large Nativity addition.

Personal Data: _____
____Want Mark _____ Mark _____ Purch. 19___ Pd $ _____

192368 **EASTER SEALS**
Boy with Basketball in Wheelchair
"Give Ability A Chance"

LE 1997   H   Current

Comments: 1995; Original Retail $30.00
1997 Easter Seals Commemorative figurine.

Personal Data: _____
____Want Mark ____ Mark _____ Purch. 19__ Pd $ _____

192384 **EASTER SEALS - ORNAMENT**
Boy with Basketball in Wheelchair
"Give Ability A Chance"

LE 1997   H   Current

Comments: 1995; Original Retail $6.00
1997 Easter Seals Commemerative ornametn. Two dimensional round ornament

Personal Data: _____
____Want Mark ____ Mark _____ Purch. 19__ Pd $ _____

Precious Moments® Collectors' Clubs participate in various fund raising activities throughout the year for Easter Seals.

Bobby and Zach had fun at Easter Seals Camp with Candy the Clown.

213624 **MINI NATIVITY - Three Kings with Gifts**
"Wee Three Kings"

                      H   Current

Comments: 1995; Original Retail $27.50
Three piece mini Nativity set.

Personal Data: _____
____Want Mark ____ Mark _____ Purch. 19__ Pd $ _____

225290 **EASTER SEALS - ORNAMENT**
Girl with Chick in Egg
"Always In His Care"

DATED 1990   NM $10

Comments: 1989; Original Retail $8.00
1990 Commemorative Easter Seals two-dimensional ornament. Same shape as Easter Seals logo.

Personal Data: _____
____Want Mark ____ Mark _____ Purch. 19__ Pd $ _____

227986 **ORNAMENT - Collectors' Club**
"Celebrating A Decade Of Loving, Caring And Sharing"

DATED 1990   NM $10

Comments: 1989; Original Retail $7.00
Special Ten-Year ornament available to Club Members Only.

Personal Data: _____
____Want Mark ____ Mark _____ Purch. 19__ Pd $ _____

230448 **PLAQUE**
"The Enesco Precious Moments Collection"

MM	$25	V	$15	TRP	$15
BA	$18	GC	$15	S	$15
FLM	$18	B	$15	H	$15

Comments: 1989; Original Retail $15.00

Personal Data: _____
____Want Mark ____ Mark _____ Purch. 19__ Pd $ _____

233196 **ORNAMENT - Girl with Dove**
"Sharing A Gift Of Love"

DATED 1991   NM $10

Comments: 1990; Original Retail $8.00
1991 Commemorative Easter Seals. Two-dimensional, heart-shaped ornament.

Personal Data: _____
____Want Mark ____ Mark _____ Purch. 19__ Pd $ _____

238899   **EASTER SEALS - ORNAMENT**
Envelope w/Girl Signing
"A Universal Love"

DATED 1992   NM $10

Comments: 1990; Original Retail $8.00
1992 Easter Seals Commemorative Ornament. No demand.

Personal Data: _____
____Want Mark ____ Mark _____ Purch. 19__ Pd $ _____

244570   **EASTER SEALS - ORNAMENT**
Girl with Pail of Shells
"It Is No Secret What God Can Do"

DATED 1994   NM $8

Comments: 1993; Original Retail $6.50
1994 Easter Seals Commemorative Ornament.

Personal Data: _____
____Want Mark ____ Mark _____ Purch. 19__ Pd $ _____

250112   **ORNAMENT - Girl with Trophy Cup**
"You're My Number One Friend"

DATED 1993   NM $10

Comments: 1992; Original Retail $8.00
1993 Easter Seals Commemorative Ornament.

Personal Data: _____
____Want Mark ____ Mark _____ Purch. 19__ Pd $ _____

408735 ♪ **MUSICAL - JACK-IN-THE-BOX**
Four Seasons Spring
"The Voice Of Spring"

LE 1990/91- 5 YEARS OLD   FLM $150
                             V $130

Comments: 1984; Original Retail $200.00
Limited to two years' production. Plays *April Love*. In my opinion, this style of doll did not have great appeal for most collectors. Why were these dolls "unpopular"? Maybe they could not be held and loved?

Personal Data: _____
____Want Mark ____ Mark _____ Purch. 19__ Pd $ _____

408743 ♪ **MUSICAL - JACK-IN-THE-BOX**
Four Seasons Summer
"Summer's Joy"

LE 1990/91 - 5 YEARS OLD
                              FLM $135
                              V $125

Comments: 1984; Original Retail $200.00
Limited to two year's production. Plays *You Are My Sunshine*. Good source reported seeing these dolls being destroyed at the Enesco warehouse in Elk Grove. Not good sellers. ***See note on 408735.***

Personal Data: _____
____Want Mark ____ Mark _____ Purch. 19__ Pd $ _____

408751 ♪ **MUSICAL - JACK-IN-THE-BOX**
Four Seasons Autumn
"Autumn's Praise"

LE 1990/91 - 5 YEARS OLD   FLM $130
                              V $125

Comments: 1984; Original Retail $200.00
Limited to two years' production. Plays *Autumn Leaves*.
See note on 408735.

Personal Data: _____
____Want Mark ____ Mark _____ Purch. 19__ Pd $ _____

408778 ♪ **MUSICAL - JACK-IN-THE-BOX**
Four Seasons Winter
"Winter's Song"

LE 1990/91 - 5 YEARS OLD   FLM $135
                              V $130

Comments: 1984; Original Retail $200.00
Limited to two years' production. Plays *Through The Eyes Of Love*.
See note on 408735

Personal Data: _____
____Want Mark ____ Mark _____ Purch. 19__ Pd $ _____

408786   **DOLL - Four Seasons Spring**
"The Voice Of Spring"

LE 1990/91 - 5 YEARS OLD
Cloth up to neck   MM $150
Porcelain breastplate   FLM $120
                              V $120

Comments: 1984; Original Retail $150.00
Limited to two years' production.

Personal Data: _____
____Want Mark ____ Mark _____ Purch. 19__ Pd $ _____

408794   *DOLL* - Four Seasons Summer
"Summer's Joy"

LE 1990/91 - 5 YEARS OLD
Cloth up to neck   MM $150
Porcelain breastplate   FLM $145
                            V $140

Comments: 1984; Original Retail $150.00
Limited to two years' production.

Personal Data: _____
____Want Mark ____ Mark _____ Purch. 19__ Pd $ _____

408808   *DOLL* - Four Seasons Autumn
"Autumn's Praise"

LE 1990/91 - 5 YEARS OLD
Cloth up to neck   MM $150
Porcelain breastplate   FLM $145
                            V $140

Comments: 1984; Original Retail $150.00
Limited to two years' production. We have found "for sale" prices below $150 on the Four Seasons Dolls. Most sales of V mark reported were below $100!

Personal Data: _____
____Want Mark ____ Mark _____ Purch. 19__ Pd $ _____

408816   *DOLL* - Four Seasons Winter
"Winter's Song"

LE 1990/91 - 5 YEARS OLD
Cloth up to neck   NM $150
Porcelain breastplate   FLM $150
                            V $150

Comments: 1984; Original Retail $150.00
Limited to two years' production.

Personal Data: _____
____Want Mark ____ Mark _____ Purch. 19__ Pd $ _____

417777   ♪   *MUSICAL* - JACK-IN-BOX
Christmas Girl
"May You Have An Old Fashioned Christmas"

LE 1991/92 - 4 YEARS OLD   FLM $135   GC $130
                                 V $135

Comments: 1990; Original Retail $200.00
Limited to two years' production. Plays *Have Yourself A Merry Little Christmas*. No sales reported. Did not sell well.
Personal Data: _____
____Want Mark ____ Mark _____ Purch. 19__ Pd $ _____

417785   *DOLL* - Christmas Girl
"May You Have An Old Fashioned Christmas"

LE 1991/92 - 4 YEARS OLD   MM $150
                                V $150
                              GC $150
                              FLM $150

Comments: 1990; Original Retail $150.00
Limited to two years' production. No sales found in research.
Personal Data: _____
____Want Mark ____ Mark _____ Purch. 19__ Pd $ _____

422282   ♪   *MUSICAL* - Jack-In-Box - Girl w/Hearts
"You Have Touched So Many Hearts"

LE 1991/92 - 4 YEARS OLD   FLM $120
                                V $110
                              GC $100

Comments: 1990; Original Retail $175.00
Limited to two years' production. Plays *Everybody Loves Somebody*. No reports of this being sold on the secondary market for 2 years. Not a popular style; poor retail seller. Overproduced; many were destroyed at company. *See #35, page XIV.*
Personal Data: _____
____Want Mark ____ Mark _____ Purch. 19__ Pd $ _____

427527   *DOLL* - Girl with Hearts
"You Have Touched So Many Hearts"

LE 1991/92 - 4 YEARS OLD   FLM $90
                                V $90
                              GC $90

Comments: 1990; Original Retail $90.00
Limited to two years' production. No reported sales on the secondary market for two years. *See #35, page XIV.*
Personal Data: _____
____Want Mark ____ Mark _____ Purch. 19__ Pd $ _____

429570   ♪   *MUSICAL ACTION DOLL* - Blue
Baby Boy Doll on Pillow, straight hair
"The Eyes Of The Lord Are Upon You"

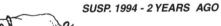

SUSP. 1994 - 2 YEARS AGO
                         FLM $75   B $65
                         V $65   TRP $65
                         GC $65

Comments: 1990; Original Retail $65.00
Plays *Brahm's Lullaby*. Fewer FLM marks. Reported with Missing Mark.
Personal Data: _____
____Want Mark ____ Mark _____ Purch. 19__ Pd $ _____

429589 ♪ *MUSICAL ACTION DOLL* - pink
Baby Girl Doll on Pillow, curly hair
"The Eyes Of The Lord Are Upon You"

SUSP. 1994 - 2 YEARS AGO FLM $75   B $65
                             V $65   TRP $65
                             GC $65

Comments: 1990; Original Retail $65.00
Plays *Brahm's Lullaby*. Very cute doll. Girl doll is more
popular than boy. Fewer FLM marks

Personal Data: _____
____Want Mark _____ Mark _____ Purch. 19__ Pd $ _____

*Friendship is the cement that
holds the whole world
together.*

Gina & Samantha Myers

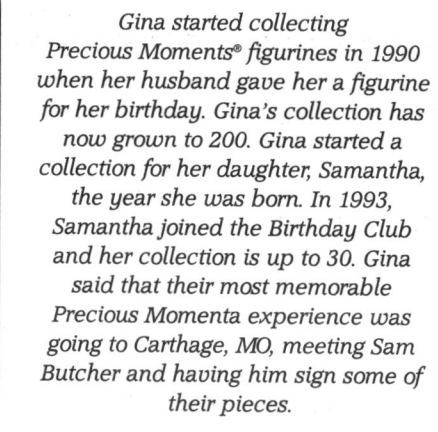

*Gina started collecting
Precious Moments® figurines in 1990
when her husband gave her a figurine
for her birthday. Gina's collection has
now grown to 200. Gina started a
collection for her daughter, Samantha,
the year she was born. In 1993,
Samantha joined the Birthday Club
and her collection is up to 30. Gina
said that their most memorable
Precious Momenta experience was
going to Carthage, MO, meeting Sam
Butcher and having him sign some of
their pieces.*

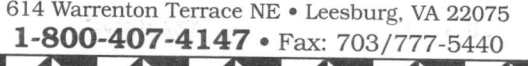

520233 **ORNAMENT** - Boy and Girl/Box
"Our First Christmas Together"

DATED 1988   FL $18.50

Comments: 1988; Original Retail $13.00
This ornament was also produced in 1986 (102350) and 1987 (112399). The only differences were the marks, style numbers and the dates. Secondary market has been thus affected. **See #28, page XIV.**

Personal Data: _____
___Want Mark ___ Mark ____ Purch. 19__ Pd $ _____

520241 **ORNAMENT** - Girl in Sleigh
"Baby's First Christmas"

DATED 1988   FL $22

Comments: 1988; Original Retail $15.00
Also produced in 1989 (523208). The Baby Boy Ornament for 1988 was 115282. **See #28, page XIV.**

Personal Data: _____
___Want Mark ___ Mark ____ Purch. 19__ Pd $ _____

520268   Angel with Trumpet (Miniature)
"Rejoice O Earth"

FL $30	V $20	TRP $17
FLM $20	GC $17	S $17
BA $18	B $17	H $17

Comments: 1988; Original Retail $13.00/$17.00
Rarely will one pay extra for a figurine on the secondary market when it's still in production. If the first mark is scarce, then the secondary market is higher. Generally Christmas pieces' first marks are not scarce.

Personal Data: _____
___Want Mark ___ Mark ____ Purch. 19__ Pd $ _____

520276   **ORNAMENT** - Puppy in Stocking
"You Are My Gift Come True"

DATED 1988   FL $23

Comments: 1988; Original Retail $12.50
10th Anniversary Ornament. No inspiration on base.
Easily found under $20 even after 8 years.

Personal Data: _____
___Want Mark ___ Mark ____ Purch. 19__ Pd $ _____

520284   **PLATE** - Girl with Reindeer
"Merry Christmas Deer"

DATED 1988   FL $55

Comments: 1988; Original Retail $50
Third issue of *Christmas Love Series*. Plates are not trading much over retail; many even for less. Easily found at above price for several years.

Personal Data: _____
___Want Mark ___ Mark ____ Purch. 19__ Pd $ _____

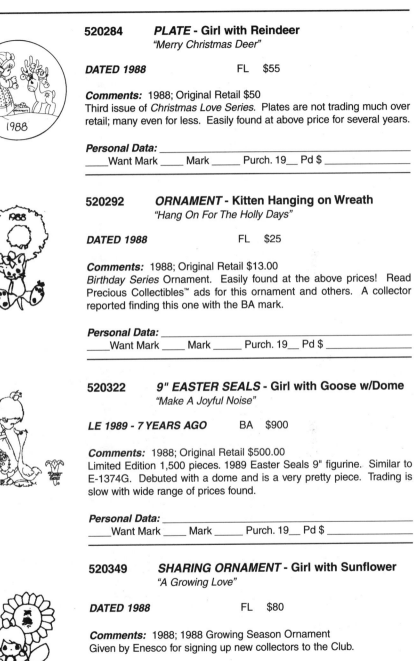

520292   **ORNAMENT** - Kitten Hanging on Wreath
"Hang On For The Holly Days"

DATED 1988   FL $25

Comments: 1988; Original Retail $13.00
Birthday Series Ornament. Easily found at the above prices! Read *Precious Collectibles™* ads for this ornament and others. A collector reported finding this one with the BA mark.

Personal Data: _____
___Want Mark ___ Mark ____ Purch. 19__ Pd $ _____

520322   **9" EASTER SEALS** - Girl with Goose w/Dome
"Make A Joyful Noise"

LE 1989 - 7 YEARS AGO   BA $900

Comments: 1988; Original Retail $500.00
Limited Edition 1,500 pieces. 1989 Easter Seals 9" figurine. Similar to E-1374G. Debuted with a dome and is a very pretty piece. Trading is slow with wide range of prices found.

Personal Data: _____
___Want Mark ___ Mark ____ Purch. 19__ Pd $ _____

520349   **SHARING ORNAMENT** - Girl with Sunflower
"A Growing Love"

DATED 1988   FL $80

Comments: 1988; 1988 Growing Season Ornament
Given by Enesco for signing up new collectors to the Club.

Personal Data: _____
___Want Mark ___ Mark ____ Purch. 19__ Pd $ _____

You're As Pretty As A Picture

A little girl named Katie wrote to Sam asking that he make a Precious Moments figurine with bangs and a cowlick. Sam responded by drawing You're As Pretty As A Picture. The frame on the prototype Katie figurine covered too much of the little girl's head, so Sam redesigned the figurine, raising the frame so that her face showed through. Sam then presented Katie with her very own figurine. This figurine has been produced as the 1996 Enesco Precious Moments Collectors' Club membership piece.

520357 **Angel with Newspaper and Dog**
"Jesus The Savior Is Born"

SUSP. 1993 - 3 YEARS AGO	FL	$52	V	$40
	BA	$45	GC	$38
	FLM	$45	B	$35

Comments: 1988; Original Retail $25.00/$32.50
Not easily found. May be due to retailers not ordering. Suspended in late '93. We predicted this in the '92 guide! What are some of your predictions?

Personal Data: _____
____Want Mark ____ Mark _____ Purch. 19__ Pd $ _____

520403 ***ORNAMENT* - Hippo**
"Hippo Holidays"

DATED 1995   S $17

Comments: 1995; Original Retail $17.00
Birthday Series Ornament.

Personal Data: _____
____Want Mark ____ Mark _____ Purch. 19__ Pd $ _____

520411 ***ORNAMENT* - Squirrel on Log**
"I'm Nuts About You"

DATED 1992   GC $23

Comments: 1992; Original Retail $16.00
Birthday Series Ornament.

Personal Data: _____
____Want Mark ____ Mark _____ Purch. 19__ Pd $ _____

520438 ***ORNAMENT* - Bunny on Ice Skates**
"Sno-Bunny Falls For You Like I Do"

DATED 1991   V $25

Comments: 1990; Original Retail $15.00
Birthday Series Ornament. Oops! The li'l silver skates made this ornament popular. Found without a date! Add $50 to secondary market value. Not marked as *Birthday Series*. Found many listed for sale in late '94 for $20!

Personal Data: _____
____Want Mark ____ Mark _____ Purch. 19__ Pd $ _____

520462 ***ORNAMENT* - Dog/Gift Box**
"Christmas Is Ruff Without You"

DATED 1989   FL $40   BA $35

Comments: 1988; Original Retail $13.00
Birthday Series Ornament. Was somewhat plentiful but popular. More trading was found on BA than FL mark the last three years. ***See #29, page XIV.***

Personal Data: _____
____Want Mark ____ Mark _____ Purch. 19__ Pd $ _____

520470 ***ORNAMENT* - Christmas Puppy**
"Take A Bow Cuz You're My Christmas Star"

DATED 1994   TRP $25

Comments: 1993; Original Retail $16.00

Personal Data: _____
____Want Mark ____ Mark _____ Purch. 19__ Pd $ _____

520489 ***ORNAMENT* - Turtle with Gift/Antlers**
"Slow Down And Enjoy The Holidays"

DATED 1993   B $22

Comments: 1992; Original Retail $16.00
Birthday Series Ornament. Sam has a super cute outdoor sign along Chapel Road requesting that we not run over the turtles.

Personal Data: _____
____Want Mark ____ Mark _____ Purch. 19__ Pd $ _____

520497 ***ORNAMENT* - Kitten with Ornament**
"Wishing You A Purr-fect Holiday"

DATED 1990 FLM $32.50

Comments: 1989; Original Retail $15.00
Birthday Series Ornament. Found without date; add $50 to the secondary market value.

Personal Data: _____
____Want Mark ____ Mark _____ Purch. 19__ Pd $ _____

520535 **Ballerina in Red Tutu**
"The Lord Turned My Life Around"

GC 40	TRP $37.50	H 37.50
B $37.50	S $37.50	

Comments: 1992; Original Retail $35.00/$37.50
Because there are other Ballerinas, maybe this one, 520578 or 520551 may be retired or suspended in the near future. Retail price increased in '96.

Personal Data: _____
____Want Mark ____ Mark _____ Purch. 19__ Pd $ _____

520543 **Ballerina in Pink Tutu**
"In The Spotlight Of His Grace"

FLM $45	B $37.50	H $37.50
V $40	TRP $37.50	
GC $38	S $37.50	

Comments: 1990; Original Retail $35.00/$37.50
Retail price increased in '96.

Personal Data: _____
____Want Mark ____ Mark _____ Purch. 19__ Pd $ _____

520551 **Ballerina in Blue Tutu**
"Lord, Turn My Life Around"

BA $50	GC $40	S $37.50
FLM $40	B $37.50	H $37.50
V $40	TRP $37.50	

Comments: 1988; Original Retail $35.00/$37.50
Retail price increased in '96.

Personal Data: _____
____Want Mark ____ Mark _____ Purch. 19__ Pd $ _____

520578 **Ballerina in Purple Tutu**
"You Deserve An Ovation"

GC $42	TRP $37.50	H $37.50
B $37.50	S $37.50	

Comments: 1990; Original Retail $35.00/$37.50
Very little trading found on this piece. Too many ballerinas at the present time – adorable but perfect for retirement or suspension. Retail price increased in '96.

Personal Data: _____
____Want Mark ____ Mark _____ Purch. 19__ Pd $ _____

520624 **Boy with X-Ray Machine**
"My Heart Is Exposed With Love"

FL $65	V $60	TRP $60
BA $60	GC $60	S $60
FLM $60	B $60	H $60

Comments: 1988; Original Retail $45.00/$60.00
I predict suspension or retirement for this piece as retailers say it is accepted mainly by the medical field/gift buyers and the nurse figurine outsells this piece. Cute piece! A must for X-ray technicians. Retail price increased to $60 in '96. Secondary market did increase but so did retail.

Personal Data: _____
____Want Mark ____ Mark _____ Purch. 19__ Pd $ _____

520632 **Clown with Mouse Wiping Tears**
"A Friend Is Someone Who Cares"

RETIRED 1995 - 1 YEAR AGO

FL $75	V $55	TRP $50
BA $70	GC $55	S $50
FLM $60	B $50	

Comments: 1988; Original Retail $30.00/$35.00
Fourteen clowns have been retired or suspended since 1988.

Personal Data: _____
____Want Mark ____ Mark _____ Purch. 19__ Pd $ _____

If you cannot lift the load off another's back, do not walk away. Try to lighten it.
Frank Tyger

520640   Angel with Butterfly
"I'm So Glad You Fluttered Into My Life"

RETIRED 1991 - 5 YEARS AGO

FL	$275	FLM	$250
BA	$250	V	$230

Comments: 1988; Original Retail $40.00/$45.00
First mark very scarce. Very few V marks as well as FL marks. Prices skyrocketed after retirement. The main reason? No "after" production!! Called "Drop Dead." High prices now coming down after an all time high in 93/94. Was up to $400 on FL. Big drop in prices in '95 and now.

Personal Data: _____
____Want Mark ____ Mark _____ Purch. 19__ Pd $ _____

520659   Bear with Cake
"Wishing You A Happy Bear Hug"

TRP	$30	S	$27.50	H	$27.50

Comments: 1992; Original Retail $27.50
Birthday Series addition.

Personal Data: _____
____Want Mark ____ Mark _____ Purch. 19__ Pd $ _____

520667   Girl with Bucket of Eggs/Chicken
"Eggspecially For You"

FL	$70	V	$55	TRP	$50
BA	$60	GC	$55	S	$50
FLM	$60	B	$50	H	$50

Comments: 1988; Original Retail $45.00/$50.00
Many call her "Rosie." I autograph this one (okayed by Sam). I write about my chickens in "Down on the Farm" articles for the *Precious Collectibles*™ magazine. Now we have ostriches, too! Maybe Sam will let me sign the Ostrich birthday piece too. ☺

Personal Data: _____
____Want Mark ____ Mark _____ Purch. 19__ Pd $ _____

520675   Boy Helping Girl at Fountain
"Your Love Is So Uplifting"

FL	$90	V	$75	TRP	$75
BA	$80	GC	$75	S	$75
FLM	$80	B	$75	H	$75

Comments: 1988; Original Retail $60.00/$75.00
Somewhat limited, as are all the extra large pieces, but not sought after on the secondary market to date. Retail went up $15 in '95, thus when secondary market prices rose, it didn't appear there was any trading on this figurine and there has been no significant increase since.

Personal Data: _____
____Want Mark ____ Mark _____ Purch. 19__ Pd $ _____

520683   Boy with Paper Over Head
"Sending You Showers Of Blessings"

RETIRED 1992 - 4 YEARS AGO

FL	$70	V	$65
BA	$65	GC	$65
FLM	$65		

Comments: 1988; Original Retail $32.50/$35.00
Very attractive piece! GC somewhat scarce when retired. Price leveled off for now.

Personal Data: _____
____Want Mark ____ Mark _____ Purch. 19__ Pd $ _____

520691   ♪ *MUSICAL* - Ballerina on Base
"Lord, Keep My Life In Balance"

SUSP. 1993 - 3 YEARS AGO

V	$85	B	$75
GC	$75		

Comments: 1990; Original Retail $60.00/$65.00
Plays *Music Box Dancer*.

Personal Data: _____
____Want Mark ____ Mark _____ Purch. 19__ Pd $ _____

520705   Baby/Father, Puppy with Bottle
"Baby's First Pet"

SUSP. 1994 - 2 YEARS AGO

FL	$80	V	$65	TRP	$55
BA	$70	GC	$58		
FLM	$65	B	$58		

Comments: 1988; Original Retail $45.00/$50.00
Fifth issue in *Baby's First Series*. Most sought after series on secondary market in last three years. Found the most trading was on FL mark.

Personal Data: _____
____Want Mark ____ Mark _____ Purch. 19__ Pd $ _____

520721   Boy/Dog/Fishing Pole
"Just A Line To Wish You A Happy Day"

FL	$90	V	$75	TRP	$75
BA	$85	GC	$75	S	$75
FLM	$80	B	$75	H	$75

Comments: 1988; Original Retail $65.00/$75.00
In my opinion, this is more scarce than collectors realize. This is true for most current large pieces. Another fisherman debuted in 1995, so this may be suspended or retired. Usually large pieces get suspended over retirement.

Personal Data: _____
____Want Mark ____ Mark _____ Purch. 19__ Pd $ _____

520748   Two Girls Having A Tea Party
"Friendship Hits The Spot"

FL	$80	V	$70	TRP	$70
BA	$70	GC	$70	S	$70
FLM	$70	B	$70	H	$70

ERROR - no table $225-250

Comments: 1988; Original Retail $55.00/$70.00
We have heard from several collectors that this piece has been found without the table. There is an "x" on one where the table was to be. Retail up to $70 in '96. Has been found with the word "Friendship" misspelled, "Freindship." Add $25 for this error.

Personal Data: _____
____Want Mark ____ Mark _____ Purch. 19__ Pd $ _____

520756   Boy by Sign Post with Bag
"Jesus Is The Only Way"

SUSP. 1993 - 3 YEARS AGO

CT	$75	FLM	$50	B	$50
FL	$65	V	$50		
BA	$60	GC	$50		

Comments: 1988; Original Retail $40.00/$45.00
"Many" of the decals were placed on the sign incorrectly which caused collectors to believe the sign was spelled incorrectly. (ex. OVEP) C-0113, the 1993 Club Membership figurine, is very similar. Probably suspended due to all the decals. We have had several reports of CT. Do you have a CT?

Personal Data: _____
____Want Mark ____ Mark _____ Purch. 19__ Pd $ _____

520764   Two Puppies
"Puppy Love"

FL	$25	V	$18	TRP	$17.50
BA	$20	GC	$18	S	$17.50
FLM	$18	B	$17.50	H	$17.50

Comments: 1988; Original Retail $12.50/$17.50
Retail price increase in '95 and again in '96.

Personal Data: _____
____Want Mark ____ Mark _____ Purch. 19__ Pd $ _____

The '97 Easter Seals piece will be a li'l boy in a wheelchair playing basketball.

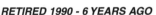

520772   Boy/Girl Indians in Canoe
"Many Moons In Same Canoe, Blessum You"

RETIRED 1990 - 6 YEARS AGO

FL	$290	FLM	$255
BA	$285		

Comments: 1988; Original Retail $50.00/$55.00
These Indians were changed from "gray" hair to darker hair on later pieces. Collectors wrote suggesting that clothes be painted. With all these problems, it's no wonder it was retired. This was the most scarce of the 1990 retired pieces. Price fluctuated from $175 to $125 in mid-1992. The price then increased in late 1992 to early 1993. **We have received two reports of a piece with FLM <u>and</u> Rosebud mark! (**Insured for $400.)

Personal Data: _____
____Want Mark ____ Mark _____ Purch. 19__ Pd $ _____

520780   Bride and Groom in Car
"Wishing You Roads Of Happiness"

FL	$90	V	$75	TRP	$75
BA	$85	GC	$75	S	$75
FLM	$80	B	$75	H	$75

Comments: 1988; Original Retail $60.00/$75.00
Also produced in crystal and as an ornament.

Personal Data: _____
____Want Mark ____ Mark _____ Purch. 19__ Pd $ _____

520799   Girl with Bridal Gown and Baseball/Bat
"Someday My Love"

RETIRED 1992 - 4 YEARS AGO

FL	$75	FLM	$70	GC	$60
BA	$70	V	$65		

Comments: 1988; Original Retail $40.00/$45.00

Personal Data: _____
____Want Mark ____ Mark _____ Purch. 19__ Pd $ _____

520802 Girl at Ladder/Blue Paint Spilled
"My Days Are Blue Without You"

SUSP. 1991 - 5 YEARS AGO

CIRCLE MOUTH			
	FL $110	FLM $90	
	BA $100	V $95	

SMILE (ERROR)		
	FL $115	
	BA $110	

Comments: 1988; Original Retail $65.00/$70.00
Find the smiling girl with FL mark as this piece has been changed to a circle mouth to represent being sad. This smile is more abundant than the Dunce's smile but as time goes by it will become scarce. Also found with frown.

Personal Data: _____
____Want Mark ____ Mark _____ Purch. 19__ Pd $ _____

520810 Grandpa with Dog
"We Need A Good Friend Through The Ruff Times"

SUSP. 1991 - 5 YEARS AGO

	FL $55	FLM $45
	BA $48	V $40

Comments: 1988; Original Retail $35.00/$37.50

Personal Data: _____
____Want Mark ____ Mark _____ Purch. 19__ Pd $ _____

520829 Girl with Trophy
"You Are My Number One"

	FL $40	V $35	TRP $35
	BA $38	GC $35	S $35
	FLM $38	B $35	H $35

Comments: 1988; Original Retail $25.00/$35.00
I look for this to be suspended or retired in the future. Retail price increase in 1995 and 1996.

Personal Data: _____
____Want Mark ____ Mark _____ Purch. 19__ Pd $ _____

520837 Bride and Groom with Candle
"The Lord Is Your Light To Happiness"

	FL $75	V $65	TRP $65
	BA $65	GC $65	S $65
	FLM $65	B $65	H $65

Comments: 1988; Original Retail $50.00/$65.00
Popular wedding gift. About fifty dollars was a price range more gift buyers were willing to pay.

Personal Data: _____
____Want Mark ____ Mark _____ Purch. 19__ Pd $ _____

520845 Boy Kneeling with Engagement Ring
"Wishing You A Perfect Choice"

FL $75	V $65	TRP $65
BA $70	GC $65	S $65
FLM $65	B $65	H $65

Comments: 1988; Original Retail $55.00/$65.00
Price increase will slow retail sales for individuals, in my opinion. Not being sought after on secondary market.

Personal Data: _____
____Want Mark ____ Mark _____ Purch. 19__ Pd $ _____

520853 Orphan Boy with Flowers
"I Belong To The Lord"

SUSP. 1991 - 5 YEARS AGO

FL $45	FLM $35
BA $38	V $35

Comments: 1988; Original Retail $25.00/$27.50
Definitely was a slow seller on gift market, no doubt the reason for suspension.

Personal Data: _____
____Want Mark ____ Mark _____ Purch. 19__ Pd $ _____

520861 Girl with Slate
"Sharing Begins In The Heart"

LE 1989 - 7 YEARS AGO   FL $75   BA $45

Comments: 1988; Original Retail $25.00
Second *Main Event* piece. No reference is written on the piece to signify "Main Event" piece. No doubt an error. Fewer events early in 1989, thus fewer first marks than BA marks.

Personal Data: _____
____Want Mark ____ Mark _____ Purch. 19__ Pd $ _____

520934 Baby with Bunny, Turtle and Box
"Heaven Bless You"

BA $50	GC $35	S $35
FLM $40	B $35	H $35
V $35	TRP $35	

Comments: 1989; Original Retail $35.00
This figurine has been seen with an HG mark. It may have been a sample ($135-155).

Personal Data: _____
____Want Mark ____ Mark _____ Purch. 19__ Pd $ _____

521000   **Boy Holding a Pearl**
"There Is No Greater Treasure Than To Have A Friend Like You"

GC $40	TRP $30	H $30
B $32	S $30	

Comments: 1992; Original Retail $30.00
Display with 531111, *Girl with Pearl in Oyster*, for a perfect seaside theme. Use sand and sea shells, etc.

Personal Data: _____
____Want Mark ____ Mark _____ Purch. 19__ Pd $ _____

521043   **Bird and Gorilla**
"To My Favorite Fan"

SUSP. 1993 - 3 years ago	BA $50	GC $22
	FLM $32	B $22
	V $25	

Comments: 1989; Original Retail $16.00
First mark, BA, was somewhat scarce. Not marked *Birthday Series*.

Personal Data: _____
____Want Mark ____ Mark _____ Purch. 19__ Pd $ _____

521175   **Kangaroo with Baby in Pouch**
"Hello World!"

FL $30	V $17.50	TRP $17.50
BA $20	GC $17.50	S $17.50
FLM $18	B $17.50	H $17.50

Comments: 1988; Original Retail $13.50/$17.50
Not marked *Birthday Series*. Retail price increase in 1995 and in 1996.

Personal Data: _____
____Want Mark ____ Mark _____ Purch. 19__ Pd $ _____

521183   **Two Girls Embracing**
"That's What Friends Are For"

FLM $55	B $50	H $50
V $50	TRP $50	
GC $50	S $50	

Comments: 1989; Original Retail $45.00/$50.00
Slow at retail. Retail price raised in 1996.

Personal Data: _____
____Want Mark ____ Mark _____ Purch. 19__ Pd $ _____

521205   **Girl with Stick Horse**
"Hope You're Up And On The Trail Again"

SUSP. 1993 - 3 YEARS AGO	BA $60	GC $50
	FLM $52	B $50
	V $50	

Comments: 1989; Original Retail $35.00
Cute piece.

Personal Data: _____
____Want Mark ____ Mark _____ Purch. 19__ Pd $ _____

521213   **Girl with Bowl of Fruit**
"The Fruit Of The Spirit Is Love"

B $35	S $32.50	
TRP $32.50	H $32.50	

Comments: 1992; Original Retail $30.00/$32.50
Seemed abundant in '93. Retail price increased in 1996. Good suspension candidate.

Personal Data: _____
____Want Mark ____ Mark _____ Purch. 19__ Pd $ _____

521221   **Boy with Basketball**
"Enter His Courts With Thanksgiving"

S $35	H $35

Comments: 1995; Original Retail $35.00

Personal Data: _____
____Want Mark ____ Mark _____ Purch. 19__ Pd $ _____

521272   **Boy on Rocking Horse**
"Take Heed When You Stand"

SUSP. 1994 - 2 YEARS AGO		
V $75	B $65	
GC $68	TRP $60	

Comments: 1990; Original Retail $55.00
One report of an unpainted hat band. Most sales found at the V level.

Personal Data: _____
____Want Mark ____ Mark _____ Purch. 19__ Pd $ _____

*The kind of wealth that life extends
is best when it's a wealth of friends.*

521280 Girl on Skates
"Happy Trip"

SUSP. 1994 - 2 YEARS AGO

BA	$100	V	$50	B	$50
FLM	$55	GC	$50	TRP	$40

Comments: 1989; Original Retail $35.00
BA somewhat scarce. Slow on secondary market.

Personal Data: _____
____Want Mark ____ Mark _____ Purch. 19__ Pd $ _____

521299 Boy and Girl Hugging
"Hug One Another"

RETIRED 1995 - 1 YEAR AGO

FLM	$90	B	$75
V	$85	TRP	$65
GC	$80	S	$65

Comments: 1990; Original Retail $45.00/$50.00
This piece was portrayed as a "dancing" couple when we visited the Precious Moments® Studio in Japan. We all "danced" to music at the studio! First time visit to Japan! Enesco planned a lifetime of memories for us! Retirement brought secondary market from $50 to $100.

Personal Data: _____
____Want Mark ____ Mark _____ Purch. 19__ Pd $ _____

521302 ORNAMENT - Little Girl with Snowball
"May All Your Christmases Be White"

SUSP. 1994 - 2 YEARS AGO	BA $38	GC	$25
	FLM $30	B	$22
	V $25	TRP	$22

Comments: 1988; Original Retail $13.50/$16.00
This little girl was a tribute to Sam's mother. When she was a little girl she wanted to mail snowballs to her relatives in Florida. (See the display at the Chapel.)

Personal Data: _____
____Want Mark ____ Mark _____ Purch. 19__ Pd $ _____

521310 Girl with Apple
"Yield Not To Temptation"

SUSP. 1993 - 3 YEARS AGO

BA	$50	GC	$35
FLM	$45	B	$35
V	$40		

Comments: 1989; Original Retail $27.50/$30.00
Very little trading on this piece for past two years.

Personal Data: _____
____Want Mark ____ Mark _____ Purch. 19__ Pd $ _____

521329 Girl with a Toad
"Have I Toad You Lately That I Love You"

H   Current

Comments: 1995; Original Retail $30.00
1996 DSR Catalog Promotion. *See #33, page XIV.*

Personal Data: _____
____Want Mark ____ Mark _____ Purch. 19__ Pd $ _____

521396 Girl with Boxing Gloves
"Faith Is A Victory"

RETIRED 1993 - 3 YEARS AGO

BA	$155	V	$130	B	$100
FLM	$130	GC	$100		

Comments: 1989; Original Retail $25.00/$27.50
Collectors questioned "no blouse" on the girl. We predicted this would be retired! Starting on Jan. 6, 1994, she began to appear on retailers' shelves again! This decreased value on the secondary market, much to the disappointment of collectors and those who paid top dollar for this piece in '93. When this Butterfly-marked piece appeared on retailers' shelves eight months after retirement it was selling at $125. Much trading being offered on this piece!! Price dropped, in my opinion, due to Jan. '94 supply. Many sales found at BA and FLM level even below these prices!

Personal Data: _____
____Want Mark ____ Mark _____ Purch. 19__ Pd $ _____

521418 Girl with Letters Y-O-U
"I'll Never Stop Loving You"

BA	$52	GC	$40	S	$40
FLM	$45	B	$40	H	$40
V	$42	TRP	$40		

Comments: 1989; Original Retail $37.50/$40.00
Retailers have written that for a faster retail sale, a great inspiration would have been "You Make A Difference." One report of "Y" missing. Retail up in '96.

Personal Data: _____
____Want Mark ____ Mark _____ Purch. 19__ Pd $ _____

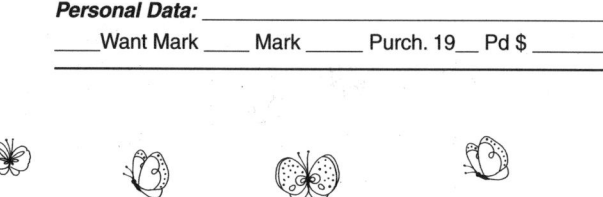

521434   **Girl with Picture of Mom and Dad**
"To A Very Special Mom And Dad"

SUSP. 1993 - 3 YEARS AGO   V $55   B $45
                                    GC $50

Comments: 1990; Original Retail $35.00
This is an unusual piece - different enough from the general line. I'd look for it if I didn't have one.

Personal Data: _____
____Want Mark ____ Mark _____ Purch. 19__ Pd $ _____

521450   **Girl with Glue on Foot**
"Lord, Help Me Stick To My Job"

BA	$52	GC	$38	S	$35
FLM	$45	B	$35	H	$35
V	$38	TRP	$35		

Comments: 1989; Original Retail $30.00/$35.00
Here is possibly one to be retired or suspended.

Personal Data: _____
____Want Mark ____ Mark _____ Purch. 19__ Pd $ _____

521477   **Girl with Telephone**
"Tell It To Jesus"

BA	$55	GC	$40	S	$40
FLM	$45	B	$40	H	$40
V	$45	TRP	$40		

Comments: 1988; Original Retail $35.00/$40.00
Popular piece. Display with PM811 *Hello, Lord It's Me Again.* The art of this piece was used on the cover of the Granby, Missouri, telephone book in 1994. Retail price increased in '96.

Personal Data: _____
____Want Mark ____ Mark _____ Purch. 19__ Pd $ _____

521485   **Girl Looking Through Hollow Log**
"There's A Light At The End Of The Tunnel"

FLM	$65	B	$60	H	$60
V	$60	TRP	$60		
GC	$60	S	$60		

Comments: 1990; Original Retail $55.00/$60.00
A suspension or retirement candidate, in my opinion. Retail price up in '96.

Personal Data: _____
____Want Mark ____ Mark _____ Purch. 19__ Pd $ _____

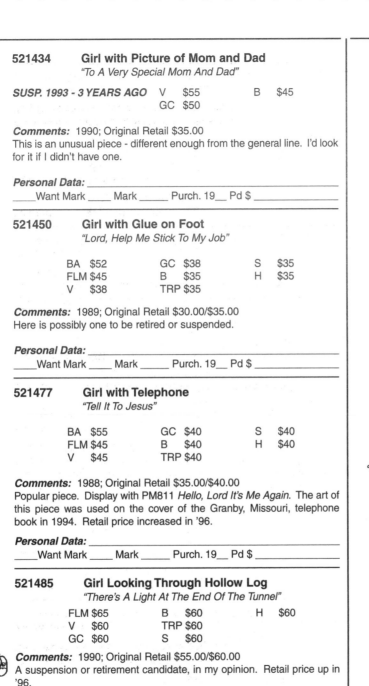

521493   **Girl with Baby**
"A Special Delivery"

V	$40	TRP	$32.50	H	$32.50
GC	$35	S	$32.50		
B	$32.50				

Comments: 1990; Original Retail $30.00/$32.50
Retail price increase in '96

Personal Data: _____
____Want Mark ____ Mark _____ Purch. 19__ Pd $ _____

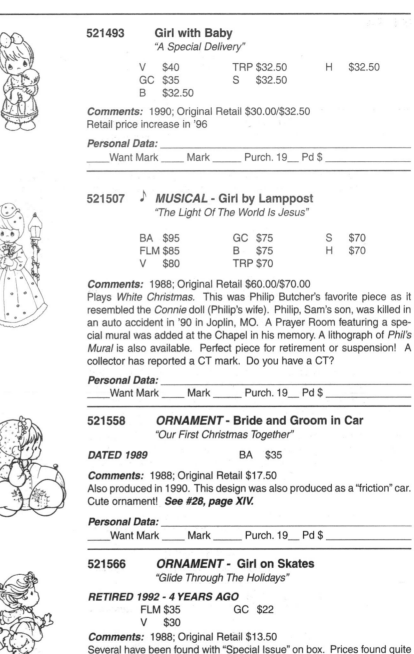

521507   ♪   **MUSICAL - Girl by Lamppost**
"The Light Of The World Is Jesus"

BA	$95	GC	$75	S	$70
FLM	$85	B	$75	H	$70
V	$80	TRP	$70		

Comments: 1988; Original Retail $60.00/$70.00
Plays *White Christmas.* This was Philip Butcher's favorite piece as it resembled the *Connie* doll (Philip's wife). Philip, Sam's son, was killed in an auto accident in '90 in Joplin, MO. A Prayer Room featuring a special mural was added at the Chapel in his memory. A lithograph of *Phil's Mural* is also available. Perfect piece for retirement or suspension! A collector has reported a CT mark. Do you have a CT?

Personal Data: _____
____Want Mark ____ Mark _____ Purch. 19__ Pd $ _____

521558   **ORNAMENT - Bride and Groom in Car**
"Our First Christmas Together"

DATED 1989   BA $35

Comments: 1988; Original Retail $17.50
Also produced in 1990. This design was also produced as a "friction" car. Cute ornament! **See #28, page XIV.**

Personal Data: _____
____Want Mark ____ Mark _____ Purch. 19__ Pd $ _____

521566   **ORNAMENT - Girl on Skates**
"Glide Through The Holidays"

RETIRED 1992 - 4 YEARS AGO
FLM	$35	GC	$22
V	$30		

Comments: 1988; Original Retail $13.50
Several have been found with "Special Issue" on box. Prices found quite readily below $25 in early '96 on GC.

Personal Data: _____
____Want Mark ____ Mark _____ Purch. 19__ Pd $ _____

521574 ORNAMENT - Girl with Baby in Sleigh
"Dashing Through The Snow"

SUSP. 1994 - 2 YEARS AGO

FLM $30	GC $25	TRP $22
V $28	B $22	

Comments: 1987; Original Retail $15.00/$16.00
Same as *January* figurine, 109983. Price up since suspension.

Personal Data: _____
____Want Mark ____ Mark _____ Purch. 19__ Pd $ _____

521590 ORNAMENT - Boy with Christmas Tree
"Don't Let The Holidays Get You Down"

RETIRED 1994 - 2 YEARS AGO

FLM $38	B $30
V $35	TRP $30
GC $32	

Comments: 1988; Original Retail $15.00/$16.00
Same as figurine 522112 which retired in 1993.

Personal Data: _____
____Want Mark ____ Mark _____ Purch. 19__ Pd $ _____

521671 Monkey Riding Camel
"Hope You're Over The Hump"

MM $25	TRP $18.50	H $18.50
B $20	S $18.50	

Comments: 1992; Original Retail $17.50/$18.50
This piece has been reported without a mark! Retail up in '96

Personal Data: _____
____Want Mark ____ Mark _____ Purch. 19__ Pd $ _____

521698 Girl/Boy with Bandaged Thumb
"Thumb-body Loves You"

FLM $70	B $60	H $60
V $65	TRP $60	
GC $65	S $60	

Comments: 1990; Original Retail $55.00/$60.00
Some thumbs are bright pinkish-red, some very pale. (One was hit harder than the other...) No difference in value. She is smiling. Some say she should have had a frown· ☺ I say suspension before too many years. If the nail is all the way down, add $25 over secondary market value.

Personal Data: _____
____Want Mark ____ Mark _____ Purch. 19__ Pd $ _____

521701 Boy and Girl with Basketball and Bat
"Shoot For The Stars And You'll Never Strike Out"

H Current

Comments: 1996; Original Retail $60.00
Boys and Girls Clubs Of America Commemorative Figurine.

Personal Data: _____
____Want Mark ____ Mark _____ Purch. 19__ Pd $ _____

521728 Boy Giving Flower to Girl
"My Love Blooms For You"

S $55	H $50

Comments: 1995; Original Retail $50.00

Personal Data: _____
____Want Mark ____ Mark _____ Purch. 19__ Pd $ _____

521779 Girl Sweeping Dirt Under Rug
"Sweep All Your Worries Away"

BA $130	GC $42	S $40
FLM $50	B $42	H $40
V $45	TRP $40	

Comments: 1989; Original Retail $40.00
A collector found this piece with two identical marks - not two different marks as other pieces have been found. The two marks were both the FLM, placed at different angles. I feel this piece would have a value of at least $300-350. BA mark scarce! Found without dog (S mark), add $75 to secondary market value. ***See #6, page XI.***

Personal Data: _____
____Want Mark ____ Mark _____ Purch. 19__ Pd $ _____

521817 Two Girls with Flowers
"Good Friends Are Forever"

BA $65	GC $55	S $55
FLM $60	B $55	H $55
V $55	TRP $55	

Comments: 1989; Original Retail $50.00/$55.00
This piece was also produced with the ROSEBUD mark, 525049 ($750). Not a great seller. Often friends do not have $55 to spend on a "friend" gift. 523623 friendship piece more popular.

Personal Data: _____
____Want Mark ____ Mark _____ Purch. 19__ Pd $ _____

521825 **Whale - Age 10**
"May Your Birthday Be Mammoth"

GC	$30	TRP	$25	H	$25
B	$28	S	$25		

Comments: 1990; Original Retail $25.00
Part of the *Birthday Train Series.*

Personal Data: _____
____Want Mark ____ Mark _____ Purch. 19__ Pd $ _____

521833 **Horse - Age 9**
"Being Nine Is Just Divine"

GC	$30	TRP	$25	H	$25
B	$28	S	$25		

Comments: 1990; Original Retail $25.00
Part of the *Birthday Train Series.* Original drawing for age 9 was a Unicorn.

Personal Data: _____
____Want Mark ____ Mark _____ Purch. 19__ Pd $ _____

521841 **Boy Whispering into Girl's Ear**
"Love Is From Above"

BA	$60	GC	$50	S	$50
FLM	$55	B	$50	H	$50
V	$52	TRP	$50		

Comments: 1989; Original Retail $45.00/$50.00
Close to suspension in my opinion. No action on secondary market. Retail price up in '96.

Personal Data: _____
____Want Mark ____ Mark _____ Purch. 19__ Pd $ _____

Bea Butler set up this attractive manger scene. By accenting the scene with angel hair, the Precious Moments® figurines look as if they are floating in heavenly clouds.

521868 **Angel Holding Commandments**
"The Greatest Of These Is Love"

SUSP. 1991 - 5 YEARS AGO

BA	$45	V	$38
FLM	$40		

Comments: 1988; Original Retail $27.50/$30.00
Many BA sales reported.

Personal Data: _____
____Want Mark ____ Mark _____ Purch. 19__ Pd $ _____

521892 **Boy Pulling Girl with Lily in Wagon**
"Easter's On Its Way"

BA	$75	GC	$70	S	$65
FLM	$72	B	$65	H	$65
V	$70	TRP	$65		

Comments: 1989; Original Retail $60.00/$65.00
Suspension candidate in my opinion.

Personal Data: _____
____Want Mark ____ Mark _____ Purch. 19__ Pd $ _____

521906 **Girl with Easter Basket Looking at Frogs**
"Hoppy Easter, Friend"

FLM	$50	B	$42	H	$40
V	$45	TRP	$40		
GC	$42	S	$40		

Comments: 1990; Original Retail $40.00
Cute piece, affordable!

Personal Data: _____
____Want Mark ____ Mark _____ Purch. 19__ Pd $ _____

521914 **Boys with Song Book**
"Perfect Harmony"

TRP	$65	H	$55
S	$55		

Comments: 1994; Original Retail $55.00

Personal Data: _____
____Want Mark ____ Mark _____ Purch. 19__ Pd $ _____

521922   Baby Sleeping on a Cloud
"Safe In The Arms Of Jesus"

GC $40	TRP $32.50	H $32.50
B $32.50	S $32.50	

Comments: 1992; Original Retail $30.00/$32.50
Child Evangelism Fellowship Figurine.

Personal Data: _____
____Want Mark ____ Mark _____ Purch. 19__ Pd $ _____

521949   Boy Standing by Tree Stump/Squirrel
"Wishing You A Cozy Season"

SUSP. 1993 - 3 YEARS AGO

BA $65	V $55	B $55
FLM $60	GC $55	

Comments: 1988; Original Retail $42.50/$45.00
More BA sales found than others.

Personal Data: _____
____Want Mark ____ Mark _____ Purch. 19__ Pd $ _____

521957   Boy with Kite
"High Hopes"

SUSP. 1993 - 3 YEARS AGO

BA $50	V $45	B $30
FLM $45	GC $35	

Comments: 1989; Original Retail $30.00
Most sales found were BA mark.

Personal Data: _____
____Want Mark ____ Mark _____ Purch. 19__ Pd $ _____

521965   Boy with Potted Flower
"To A Special Mum"

FLM $45	B $38	H $35
V $40	TRP $35	
GC $38	S $35	

Comments: 1990; Original Retail $30.00/$35.00

Personal Data: _____
____Want Mark ____ Mark _____ Purch. 19__ Pd $ _____

*Man to marriage counselor: "She went from hard-to-get
to hard-to-handle to hard-to-take."*

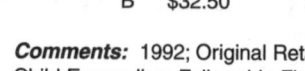

521981   Boy Marching with Drum
"Marching To The Beat Of Freedom's Drum"

S $35	H $35

Comments: 1995; Original Retail $35.00

Personal Data: _____
____Want Mark ____ Mark _____ Purch. 19__ Pd $ _____

522015   Boy with Apple and School Book
"To The Apple Of God's Eye"

B $42	S $35
TRP $35	H $35

Comments: 1992; Original Retail $32.50
Slow seller. Cute piece. Retail up in '96.

Personal Data: _____
____Want Mark ____ Mark _____ Purch. 19__ Pd $ _____

522023   Football Player Among Leaves
"May Your Life Be Blessed With Touchdowns"

BA $65	GC $55	S $50
FLM $60	B $50	H $50
FL $55	TRP $50	

Comments: 1988; Original Retail $45.00/$50.00
This was a very popular J&D poster. Figurines should have a leaf on the boy's leg; several have been found without the leaf. Add $45-50 over secondary market value for pieces without the leaf. Bases on these pieces and several others are a darker-toned tan compared to the general collection. A decision was evidently made at the factory during production as we notified Enesco of this change and their response was that they would "look into it." Other pieces have also been found with dark-toned bases similar to another collectible (Memories of Yesterday) produced by the same factory. (In my opinion, the factory made this change and Enesco later okayed it as so many were already produced this way.) Perfect for a retirement piece.

Personal Data: _____
____Want Mark ____ Mark _____ Purch. 19__ Pd $ _____

522031   Boy and Turkey at Thanksgiving Table
"Thank You Lord For Everything"

SUSP. 1993 - 3 YEARS AGO

BA $90	V $78	B $75
FLM $85	GC $75	

Comments: 1988; Original Retail $55.00
This was different from the "norm." Really cute piece!

Personal Data: _____
____Want Mark ____ Mark _____ Purch. 19__ Pd $ _____

522058 **Boy with Candle/Bedtime Stories**
"Now I Lay Me Down To Sleep"

TRP $38		H	$32.50
S	$35		

Comments: 1994; Original Retail $30.00/$32.50
Color flyers from Enesco show the prototype for this figurine having a teddy bear by the boy's feet. Neither the actual figurine nor the line art have the teddy bear.

Personal Data: _____
____Want Mark ____ Mark _____ Purch. 19__ Pd $ _____

522082 **Boy Trimming Globe**
"May Your World Be Trimmed With Joy"

V	$68	TRP $55
GC	$60	S	$55
B	$55	H	$55

Comments: 1990; Original Retail $55.00
We've received reports of this being a slow seller due to the retail price. Perhaps this will be a retirement or suspension candidate in the future as collectors have not sought him out compared to other Christmas pieces.

Personal Data: _____
____Want Mark ____ Mark _____ Purch. 19__ Pd $ _____

522090 **Girl/Boy with Water Hose**
"There Shall Be Showers Of Blessings"

BA	$85	GC	$75	S	$70
FLM	$75	B	$70	H	$70
V	$70	TRP $70		

Comments: 1989; Original Retail $60.00/$70.00
Cute piece, but only avid collectors would pay $70 for the inspiration.

Personal Data: _____
____Want Mark ____ Mark _____ Purch. 19__ Pd $ _____

A thankful heart enjoys blessings twice –
when they're received and when they're remembered.

522104 **Girl with Chickens/Dog/Eggs**
"It's No Yoke When I Say I Love You"

SUSP. 1994 - 2 YEARS AGO	V	$100	B	$90
	GC	$90	TRP	$90

Comments: 1990; Original Retail $60.00/$65.00
The retail price made her a slow seller. She is a very attractive piece! Suspension usually increases the sales for earlier marks. Only produced four years.

Personal Data: _____
____Want Mark ____ Mark _____ Purch. 19__ Pd $ _____

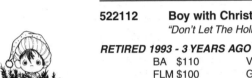

522112 **Boy with Christmas Tree Across Lap**
"Don't Let The Holidays Get You Down"

RETIRED 1993 - 3 YEARS AGO					
BA	$110	V	$100	B	$85
FLM	$100	GC	$95	MM	$95

Comments: 1988; Original Retail $42.50/$45.00
Not abundant at retirement time. Was found without the hatchet. Nice piece!

Personal Data: _____
____Want Mark ____ Mark _____ Purch. 19__ Pd $ _____

522120 **Boy/Gift Box with Dog, Ball and Bat**
"Wishing You A Very Successful Season"

BA	$80	GC	$70	S	$70
FLM	$75	B	$70	H	$70
V	$75	TRP $70		

Comments: 1988; Original Retail $60.00/$70.00
Very limited amount of trading on this piece. In my opinion, higher priced figurines ($60-70), if not very scarce, do not become popular pieces in future trades on the secondary market. This baseball one is probably a "strike out." Insure at these prices.

Personal Data: _____
____Want Mark ____ Mark _____ Purch. 19__ Pd $ _____

522201 **Boy and Girl on Motorcycle**
"Bon Voyage"

BA	$120	GC	$95	S	$95
FLM	$100	B	$95	H	$90
V	$95	TRP $95		

Comments: 1988; Original Retail $75.00/$90.00
Super nice piece!

Personal Data: _____
____Want Mark ____ Mark _____ Purch. 19__ Pd $ _____

522244 ♪ MUSICAL - Boy Looking in Package
"Do Not Open Till Christmas"

SUSP. 1994 - 2 YEARS AGO

GC	$95	TRP	$85
B	$90		

Comments: 1992; Original Retail $75.00
Plays *Toyland*. Very slow seller on secondary market to date.

Personal Data: _____
____Want Mark ____ Mark ____ Purch. 19__ Pd $ _____

522252 Angel on Cloud Decorating Manger
"He Is The Star Of The Morning"

SUSP. 1993 - 3 YEARS AGO

BA	$80	V	$72	B	$70
FLM	$75	GC	$70		

Comments: 1988; Original Retail $55.00/$60.00
(Also found with double GC mark - insure for $150 over secondary market value.)

Personal Data: _____
____Want Mark ____ Mark ____ Purch. 19__ Pd $ _____

522260 Giraffe with Baby in Mouth
"To Be With You Is Uplifting"

RETIRED 1994 - 2 YEARS AGO

BA	$48	GC	$35
FLM	$45	B	$35
V	$40	TRP	$35

Comments: 1988; Original Retail $20.00/$22.50
Part of the *Birthday Series*. Popular with giraffe collectors. Easily found at these prices. BA mark may be found for less if you look.

Personal Data: _____
____Want Mark ____ Mark ____ Purch. 19__ Pd $ _____

522279 Girl Looking in Bird Bath
"A Reflection Of His Love"

FLM	$70	B	$55	H	$50
V	$60	TRP	$55		
GC	$55	S	$50		

Comments: 1990; Original Retail $50.00
Reflection in birdbath – so clever! Prediction: retail price may go up on this piece. Buy now. She's different and nice to own. Has a white water reflection but has also been seen with a blue water reflection.

Personal Data: _____
____Want Mark ____ Mark ____ Purch. 19__ Pd $ _____

522287 Girl Kneeling
"Thinking Of You Is What I Really Like To Do"

BA	$42	GC	$32.50	S	$32.50
FLM	$35	B	$32.50	H	$32.50
V	$35	TRP	$32.50		

Comments: 1989; Original Retail $30.00/$32.50
Retail up in '96.

Personal Data: _____
____Want Mark ____ Mark ____ Purch. 19__ Pd $ _____

522317 Girl Putting Ornaments on Deer Antlers
"Merry Christmas Deer"

RETIRED 1995 - 1 YEAR AGO

BA	$100	GC	$80	S	$70
FLM	$90	B	$70		
V	$85	TRP	$70		

Comments: 1988; Original Retail $50.00/$60.00
"PM" logo omitted on all BA pieces. FLM marks are also being found without the "PM" logo. Retired Nov. 4, 1995.

Personal Data: _____
____Want Mark ____ Mark ____ Purch. 19__ Pd $ _____

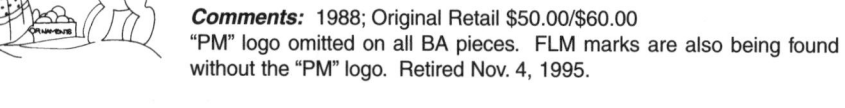

522333 Boy and Girl with Pie
"Sweeter As The Years Go By"

H	Current

Comments: 1995; Original Retail $60.00
Couple with freshly baked pie.

Personal Data: _____
____Want Mark ____ Mark ____ Purch. 19__ Pd $ _____

522376 EASTER SEALS - Girl with Easter Lily
"His Love Will Shine On You"

LE 1989 - 7 YEARS OLD

FL	$50	BA	$45

Comments: 1988; Original Retail $30.00
1989 Commemorative Easter Seals Limited Figurine Edition. Easter Lily decal appears on this piece. Watch for "Club Friends" on TV networks during Easter Seals Shows. They are great volunteers. *Precious Collectibles*™ presented Easter Seals a check on TV from contributions at one of our conventions.

Personal Data: _____
____Want Mark ____ Mark ____ Purch. 19__ Pd $ _____

May the roof above you never fall in and your friends gathered below never fall out.

522546   **Angel with Violin**
"Oh Holy Night"

DATED 1989   BA $35

Comments: 1988; Original Retail $25.00

Personal Data: _____
____Want Mark ____ Mark _____ Purch. 19__ Pd $ _____

522554   ***THIMBLE* - Angel with Violin**
"Oh Holy Night"

DATED 1989   BA $22

Comments: 1988; Original Retail $7.50

Personal Data: _____
____Want Mark ____ Mark _____ Purch. 19__ Pd $ _____

522821   ***BELL* - Angel with Violin**
"Oh Holy Night"

DATED 1989   BA $35

Comments: 1988; Original Retail $25.00

Personal Data: _____
____Want Mark ____ Mark _____ Purch. 19__ Pd $ _____

522848   ***ORNAMENT* - Angel with Violin**
"Oh Holy Night"

DATED 1989   BA $28

Comments: 1988; Original Retail $13.50

Personal Data: _____
____Want Mark ____ Mark _____ Purch. 19__ Pd $ _____

522856   **Bear in Rocking Chair**
"Have A Beary Merry Christmas"

| **SUSP. 1992 - 4 YEARS AGO** | BA | $30 | V | $25 |
| | FLM | $28 | GC | $22 |

Comments: 1988; Original Retail $15.00/$16.50
Sixth addition to *Family Christmas Scene*.

Personal Data: _____
____Want Mark ____ Mark _____ Purch. 19__ Pd $ _____

522864   **Grandpa Fishing with "Just Retired" on Chair**
"Just A Line To Say You're Special"

TRP $55   S $50   H $45

Comments: 1994; Original Retail $45.00

Personal Data: _____
____Want Mark ____ Mark _____ Purch. 19__ Pd $ _____

522910   ***ORNAMENT* - Girl with Goose**
"Make A Joyful Noise"

BA	$28	GC	$17	S	$17
FLM	$22	B	$17	H	$17
V	$20	TRP	$17		

Comments: 1988; Original Retail $15.00/$17.00
Be sure to have this ornament. "Almost" the logo for this collection.

Personal Data: _____
____Want Mark ____ Mark _____ Purch. 19__ Pd $ _____

522929   ***ORNAMENT* - Boy and Girl on Stump**
"Love One Another"

BA	$25	GC	$20	S	$18.50
FLM	$25	B	$20	H	$18.50
V	$22	TRP	$20		

Comments: 1976; Original Retail $17.50/$18.50
Very little trading found on this ornament. It's my opinion the avid collector should have this, as it is identical to E-1376 which is considered the first piece in the Precious Moments art collection. Still produced with Jonathan & David license name.

Personal Data: _____
____Want Mark ____ Mark _____ Purch. 19__ Pd $ _____

522937   **ORNAMENT - Boy and Girl in Boat**
"Friends Never Drift Apart"

RETIRED 1995 - 1 YEAR AGO

FLM	$50	B	$35
V	$45	TRP	$35
GC	$45	S	$35

Comments: 1989; Original Retail $17.50/$18.50
Somewhat heavier than others. Predicted this could be retired or suspended for that reason. Prediction came true Nov. 4, 1995!

Personal Data: _____
____Want Mark ____ Mark _____ Purch. 19___ Pd $ _____

522945   **ORNAMENT - Bride with Groom Popping Out of Trunk**
"Our First Christmas Together"

DATED 1991   V $25

Comments: 1989; Original Retail $17.50

Personal Data: _____
____Want Mark ____ Mark _____ Purch. 19___ Pd $ _____

522953   **ORNAMENT - Girl with Cross**
"I Believe In The Old Rugged Cross"

SUSP. 1994 - 2 YEARS AGO	BA	$35	GC	$22
	FLM	$30	B	$22
	V	$25	TRP	$20

Comments: 1988; Original Retail $15.00/$16.00
Popular ornament. Suspension has speeded up the trading!

Personal Data: _____
____Want Mark ____ Mark _____ Purch. 19___ Pd $ _____

522961   **SHARING SEASON ORNAMENT**
Girl with Box of Puppies
"Always Room For One More"

       BA $95

Comments: 1988; 1989 Sharing Season Ornament given to collectors when they signed up two new Enesco Collector's Club Members. Yes, you may have more than one membership. Many signed up two new memberships for themselves. They received club pieces and free ornaments.

Personal Data: _____
____Want Mark ____ Mark _____ Purch. 19___ Pd $ _____

522988   **MINI NATIVITY - Girl Sweeping**
"Isn't He Precious"

SUSP. 1993 - 3 YEARS AGO

BA	$30	V	$25	B	$22
FLM	$28	GC	$25		

Comments: 1988; Original Retail $15.00/$16.50
Addition to Miniature Nativity.

Personal Data: _____
____Want Mark ____ Mark _____ Purch. 19___ Pd $ _____

522996   **MINI NATIVITY - Mama and Baby Bunnies**
"Some Bunny's Sleeping"

SUSP. 1993 - 3 YEARS AGO	FLM	$25	GC	$18
	V	$20	B	$18

Comments: 1989; Original Retail $12.00
Addition to Miniature Nativity. Cute with Noah's Ark set, too. Not really sought after to date.

Personal Data: _____
____Want Mark ____ Mark _____ Purch. 19___ Pd $ _____

523003   **PLATE - Family Series**
"May Your Christmas Be A Happy Home"

DATED 1989   BA $65

Comments: 1988; Original Retail $50.00
Fourth issue of *Christmas Love Series*. Attractive plate. Send us a photo of your plate displays. Not many plates being traded.

Personal Data: _____
____Want Mark ____ Mark _____ Purch. 19___ Pd $ _____

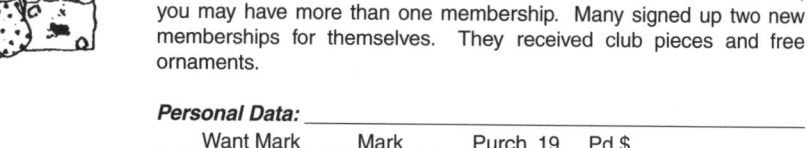

523011   **Chapel**
"There's A Christian Welcome Here"

SUSP. 1995 - 1 YEAR AGO

NM WITHOUT BROW	$110	V	$55
NM WITH BROW	$90	GC	$50

Comments: 1988; Original Retail $45.00
The Chapel first debuted in 1989. The first allotment (several thousand) had no eyebrow. "NMs" were still being offered in 1991 at the Precious Moments Chapel in Carthage, Missouri. In late 1992 more "no eyebrow" NM figurines were found at the Chapel. This piece was sold only to visitors at the Chapel at $45 each. Many bought extra to bring back to collectors at home in the beginning. *Precious Collectibles'* first convention at the Chapel drew over 1600 avid collectors. Many NMs were sold that weekend.

Personal Data: _____
___Want Mark ___ Mark _____ Purch. 19__ Pd $ _____

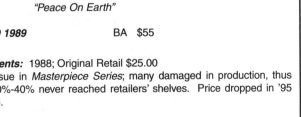

523038   **Boy Painting Picture with Animals**
"He Is My Inspiration"

NM $60-70

Comments: 1990; Original Retail $60.00
Available only at the Chapel Gift Shoppe. Debuted in 1991. Some pieces found without palette, add $100 to secondary market price. As reported by Chapel Gift Shoppe, this piece has not been assigned a mark. "I would like to see the Chapel have an exclusive Chapel imprint with year mark on the bottom of such figurines." Hint! Hint!

Personal Data: _____
___Want Mark ___ Mark _____ Purch. 19__ Pd $ _____

523062   *ORNAMENT* - **Round Porcelain Ball/Stand**
"Peace On Earth"

DATED 1989   BA $55

Comments: 1988; Original Retail $25.00
First issue in *Masterpiece Series*; many damaged in production, thus over 30%-40% never reached retailers' shelves. Price dropped in '95 and '96.

Personal Data: _____
___Want Mark ___ Mark _____ Purch. 19__ Pd $ _____

The passing of years makes youngsters ponder,
why Dad gets grayer and Mom gets blonder.

523097   **Girl Angel with Book**
"Jesus Is The Sweetest Name I Know"

SUSP. 1993 - 3 YEARS AGO

BA	$40	V	$35	B	$30
FLM	$35	GC	$30		

Comments: 1988; Original Retail $22.50/$25.00

Personal Data: _____
___Want Mark ___ Mark _____ Purch. 19__ Pd $ _____

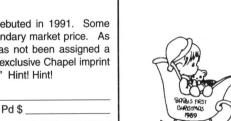

523178   **Girl/Stork with Bundle**
"Joy On Arrival"

FLM	$70	B	$55	H	$55
V	$60	TRP	$55		
GC	$55	S	$55		

Comments: 1990; Original Retail $50.00/$55.00
Very "sweet" piece. FLM not as abundant in my opinion. Retail up in '96.

Personal Data: _____
___Want Mark ___ Mark _____ Purch. 19__ Pd $ _____

523194   *ORNAMENT* - **Baby Boy in Sleigh with Bear**
"Baby's First Christmas 1989"

DATED 1989   BA $22.50

Comments: 1988; Original Retail $15.00
Also produced in 1988 (115282). *See #29, page XIV.*

Personal Data: _____
___Want Mark ___ Mark _____ Purch. 19__ Pd $ _____

523208   *ORNAMENT* - **Baby Girl in Sleigh with Doll**
"Baby's First Christmas 1989"

DATED 1989   BA $25

Comments: 1988; Original Retail $15.00
Identical to 1988 (520241). The identical design produced two years has kept the secondary market from increasing as compared to ornament designs produced for one year only. *See #28, page XIV.*

Personal Data: _____
___Want Mark ___ Mark _____ Purch. 19__ Pd $ _____

523224   ***ORNAMENT* - Girl with Stick Horse**
"Happy Trails Is Trusting Jesus"

SUSP. 1994 - 2 YEARS AGO   V $32.50   B $28
                                     GC $30   TRP $25

Comments: 1989; Original Retail $15.00/$16.00
Not easy to find. FLM reported. Do you have a FLM?

Personal Data: _____
____Want Mark ____ Mark _____ Purch. 19__ Pd $ _____

523283   **9"** ***EASTER SEALS*** **- Girl Holding String
of Hearts with Dome**
"You Have Touched So Many Hearts"

LE 1990 - 6 YEARS OLD   BA $550
                                  FLM $550

Comments: 1982; Original Retail $500.00
1990 Easter Seals 9" piece. Limited Edition 2000. Similar to figurine
E-2821. Plentiful for demand. Prices found $400 up. ***See #25, page XIV.***

Personal Data: _____
____Want Mark ____ Mark _____ Purch. 19__ Pd $ _____

523291   **Girl Giving Alms to Poor Boy**
*"Blessed Are The Merciful, For They Shall
Obtain Mercy"*

LE 1994 - 2 YEARS OLD   NM $70   TRP $60

Comments: 1991; Projected Original Retail $55.00
Fifth in the Seven *Beatitudes Window Figurine Series*. Debuted in 1994.
Available at the Chapel only. Limited to one year production from the
release date. Unpainted mouse has been reported. ***See #40, page XV.***

Personal Data: _____
____Want Mark ____ Mark _____ Purch. 19__ Pd $ _____

523313   **Indian with Deer**
*"Blessed Are The Meek, For They Shall
Inherit The Earth"*

LE 1993/94 - 2 YEARS OLD   B $60
                                      TRP $55

Comments: 1991; Original Retail $55.00
Third in the Seven *Beatitudes Window Figurine Series*. Debuted in 1993.
Available at the Chapel only. Limited to one year production from the
release date. ***See #40, page XV.***

Personal Data: _____
____Want Mark ____ Mark _____ Purch. 19__ Pd $ _____

523321   **Girl Praying**
*"Blessed Are They Which Do Hunger And Thirst
After Righteousness, For They Shall Be Filled"*

LE 1993 - 3 YEARS OLD   B $60

Comments: 1991; Original Retail $55.00
Fourth in the Seven *Beatitudes Window Figurine Series*. Debuted in
Sept. 1993. Available at the Chapel only. ***See #40, page XV.***

Personal Data: _____
____Want Mark ____ Mark _____ Purch. 19__ Pd $ _____

523348   **Girl with Butterfly**
*"Blessed Are The Peacemakers, For They
Shall Be Called The Children Of God"*

LE 1995   TRP $55   S $55

Comments: 1991; Projected Original Retail $55.00
Seventh in the Seven *Beatitudes Window Figurine Series*. **This piece
debuted in 1995.** Available at Chapel only. Limited to one year production from the release date. ***See #40, page XV.***

Personal Data: _____
____Want Mark ____ Mark _____ Purch. 19__ Pd $ _____

523380   **Girl Crying**
*"Blessed Are They That Mourn,
For They Shall Be Comforted"*

LE 1991/92 - 4 YEARS OLD   GC $60
                                     B $60

Comments: 1991; Original Retail $55.00
Second in the Seven *Beatitudes Window Figurine Series*. Available at
Chapel only. Debuted in 1992. Limited to one year production from the
release date. ***See #40, page XV.***

Personal Data: _____
____Want Mark ____ Mark _____ Purch. 19__ Pd $ _____

523399   **Girl Sitting with Birds**
*"Blessed Are The Pure In Heart,
For They Shall See God"*

LE 1994/95   TRP $55   S $55

Comments: 1991; Projected Original Retail $55.00
Sixth in the Seven *Beatitudes Window Figurine Series*. This piece
debuted in late '94. Available at Chapel only. Limited to one year production from the release date. ***See #40, page XV.***

Personal Data: _____
____Want Mark ____ Mark _____ Purch. 19__ Pd $ _____

523437   **Princess Washing Servant's Feet**
"Blessed Are The Poor In Spirit, For Theirs Is The Kingdom Of Heaven"

LE 1992 - 4 YEARS OLD   GC $60

Comments: 1991; Original Retail $55.00
First in the Seven *Beatitudes Window Figurine Series*. Debuted in 1992. Available through collectors' ads in *Precious Collectibles*™. Limited to one year production after release date. ***See #40, page XV.***

Personal Data: _____
____Want Mark ____ Mark _____ Purch. 19__ Pd $ _____

523453   **Expectant Mother**
"The Good Lord Always Delivers"

BA	$40	GC	$30	S	$30
FLM	$35	B	$30	H	$30
V	$32	TRP	$30		

Comments: 1989; Original Retail $27.50/$30.00

Personal Data: _____
____Want Mark ____ Mark _____ Purch. 19__ Pd $ _____

523496   **Girl with Bible and Cross**
"This Day Has Been Made In Heaven"

BA	$45	GC	$35	S	$35
FLM	$40	B	$35	H	$35
V	$35	TRP	$35		

Comments: 1989; Original Retail $30.00/$35.00
Could be a suspension candidate. Slow seller. A collector found this piece with double marks – B and TRP. Add $100 to the secondary market value. Retail price raised in 1996.

Personal Data: _____
____Want Mark ____ Mark _____ Purch. 19__ Pd $ _____

523518   **Girl with Heart Behind Back**
"God Is Love Dear Valentine"

BA	$45	GC	$30	S	$30
FLM	$38	B	$30	H	$30
V	$35	TRP	$30		

Comments: 1989; Original Retail $27.50/$30.00

Personal Data: _____
____Want Mark ____ Mark _____ Purch. 19__ Pd $ _____

523526   **Girl with Fan**
"I'm A Precious Moments Fan"

LE 1990 - 6 YEARS OLD   BA $52
                              FLM $40

Comments: 1988; Original Retail $25.00
1990 Special Event figurine. Generally, Special Event figurines are easily found.

Personal Data: _____
____Want Mark ____ Mark _____ Purch. 19__ Pd $ _____

523534   ***EGG WITH SEPARATE BASE -***
               Girl with Cross
"I Will Cherish The Old Rugged Cross"

DATED 1991   FLM $42.50
                   V $35

Comments: 1990; Original Retail $27.50
This egg is a "bas-relief" – the design is in the mold, rather than on a decal as the small, dated Easter eggs. This piece is also larger than the first dated porcelain eggs. Slow seller!

Personal Data: _____
____Want Mark ____ Mark _____ Purch. 19__ Pd $ _____

523542   **Girl at Typewriter**
"You Are The Type I Love"

V	$55	TRP	$45
GC	$50	S	$45
B	$40-45	H	$45

Comments: 1990; Original Retail $40.00/$45.00
Not being sought after on secondary market to date. Retail price up in '96.

Personal Data: _____
____Want Mark ____ Mark _____ Purch. 19__ Pd $ _____

523593   **Girl Holding a Bird**
"The Lord Will Provide"

LE 1993 - 3 YEARS OLD   GC $55
                              B $50

Comments: 1993; Original Retail $40.00
1993 Limited Edition. Beautiful! Display her with the '92 Limited Edition piece, *You Are My Happiness*. A perfect display!

Personal Data: _____
____Want Mark ____ Mark _____ Purch. 19__ Pd $ _____

523615   **Girl Climbing Ladder to "Air Mail" Box**
"Good News Is So Uplifting"

V	$80	TRP	$70
GC	$75	S	$70
B	$70	H	$70

Comments: 1990; Original Retail $60.00/$70.00
A suspension candidate! Retail up in '96.

Personal Data: _____

____Want Mark ____ Mark _____ Purch. 19__ Pd $ _____

523623   **Two Girls Feeding a Kitten**
"I'm So Glad That God Blessed Me With A Friend Like You"

RETIRED 1995 - 1 YEAR AGO

GC	$80	TRP	$70
B	$75	S	$65

Comments: 1992; Original Retail $50.00/$55.00

Personal Data: _____

____Want Mark ____ Mark _____ Purch. 19__ Pd $ _____

523631   **Girl at Gate**
"I Will Always Be Thinking Of You"

B	$55	S	$45
TRP	$50	H	$45

Comments: 1993; Original Retail $45.00
Has been found with the title decal placed backwards on the bottom.

Personal Data: _____

____Want Mark ____ Mark _____ Purch. 19__ Pd $ _____

523682 ♪ **MUSICAL - Girl with Bible and Cross**
"This Day Has Been Made In Heaven"

V	$75	TRP	$65
GC	$70	S	$65
B	$65	H	$65

Comments: 1990; Original Retail $60.00/$65.00
Plays *Amazing Grace*. Retail up in '96.

Personal Data: _____

____Want Mark ____ Mark _____ Purch. 19__ Pd $ _____

523704   **ORNAMENT - Round Porcelain Ball/Stand**
"May Your Christmas Be A Happy Home"

DATED 1990

FLM Blue Shirt	$40
FLM Yellow Shirt	$65

Comments: 1989; Original Retail $27.50
Second issue of *Masterpiece Series*. The first shipments had yellow shirts on the little boy; the following shipments arrived with blue shirts. There are fewer yellow shirts. Easily found at above prices. Now said to be found in FLM with pink shirt. Do you have a pink shirt?

Personal Data: _____

____Want Mark ____ Mark _____ Purch. 19__ Pd $ _____

523739   **Nurse with Alarm Clock**
"Time Heals"

FLM	$55	B	$40	H	$40
V	$45	TRP	$40		
GC	$40	S	$40		

Comments: 1989; Original Retail $37.50/$40.00
Has been found with no eyebrows. This has been found on several pieces since 1988. Three nurse figurines on the market. Possibly one may be suspended or retired soon. Reported with a MM. Retail price is up in '96.

Personal Data: _____

____Want Mark ____ Mark _____ Purch. 19__ Pd $ _____

523747   **Boy and Girl Kissing Under Mistletoe**
"Blessings From Above"

RETIRED 1994 - 2 YEARS AGO

FLM	$125	B	$90
V	$105	TRP	$90
GC	$95		

Comments: 1989; Original Retail $45.00/$50.00
More produced after retirement announcement.

Personal Data: _____

____Want Mark ____ Mark _____ Purch. 19__ Pd $ _____

523755   **Girl with Angel Jack-in-Box**
"Just Poppin' In To Say Halo!"

TRP	$55	H	$45
S	$45		

Comments: 1992; Original Retail $45.00

Personal Data: _____

____Want Mark ____ Mark _____ Purch. 19__ Pd $ _____

523763   **Boy with /Alphabet Blocks**
"I Can't Spell Success Without You"

SUSP. 1994 - 2 YEARS AGO   MM $85   GC $60
                          FLM $75   B $60
                          V $65   TRP $60

Comments: 1990; Original Retail $40.00/$45.00
Very little trading found on this piece. The mark most traded seems to be the V mark. This piece has been found without the embossed *Sam B.* Add $25 to the secondary market value. This piece has also been reported with a MM.

Personal Data: _____
____Want Mark ____ Mark _____ Purch. 19__ Pd $ _____

523771   **ORNAMENT - Girl with Pie**
"Baby's First Christmas"

DATED 1990   FLM $25

Comments: 1989; Original Retail $15.00

Personal Data: _____
____Want Mark ____ Mark _____ Purch. 19__ Pd $ _____

523798   **ORNAMENT - Boy with Pie**
"Baby's First Christmas"

DATED 1990   FLM $25

Comments: 1989; Original Retail $15.00

Personal Data: _____
____Want Mark ____ Mark _____ Purch. 19__ Pd $ _____

523801   **PLATE - Girl Selling Ice Cream**
"Wishing You A Yummy Christmas"

DATED 1990   FLM $57.50

Comments: 1989; Original Retail $50.00
First issue of *Christmas Blessings Series.* Very few plates are being traded on the secondary market.

Personal Data: _____
____Want Mark ____ Mark _____ Purch. 19__ Pd $ _____

523828   **BELL - Girl with Candle and Book**
"Once Upon A Holy Night"

DATED 1990   FLM $35

Comments: 1989; Original Retail $25.00

Personal Data: _____
____Want Mark ____ Mark _____ Purch. 19__ Pd $ _____

523836   **Girl with Candle and Book**
"Once Upon A Holy Night"

DATED 1990   FLM $37.50

Comments: 1989; Original Retail $25.00
1990 is written for the viewer to read, not the little girl. Original pictures of the "sample piece" had "1990" turned toward the girl. Any chance you have something different? *See #7, page VII.*

Personal Data: _____
____Want Mark ____ Mark _____ Purch. 19__ Pd $ _____

523844   **THIMBLE - Girl with Candle and Book**
"Once Upon A Holy Night"

DATED 1990   FLM $18.50

Comments: 1989; Original Retail $8.00

Personal Data: _____
____Want Mark ____ Mark _____ Purch. 19__ Pd $ _____

523852   **ORNAMENT - Girl with Candle and Book**
"Once Upon A Holy Night"

DATED 1990   FLM $25

Comments: 1989; Original Retail $15.00

Personal Data: _____
____Want Mark ____ Mark _____ Purch. 19__ Pd $ _____

---

*Courtship is that time
during which the female decides
whether or not she can do any better.*

523860   *PLATE* **- Girl at Bird House**
"Blessings From Me To Thee"

DATED 1991   V $60

Comments: 1990; Original Retail $50.00
Very little trading found.

Personal Data: _____
____Want Mark _____ Mark _____ Purch. 19__ Pd $ _____

523879   *9" EASTER SEALS* **- Girl with Butterfly**
with Dome
"We Are God's Workmanship"

LE 1990 - 6 YEARS OLD   FLM $600-625
                               V $550-625

Comments: 1982; Original Retail $500.00
1990 Easter Seals 9" Figurine with Dome. Limited Edition 2,000 pieces.
Similar to E-9258. Prices seem to be decreasing somewhat on most of
the 9" Easter Seals pieces. They will not drop too much more, in my
opinion.

Personal Data: _____
____Want Mark _____ Mark _____ Purch. 19__ Pd $ _____

523941   **Mother Rocking Baby**
"Love Never Leaves A Mother's Arms"

      S $40   H $40

Comments: 1995; Original Retail $40.00

Personal Data: _____
____Want Mark _____ Mark _____ Purch. 19__ Pd $ _____

524069   **Boy Eating Cake with Fingers**
"Baby's First Birthday"

      GC $32   TRP $25   H $25
      B $27.50   S $25

Comments: 1992; Original Retail $25.00
Addition to *Baby's First Series*.

Personal Data: _____
____Want Mark _____ Mark _____ Purch. 19__ Pd $ _____

524077   **Baby in High Chair**
"Baby's First Meal'

FLM $60   B $40   H $40
V $50   TRP $40
GC $45   S $40

Comments: 1990; Original Retail $35.00/$40.00
6th issue in *Baby's First Series*. Becoming a VERY popular series.
Baby's First Trip is the most sought after in the past year. Retail price up
in '96.

Personal Data: _____
____Want Mark _____ Mark _____ Purch. 19__ Pd $ _____

524085   **Girl in Tree Swing**
"My Warmest Thoughts Are You"

      V $75   TRP $60
      GC $65   S $60
      B $65   H $60

Comments: 1990; Original Retail $55.00/$60.00
This figurine differs from original artwork as shown at left; the figurine
has no hearts on the tree, the bluebird and leaves are in different posi-
tions and the girl has bows in her hair instead of wearing a bonnet. It's
my opinion dealers did not order this figurine in large quantities, so it may
be hard to find if suspended.

Personal Data: _____
____Want Mark _____ Mark _____ Purch. 19__ Pd $ _____

524123   **Girl in Coat with Bunny**
"Good Friends Are For Always"

      V $40   B $32.50   S $32.50
      GC $35   TRP $32.50   H $32.50

Comments: 1990; Original Retail $27.50/$32.50
Retail price increased in 1995.

Personal Data: _____
____Want Mark _____ Mark _____ Purch. 19__ Pd $ _____

524131   *ORNAMENT* **- Girl Holding Bunny**
"Good Friends Are For Always"

      GC $25   TRP $17   H $17
      B $17   S $17

Comments: 1992; Original Retail $15.00/$17.00
Retail price last increased in 1995.

Personal Data: _____
____Want Mark _____ Mark _____ Purch. 19__ Pd $ _____

524158   **Girl Kneeling at Altar with Bible**
"Lord Teach Us To Pray"

TRP $50

Comments: 1993; Original Retail $35.00
Commemorative 1994 National Day of Prayer Figurine.

Personal Data: _____
____ Want Mark ____ Mark _____ Purch. 19__ Pd $ _____

524166   **Girl with Bird**
"May Your Christmas Be Merry"

DATED 1991   V $37.50

Comments: 1990; Original Retail $27.50
It takes several years to see a large increase in the secondary market on dated pieces. This dated piece is not as scarce as previous years' dated figurines.

Personal Data: _____
____ Want Mark ____ Mark _____ Purch. 19__ Pd $ _____

524174   **ORNAMENT - Girl with Bird**
"May Your Christmas Be Merry"

DATED 1991   V $27.50

Comments: 1990; Original Retail $15.00

Personal Data: _____
____ Want Mark ____ Mark _____ Purch. 19__ Pd $ _____

Remember, just when it seems there's no hope...that's the time miracles happen.
Rosie Wells

524182   **BELL - Girl with Bird**
"May Your Christmas Be Merry"

DATED 1991   V $35

Comments: 1990; Original Retail $25.00

Personal Data: _____
____ Want Mark ____ Mark _____ Purch. 19__ Pd $ _____

524190   **THIMBLE - Girl with Bird**
"May Your Christmas Be Merry"

DATED 1991   V $25

Comments: 1990; Original Retail $8.00

Personal Data: _____
____ Want Mark ____ Mark _____ Purch. 19__ Pd $ _____

524212   **Girl with Kitten**
"Walk In The Sonshine"

S $35   H $35

Comments: 1994; Original Retail $35.00
First marks still on retailers' shelves. Look for it if you want this piece.

Personal Data: _____
____ Want Mark ____ Mark _____ Purch. 19__ Pd $ _____

524263   **Girl with Daisy**
"HE Loves Me"

LE 1991 - 5 YEARS OLD   FLM $55   GC $35
                                V $47.50

Comments: 1990; Original Retail $35.00
1991 Limited Edition. A cold cast material was used for the flower. It's a great life with Jesus walking beside you every minute of the day. "Jesus Does Love You!" He died for you, so you can ask God to forgive you of your sins! It's a great life with Jesus walking beside you every minute of the day...

Personal Data: _____
____ Want Mark ____ Mark _____ Purch. 19__ Pd $ _____

524271   **Girl with Watering Can and Plant**
"Friendship Grows When You Plant A Seed"

RETIRED 1994 - 2 YEARS AGO

V	$100	B	$75
GC	$85	TRP	$75

Comments: 1990; Original Retail $40.00
Hardest one of '94 retirement pieces to find. No production after announcement. Not a big increase seen in value on secondary market from last year's values. Many sales found.

Personal Data: _____
____Want Mark ____ Mark _____ Purch. 19__ Pd $ _____
_____

524298   **Girl Blowing Cake Off the Table**
"May Your Every Wish Come True"

GC	$60	TRP	$50	H	$50
B	$55	S	$50		

Comments: 1992; Original Retail $50.00
The Enesco brochure shows four candles; the piece has five. (Just in case you get excited.)

Personal Data: _____
____Want Mark ____ Mark _____ Purch. 19__ Pd $ _____
_____

524301   **Girl with Birthday Cake**
"May Your Birthday Be A Blessing"

FLM	$55	B	$35	H	$35
V	$40	TRP	$35		
GC	$37.50	S	$35		

Comments: 1990; Original Retail $30.00/$35.00
A cold cast material was used for the birthday cake and candles. Excellent gift which is affordable for birthdays. Retail price increase in 1995 and now in '96. Hopefully this piece will remain at this price when received as a gift; just could "start a new collector."

Personal Data: _____
____Want Mark ____ Mark _____ Purch. 19__ Pd $ _____
_____

Do something every day to make someone happy, even if it means leaving him or her alone.

Grandparent – one of those things
"so simple a child can operate."

Gramma and Hunter Wells

524336   **Boy and Girl Sharing Soda**
"Our Friendship Is Soda-Licious"

GC	$85	TRP	$70	H	$70
B	$75	S	$70		

Comments: 1992; Original Retail $65.00/$70.00
Higher priced retail pieces may be "hard to find" in the future. Retailers do not order as many of these pieces as the more "affordable" figurines under fifty dollars sell more quickly in the gift line. Not too abundant. Retail price up in '96.

Personal Data: _____
____Want Mark ____ Mark _____ Purch. 19__ Pd $ _____
_____

524352   **Girl Looking at Globe**
"What The World Needs Now"

V	$65	TRP	$50	
GC	$55	S	$50	
B	$50	H	$50	

Comments: 1990; Original Retail $50.00
Several have been found without the Bible. First marks for recent years' figurines are the most traded on the secondary market... thereafter most do not go up in value until they are five or six years old (not including rare, suspended and retired).
Personal Data: _____
____Want Mark ____ Mark _____ Purch. 19__ Pd $ _____
_____

524379   **Girl/Flower Picked from Box Behind Her**
"So Glad I Picked You As A Friend"

B	$55
TRP	$45

Comments: 1993; Original Retail $40.00
Only those DSR shops participating in the 1994 Spring catalog offer were able to order this figurine. ***See #31, page XIV.***

Personal Data: _____
____Want Mark ____ Mark _____ Purch. 19__ Pd $ _____
_____

524387   *EASTER SEALS* **- Girl with Basket of Roses**
"Take Time To Smell The Flowers"

LE 1995 - ONE YEAR OLD

TRP $40		S	$35

Comments: 1994; Original Retail $30.00
1995 Easter Seals Commemorative Figurine. Pretty! Has been more popular than some of the other past Easter Seals pieces.

Personal Data: _____
____Want Mark ____ Mark _____ Purch. 19__ Pd $ _____

524395   **Girl Holding Kitten**
"You Are Such A Purr-fect Friend"

GC	$50	TRP	$35	H	$35
B	$45	S	$35		

Comments: 1992; Original Retail $35.00
Has been found with two B marks. Very similar to '95 piece #136263 and LE #526185. Pretty!

Personal Data: _____
____Want Mark ____ Mark _____ Purch. 19__ Pd $ _____

524425   **Girl with Butterfly Net and Butterfly**
"May Only Good Things Come Your Way"

FLM	$55	B	$37.50	H	$37.50
V	$48	TRP	$37.50		
GC	$40	S	$37.50		

Comments: 1990; Original Retail $30.00/$37.50
Many confuse this piece with the retired Butterfly Angel (520640). Retail price increased last in 1995. Do not over insure.

Personal Data: _____
____Want Mark ____ Mark _____ Purch. 19__ Pd $ _____

524441   **Boy and Girl Kissing**
"Sealed With A Kiss"

GC	$65	TRP	$60	H	$60
B	$60	S	$60		

Comments: 1992; Original Retail $50.00/$60.00
Retail price increase of 10% in 1995 and nearly that again in '96.

Personal Data: _____
____Want Mark ____ Mark _____ Purch. 19__ Pd $ _____

524468   **Boy with Bell**
"A Special Chime For Jesus"

B	$37.50	S	$32.50	
TRP	$32.50	H	$32.50	

Comments: 1992; Original Retail $32.50
Boy's pajamas found to be from very light to bright red and orange.

Personal Data: _____
____Want Mark ____ Mark _____ Purch. 19__ Pd $ _____

524476   **Girl Decorating Christmas Tree**
"God Cared Enough To Send His Best"

TRP $60		H	$50
S	$50		

Comments: 1994; Original Retail $50.00
If you like this piece, buy it now!

Personal Data: _____
____Want Mark ____ Mark _____ Purch. 19__ Pd $ _____

524484   **Cat with Mouse on Cheese (2 pc. set)**
"Not A Creature Was Stirring"

SUSP. 1994 - 2 YEARS AGO

FLM	$27.50	B	$22
V	$25	TRP	$22
GC	$25		

Comments: 1989; Original Retail $17.00
The cat has been found with only one eyebrow. Not unusual to hear about missing eyebrows.

Personal Data: _____
____Want Mark ____ Mark _____ Purch. 19__ Pd $ _____

524492   **Cat with Bird in Cage**
"Can't Be Without You"

FLM $25		B	$17.50	H	$17.50
V	$20	TRP	$17.50		
GC	$17.50	S	$17.50		

Comments: 1990; Original Retail $16.00/$17.50
Retail price increase in 1995 and 1996!

Personal Data: _____
____Want Mark ____ Mark _____ Purch. 19__ Pd $ _____

524506   **Pig with Gift**
"Oinky Birthday"

B	$18	S	$14.50
TRP	$14.50	H	$14.50

Comments: 1993; Original Retail $13.50/$14.50
Birthday Series Addition. Retail up in 1996.

Personal Data: _____
____Want Mark ____ Mark _____ Purch. 19__ Pd $ _____

524522   ***EASTER SEALS* - Girl with Chick in Egg**
"Always In His Care"

LE 1990 - 6 YEARS OLD   BA $40
                               FLM $35

Comments: 1989; Original Retail $30.00
1990 Easter Seals Limited Edition Figurine. Easter Seals Logo on base.
Easter Seals pieces are usually abundant.

Personal Data: _____
____Want Mark ____ Mark _____ Purch. 19__ Pd $ _____

524875   **Bear in Package**
"Happy Birthday Dear Jesus"

SUSP. 1993 - 3 YEARS AGO   FLM $25   GC $18
                                      V $20   B $18

Comments: 1989; Original Retail $13.50
Addition to regular Nativity Set.

Personal Data: _____
____Want Mark ____ Mark _____ Purch. 19__ Pd $ _____

524883   **Christmas Fireplace**

SUSP. 1992 - 4 YEARS AGO   FLM $55   GC $45
                                      V $45

Comments: 1989; Original Retail $37.50
Seventh addition to *Family Christmas Scene*.

Personal Data: _____
____Want Mark ____ Mark _____ Purch. 19__ Pd $ _____

524905   **Boy on Skis**
"It's So Uplifting To Have A Friend Like You"

GC	$55	TRP	$45	H	$45
B	$45	S	$45		

Comments: 1992; Original Retail $40.00/$45.00
Retail price increased 10% in 1995.

Personal Data: _____
____Want Mark ____ Mark _____ Purch. 19__ Pd $ _____

524913   **Girl with Melting Snowman**
"We're Going To Miss You"

FLM	$65	B	$50	H	$50
V	$60	TRP	$50		
GC	$55	S	$50		

Comments: 1989; Original Retail $50.00
This is an attractive piece. Three snowmen have been produced. 12351
was suspended in 1988, and there was a snowman added to the Sugar
Town collection in 1993.

Personal Data: _____
____Want Mark ____ Mark _____ Purch. 19__ Pd $ _____

524921   **Two Angels on Stool**
"Angels We Have Heard On High"

V	$75	TRP	$65
GC	$70	S	$65
B	$65	H	$65

Comments: 1990; Original Retail $60.00/$65.00
It's been reported the little black angel's hand is not painted on many.
Add $10-15 to these pieces at this time for insuring.

Personal Data: _____
____Want Mark ____ Mark _____ Purch. 19__ Pd $ _____

525049   **Two Girls with Flowers**
"Good Friends Are Forever"

ROSEBUD MARK WITH EMBOSSED BA MARK   **$750**

Comments: 1989. Also produced as 521817 in the regular line.
Given away at store events – one per DSR. Many went to the "general
public," not all to collectors. Under 500 produced. Would be hard to
replace if broken. Very few sold or traded. Insure at $750 to replace.

Personal Data: _____
____Want Mark ____ Mark _____ Purch. 19__ Pd $ _____

525057   ***ORNAMENT*** **- Girl with Packages**
"Bundles Of Joy"

LE 1990 - 6 YEARS OLD   FLM $28

Comments: 1989; Original Retail $17.50
1990 Limited Edition. This ornament was available exclusively to
Precious Moments® Collectors Centers as a special sale item.

Personal Data: _____
____Want Mark _____ Mark _____ Purch. 19__ Pd $ _____

525278   ***MINI NATIVITY*** **- Pig with Chicken on Back**
"Tubby's First Christmas"

GC $18	TRP $10	H $10
B $10	S $10	

Comments: 1992; Original Retail $10.00
Addition to the Miniature Nativity.

Personal Data: _____
____Want Mark _____ Mark _____ Purch. 19__ Pd $ _____

525286   ***MINI NATIVITY*** **- Boy Angel with Doctor's Bag**
"It's A Perfect Boy"

V $25	TRP $17
GC $20	S $17
B $18.50	H $17

Comments: 1990; Original Retail $16.50/$17.00
Addition to Miniature Nativity.

Personal Data: _____
____Want Mark _____ Mark _____ Purch. 19__ Pd $ _____

525316   **Girl Praying in Front of Window**
"May Your Future Be Blessed"

GC $50	TRP $40	H $40
B $45	S $40	

Comments: 1992; Original Retail $35.00/$40.00
Suspension candidate. Retail up in 1995 and 1996.

Personal Data: _____
____Want Mark _____ Mark _____ Purch. 19__ Pd $ _____

525324   ***ORNAMENT*** **- Bride and Groom in Car**
"Our First Christmas Together"

DATED 1990   FLM $25

Comments: 1989; Original Retail $17.50
Same design as 521558. Debuted in crystal at $50. Crystal is not con-
sidered a "hot" Precious Moments® "collectible." **See #28, page XIV.**

Personal Data: _____
____Want Mark _____ Mark _____ Purch. 19__ Pd $ _____

525332   ***ORNAMENT*** **- Ballerina on One Toe
w/Purple Tutu**
"Lord Keep Me On My Toes"

GC $22.50	TRP $17	H $17
B $18	S $17	

Comments: 1992; Original Retail $15.00/$17.00
Displays well hanging from a display ornament stand. Retail price
increased in 1995.

Personal Data: _____
____Want Mark _____ Mark _____ Purch. 19__ Pd $ _____

525898   **Two Angels Ringing a Bell**
"Ring Those Christmas Bells"

GC $115	TRP $100	H $100
B $110	S $100	

Comments: 1992; Original Retail $95.00/$100.00
This is a very large, attractive piece. It will never do much on the secondary market unless retired or a change is made, etc. Retail price
increased in 1995.

Personal Data: _____
____Want Mark _____ Mark _____ Purch. 19__ Pd $ _____

525960   ***EGG WITH SEPARATE BASE*** **-
Girl w/Butterfly**
"We Are God's Workmanship"

DATED 1992   V $35
               GC $27.50

Comments: 1990; Original Retail $27.50
Eggs are beautiful but not sought after.

Personal Data: _____
____Want Mark _____ Mark _____ Purch. 19__ Pd $ _____

525979   **Boy Hitching a Ride with Angel**
"Going Home"

V	$75	TRP	$60
GC	$65	S	$60
B	$65	H	$60

Comments: 1991; Original Retail $60.00
Dedicated to the memory of Philip Butcher.

Personal Data: _____
___Want Mark ___ Mark ___ Purch. 19__ Pd $ _____

526010   **9" EASTER SEALS -**
Girl Holding Cat with Dome
"You Are Such A Purr-fect Friend"

LE 1992 - 4 YEARS OLD		V	$600-650
		GC	$550-600

Comments: 1990; Original Retail $500.00
1992 Easter Seals 9" Commemorative Figurine. At 2,000 production, this quantity supplied the demand. Very attractive piece!

Personal Data: _____
___Want Mark ___ Mark ___ Purch. 19__ Pd $ _____

526037   **Boy with Gold Crown/Jeweled Ring**
"A Prince Of A Guy"

S	$35
H	Current

Comments: 1994; Original Retail $35.00
This figurine was available in the Fall of 1995 through special buying programs. Only the "catalog" exclusive figurines were to have the Ship mark and "1995 Catalog Exclusive" on the bases; however, the Princess did not come with the notation. The base of the Prince figurine did say "1995 Catalog Exclusive." In late '95, the Prince and Princess (from the Spring '96 line) arrived at retailers' with the Ship mark. In my opinion, it would be difficult to know whether the Princess was a part of the catalog exclusive or the '96 line.

Personal Data: _____
___Want Mark ___ Mark ___ Purch. 19__ Pd $ _____

526053   **Girl with Gold Crown/Jeweled Ring**
"Pretty As A Princess"

S	$35
H	Current

Comments: 1994; Original Retail $35.00
This figurine was available in the Spring of 1995 through special buying programs. See *Boy with Gold Crown/Jeweled Ring* for extra information. Found with one of points on her crown left unpainted.

Personal Data: _____
___Want Mark ___ Mark ___ Purch. 19__ Pd $ _____

526142   **Girl Holding Map of Carthage**
"I Would Be Lost Without You"

V	$38	TRP	$30
GC	$35	S	$30
B	$30	H	$30

Comments: 1990; Original Retail $27.50/$30.00
This was reported to be a First in Series, however no Second in Series followed. Most "gift buyers" will not understand why Carthage and Joplin are marked on the figurine. Probably a future suspension piece.

Personal Data: _____
___Want Mark ___ Mark ___ Purch. 19__ Pd $ _____

526150   **Boy with Duck**
"Friends To The Very End"

B	$55	S	$45
TRP	$45	H	$45

Comments: 1993; Original Retail $40.00/$45.00
Ouch! Cute piece! Retail up in 1996 – ouch!

Personal Data: _____
___Want Mark ___ Mark ___ Purch. 19__ Pd $ _____

526185   **Girl Holding Bouquet of Roses**
"You Are My Happiness"

LE 1992 - 4 YEARS OLD		V	$70
		GC	$60

Comments: 1990; Original Retail $37.50
Limited to One Year Production (1992). A beautiful piece! Expect a secondary market rise in another year or two. This was the easiest of pieces to sell as a gift item in 1992. Get this piece and display her with the '93 L.E. figurine 523593. She's so pretty and I feel she's a must for your collection.

Personal Data: _____
___Want Mark ___ Mark ___ Purch. 19__ Pd $ _____

526193   **Girl Golfer**
"You Suit Me To A Tee"

TRP	$40	H	$35
S	$35		

Comments: 1993; Original Retail $35.00

Personal Data: _____
___Want Mark ___ Mark ___ Purch. 19__ Pd $ _____

526487 **Boy with Box of Valentine Candy**
"Sharing Sweet Moments Together"

B	$55	S	$45
TRP	$45	H	$45

Comments: 1993; Original Retail $45.00

Personal Data: _____
___Want Mark ___ Mark ___ Purch. 19__ Pd $ _____

526568 **Welcome Home - Navy**
"Bless Those Who Serve Their Country"

SUSP. 1992 - 4 YEARS AGO FLG $115 FLG★ $115

Comments: 1990; Original Retail $32.50
Pieces were abundant when produced in 1991. The sailor is the most sought after.

Personal Data: _____
___Want Mark ___ Mark ___ Purch. 19__ Pd $ _____

526576 **Welcome Home - Army**
"Bless Those Who Serve Their Country"

SUSP. 1992 - 4 YEARS AGO FLG $48 FLG★ $48

Comments: 1990; Original Retail $32.50

Personal Data: _____
___Want Mark ___ Mark ___ Purch. 19__ Pd $ _____

526584 **Welcome Home - Air Force**
"Bless Those Who Serve Their Country"

SUSP. 1992 - 4 YEARS AGO FLG $48 FLG★ $48

Comments: 1990; Original Retail $32.50.

Personal Data: _____
___Want Mark ___ Mark ___ Purch. 19__ Pd $ _____

526827 **EASTER SEALS - Girl with Piggy Bank/Coin**
"You Can Always Count On Me"

H Current

Comments: 1995; Original Retail $30.00

Personal Data: _____
___Want Mark ___ Mark ___ Purch. 19__ Pd $ _____

526835 **Praying Angel**
"The Lord Is With You"

S $27.50 H Current

Comments: 1995; Original Retail $27.50.

Personal Data: _____
___Want Mark ___ Mark ___ Purch. 19__ Pd $ _____

526886 **9" EASTER SEALS -**
Angel with World in Hands
"He's Got The Whole World In His Hands"

LE 1995 - ONE YEAR AGO S $550-600 H $500

Comments: 1994; 9" Easter Seals Commemorative Figurine for 1995 Limited to 2,000 Numbered Pieces. **See #25, page XIV.**

Personal Data: _____
___Want Mark ___ Mark ___ Purch. 19__ Pd $ _____

526916 ♪ **MUSICAL - Girl by Wishing Well**
"Wishing You Were Here"

GC	$125	TRP	$110	H	$100
B	$115	S	$100		

Comments: 1992; Original Retail $100.00
Plays *When You Wish Upon A Star*. This is a large piece. Nice... not overproduced due to size. Since this has a higher retail price, retailers order less, thus not a big production is required for retailer demand. It is likely that this piece will be suspended. I feel she is different from the norm and a nice piece for you to include in your collection, if affordable for you. Place on bottom shelf in your cabinet with glass shelves.

Personal Data: _____
___Want Mark ___ Mark ___ Purch. 19__ Pd $ _____

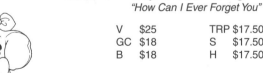

526924 **Elephant with String Around Trunk**
"How Can I Ever Forget You"

V	$25	TRP	$17.50
GC	$18	S	$17.50
B	$18	H	$17.50

Comments: 1990; Original Retail $15.00/$17.50
Addition to *Birthday Series*. Retail price increased in 1995 and 1996.

Personal Data: _____
___Want Mark ___ Mark ___ Purch. 19__ Pd $ _____

526940   *BALL ORNAMENT* - Girl with Bird
"May Your Christmas Be Merry"

DATED 1991   V $37.50

Comments: 1990; Original Retail $30.00
Not a lot of trading found on this piece. Date reported missing, even upside down.

Personal Data: _____
____Want Mark _____ Mark _____ Purch. 19__ Pd $ _____

526959   *NATIVITY* - Three Penguin Kings
"We Have Come From Afar"

SUSP. 1994 - 2 YEARS AGO	V	$28	TRP	$20
	GC	$25	B	$22

Comments: 1990; Original Retail $17.50
Addition to Nativity.

Personal Data: _____
____Want Mark _____ Mark _____ Purch. 19__ Pd $ _____

527084   *ORNAMENT* - Boy with Drum
"Baby's First Christmas"

DATED 1991   V $25

Comments: 1990; Original Retail $15.00
Cute ornament!

Personal Data: _____
____Want Mark _____ Mark _____ Purch. 19__ Pd $ _____

527092   *ORNAMENT* - Girl with Drum
"Baby's First Christmas"

DATED 1991   V $25

Comments: 1990; Original Retail $15.00

Personal Data: _____
____Want Mark _____ Mark _____ Purch. 19__ Pd $ _____

527106   *CHAPEL EXCLUSIVE* - Angel by the Cave
"He Is Not Here For He Is Risen As He Said"

Error: *Math.* corrected to *Matt.* June of '94

NM - Matt - $95
NM - Math. - $100
TRP - Matt - $60

Comments: 1993; Original Retail $60.00
Available exclusively through the Precious Moments® Chapel. When you visit the Chapel, look for the angel by the "real" cave entrance.

Personal Data: _____
____Want Mark _____ Mark _____ Purch. 19__ Pd $ _____

527114   *EASTER SEALS* - Girl with Blue Bird
"Sharing A Gift Of Love"

LE 1991- 5 YEARS OLD	FLM	$55
	V	$45

Comments: 1990; Original Retail $30.00
1991 Easter Seals Commemorative Figurine.

Personal Data: _____
____Want Mark _____ Mark _____ Purch. 19__ Pd $ _____

527122   **Girl with Puppy in Blanket**
"You Can Always Bring A Friend"

LE 1991 - 5 YEARS OLD	FLM	$60
	V	$55

Comments: 1990; Original Retail $27.50
1991 Main Event Figurine. Has been found with FL mark.

Personal Data: _____
____Want Mark _____ Mark _____ Purch. 19__ Pd $ _____

527165   *ORNAMENT* - Expectant Mother
"The Good Lord Always Delivers"

SUSP. 1993 - 3 YEARS AGO	V	$22
	GC	$20
	B	$20

Comments: 1990; Original Retail $15.00
Not sought after.

Personal Data: _____
____Want Mark _____ Mark _____ Purch. 19__ Pd $ _____

527173   ***EASTER SEALS* - Girl Signing "I Love You"**
"A Universal Love"

LE 1992 - 4 YEARS OLD   V $95
                              GC $85

Comments: 1990; Original Retail $32.50
1992 Limited Edition Commemorative Easter Seals Figurine. Easter Seals pieces quite abundant, but this piece is very, very sought after.

Personal Data: _____
____Want Mark ____ Mark _____ Purch. 19__ Pd $ _____

527211   ***ORNAMENT* - Girl Carrying Candle**
"Share In The Warmth Of Christmas"

B $20   S $17
TRP $18   H $17

Comments: 1992; Original Retail $15.00/$17.00
Retail price increased in 1995.

Personal Data: _____
____Want Mark ____ Mark _____ Purch. 19__ Pd $ _____

527238   **Baby Speaking into Microphone**
"Baby's First Word"

MM $40   GC $25   TRP $25
B $30   S $25   H $25

Comments: 1992; Original Retail $25.00
1992 Addition to *Baby's First Series*. Found with MM.

Personal Data: _____
____Want Mark ____ Mark _____ Purch. 19__ Pd $ _____

527270   **Two Dogs Hugging**
"Let's Be Friends"

V $25   TRP $17.50
GC $18   S $17.50
B $17.50   H $17.50

Comments: 1990; Original Retail $15.00/$17.00
Part of *Birthday Series*. Retail price increase in 1995.

Personal Data: _____
____Want Mark ____ Mark _____ Purch. 19__ Pd $ _____

527289   **Welcome Home - Girl Soldier**
"Bless Those Who Serve Their Country"

SUSP. 1992 - 4 YEARS AGO   FLG $50   FLG★ $50

Comments: 1990; Original Retail $32.50
Has been found with blue emblem or white emblem on her hat. Soldier figurines not as plentiful since suspended.

Personal Data: _____
____Want Mark ____ Mark _____ Purch. 19__ Pd $ _____

527297   **Welcome Home - Black Soldier**
"Bless Those Who Serve Their Country"

SUSP. 1992 - 4 YEARS AGO   FLG $48   FLG★ $48

Comments: 1990; Original Retail $32.50
We have heard many reports that this African-American man's hand is not painted to match his face color (the hand was left unpainted). Display these military pieces with a small flag as the background or with red, white and blue carnations. May be found for less if you search.

Personal Data: _____
____Want Mark ____ Mark _____ Purch. 19__ Pd $ _____

527319   **Girl Wading with Duck**
"An Event Worth Wading For"

V $45
GC $40

Comments: 1990; Original Retail $32.50
1992 Special Event piece. Usually first marks are only found at early events until around May or June. Easily found at these prices.

Personal Data: _____
____Want Mark ____ Mark _____ Purch. 19__ Pd $ _____

*Joseph's tomb was not a tomb at all -
it was just a stopping place for Christ
on his way to heaven.*

527327 **_ORNAMENT_ - Soldier**
"Onward Christmas Soldiers"

TRP $22	S $18	H $16

Comments: 1993; Original Retail $16.00

Personal Data: _____
____Want Mark ____ Mark _____ Purch. 19__ Pd $ _____

527335 **Indian Girl with Tulip**
"Bless-um You"

GC $45	TRP $35	H $35
B $42	S $35	

Comments: 1992; Original Retail $35.00
This piece has been found with a GC and a B mark, one on top of the other! Add $100 to GC mark. Another collector found that one of the hearts on the headband was not painted - add $25.

Personal Data: _____
____Want Mark ____ Mark _____ Purch. 19__ Pd $ _____

527343 **Chicken Blowing out Birthday Candle**
"Happy Birdie"

GC $24	TRP $17.50	H $17.50
B $17.50	S $17.50	

Comments: 1992; Original Retail $16.00/$17.50
1992 Addition to *Birthday Series.* Retail price increased in 1995 and 1996.

Personal Data: _____
____Want Mark ____ Mark _____ Purch. 19__ Pd $ _____

527378 **Girl Decorating Boy**
"You Are My Favorite Star"

GC $75	TRP $62	H $60
B $60-65	S $60	

Comments: 1992; Original Retail $60.00
A collector has this piece without the "PM" logo.

Personal Data: _____
____Want Mark ____ Mark _____ Purch. 19__ Pd $ _____

527386 **Columbus in Ship**
"This Land Is Our Land"

LE 1992 - 4 YEARS OLD   V $350-$425
GC $350-$400

Comments: 1990; Original Retail $350.00
Commemorative. State tax would have been at least $15 to $25. Many hats lost the paint; it was rubbed or chipped off in shipping. It's my opinion that 15,000 - 20,000 were produced... no higher than 30,000 or 35,000. Just my guess... The redemption period for this piece was "extended." I feel it will be several years before any significant secondary market increase is noticed. Probably available for $350 or less if you seek out ads, etc.

Personal Data: _____
____Want Mark ____ Mark _____ Purch. 19__ Pd $ _____

527475 **_ORNAMENT_ - Baby Girl on Candy Cane**
"Baby's First Christmas"

DATED 1992   GC $22

Comments: 1992; Original Retail $15.00

Personal Data: _____
____Want Mark ____ Mark _____ Purch. 19__ Pd $ _____

527483 **_ORNAMENT_ - Baby Boy on Candy Cane**
"Baby's First Christmas"

DATED 1992   GC $20

Comments: 1992; Original Retail $15.00

Personal Data: _____
____Want Mark ____ Mark _____ Purch. 19__ Pd $ _____

527521 **Welcome Home - Marines**
"Bless Those Who Serve Their Country"

SUSP. 1992 - 4 YEARS AGO   FLG $40-$50   FLG★ $50

Comments: 1990; Original Retail $32.50
Still on retailers' shelves. This has been found with no printing on the bottom.

Personal Data: _____
____Want Mark ____ Mark _____ Purch. 19__ Pd $ _____

527556   **Girl Sharing Wordless Book with Two Children**

"Bring The Little Ones To Jesus"

V	$120	TRP	$90
GC	$100	S	$90
B	$95	H	$90

Comments: 1990; Original Retail $90.00
First in a Series of figurines to benefit Child Evangelism Fellowship (CEF), an international, interdenominational group which works with children. See Vol. 9, #3, page 20 of *Precious Collectibles*™ for the story of this figurine. The Damien-Dutton figurine rose higher on the secondary market due to a special offering directly from the Society and was available for a limited production year.

Personal Data: _____
____ Want Mark ____ Mark _____ Purch. 19__ Pd $ _____

527564   **Uncle Sam Kneeling**

"God Bless The USA"

LE 1992 - 4 YEARS OLD

		V	$35
		GC	$32.50

Comments: 1990; Original Retail $32.50
1992 National Day of Prayer Figurine. Display with military pieces. Sam presented President Bush with a similar figurine. (Many "sales" below $35 found on V mark).

Personal Data: _____
____ Want Mark ____ Mark _____ Purch. 19__ Pd $ _____

Sam Butcher presented a special 9" Uncle Sam figurine to President Bush during the National Prayer Day observance at the White House in 1992. Pictured left to right: James D. Ford, chaplain for the House of Representatives; Barbara Bush; President Bush; Vonette Bright, chairman of National Prayer Day; entertainer Pat Boone; and Sam. Sam said the experience "was one of the most thrilling highlights of my life."

527580   **Girl Wrapped with Ribbon**

"Tied Up For The Holidays"

B	$48	S	$40
TRP	$42	H	$40

Comments: 1992; Original Retail $40.00

Personal Data: _____
____ Want Mark ____ Mark _____ Purch. 19__ Pd $ _____

527599   **Boy on Sled with Turtle**

"Bringing You A Merry Christmas"

RETIRED 1995 – ONE YEAR AGO

B	$110 up	S	$85
TRP	$95		

Comments: 1992; Original Retail $45.00
Retired late 1995 - Value could go up 5-10%

Personal Data: _____
____ Want Mark ____ Mark _____ Purch. 19__ Pd $ _____

527629   **Boy in Santa Suit**

"Wishing You A Ho Ho Ho"

GC	$55	S	$40
B	$45	H	$40
TRP	$45		

Comments: 1992; Original Retail $40.00
Christmas pieces not found at shows, etc., as much as the regular line.

Personal Data _____
____ Want Mark ____ Mark _____ Purch. 19__ Pd $ _____

527661   **Girl with String of Hearts**

"You Have Touched So Many Hearts"

V	$38-42	TRP	$37.50
GC	$37.50	S	$37.50
B	$37.50	H	$37.50

Comments: 1982; Original Retail $35.00/$37.50
Identical to E-2821, except this figurine comes with letters to personalize the hearts. That piece will surely be suspended! The letters just did not produce quality results, in my opinion... at least not on my piece. ®
(Looks almost as bad as "my painted" piece I painted in the Orient! Skill is definitely required to paint these li'l figurines! I probably would be fired the first day!) Retail price increase in 1995. This is probably a very good piece that retails well for gift sales.

Personal Data _____
____ Want Mark ____ Mark _____ Purch. 19__ Pd $ _____

527688   **Girl Holding Christmas List**
"But The Greatest Of These Is Love"

DATED 1992   GC $30
                           MM $35

Comments: 1992; Original Retail $27.50
1992 Dated Figurine. This has been found without the inspiration decal on the bottom; also found with a MM. Easily found at these prices.

Personal Data_____
___Want Mark ____ Mark _____ Purch. 19__ Pd $ _____

527696   **ORNAMENT - Girl Holding Christmas List**
"But The Greatest Of These Is Love"

DATED 1992   GC $32.50

Comments: 1992; Original Retail $15.00
Found without the inspiration decal on the bottom.

Personal Data_____
___Want Mark ____ Mark _____ Purch. 19__ Pd $ _____

527718   **THIMBLE - Girl Holding Christmas List**
"But The Greatest Of These Is Love"

DATED 1992   GC $20

Comments: 1992; Original Retail $8.00

Personal Data: _____
___Want Mark ____ Mark _____ Purch. 19__ Pd $ _____

527726   **BELL - Girl Holding Christmas List**
"But The Greatest Of These Is Love"

DATED 1992   GC $25

Comments: 1992; Original Retail $25.00
Has been found without a mark.

Personal Data: _____
___Want Mark ____ Mark _____ Purch. 19__ Pd $ _____

527734   **BALL ORNAMENT - Girl Holding Christmas List**
"But The Greatest Of These Is Love"

DATED 1992   GC $37.50

Comments: 1992; Original Retail $30.00
Ball ornaments are beautiful but not popular or sought after.

Personal Data: _____
___Want Mark ____ Mark _____ Purch. 19__ Pd $ _____

527742   **PLATE - Girl Holding Christmas List**
"But The Greatest Of These Is Love"

DATED 1992   GC $50

Comments: 1992; Original Retail $50.00

Personal Data: _____
___Want Mark ____ Mark _____ Purch. 19__ Pd $ _____

527750   **NATIVITY - Angel Holding a Blanket**
"Wishing You A Comfy Christmas"

GC $40   TRP $30   H $30
B $30   S $30

Comments: 1992; Original Retail $27.50/$30.00
This is an addition to the Nativity set. Retail price increased in 1995. A fun gift for children who love their blankets.

Personal Data: _____
___Want Mark ____ Mark _____ Purch. 19__ Pd $ _____

527769   **Octopus Holding Fish**
"I Only Have Arms For You"

GC $22.50   TRP $17.50   H $17.50
B $17   S $17.50

Comments: 1992; Original Retail $15.00/$17.50
This is an addition to the *Birthday Series*. Retail price increased in 1995 and 1996.

Personal Data: _____
___Want Mark ____ Mark _____ Purch. 19__ Pd $ _____

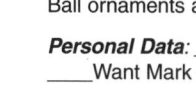

527777   **Columbus with Flag and Bear**
"This Land Is Our Land"

LE 1992 - 4 YEARS OLD   GC $40

Comments: 1990; Original Retail $35.00
Seemed to be a slow seller. Commemorative pieces have always seemed to be overproduced, probably due to retailers' orders.

Personal Data: _____
___Want Mark ____ Mark _____ Purch. 19__ Pd $ _____

If you see a friend without a smile, please give him one of yours.

Wintertime at the Chapel

Remember When

"This is the most important work of my life."

Clubs

VARIATIONS

1. One type of error collectors are interested in is that of a piece missing a visible decal. (See #2.)
2. The Angel holding the Ten Commandments, *The Greatest of These Is Love.* Compare this piece to #1 which is missing the "Crayons" decal on the pocket.
3. Tippy is missing his name decal on the *Puppy Love* figurine on the left
4. Dr. Sam Sugar (the doctor who delivered Sam Butcher) signed these two *Sugar Town* pieces for Millie Carey.
5. Figurines licensed by the Jonathan & David Company were produced with smaller heads than later figurines licensed by the Samuel J. Butcher Company. Notice the difference in the appearance of these *God Is Love* figurines.
6. This picture of six "fake" Precious Moments figurines was sent to us by Helen Starling.
7. The oldest Precious Moments boxes were plain brown cardboard with a simple paper label. This is a box for the coveted "Free Puppies" figurine.
8. The artwork of *But Love Goes On Forever* was produced as a figurine and a night light as well as Membership Plaques and Club Welcome Gift.
9. The 9" version of *Many Moons In Same Canoe, Bless-um You* appears in Precious Moments Chapel display *Will You Be Ready When Jesus Comes?*.
10. Here we have a frowning *Faith Takes the Plunge* as well as the smiling version.
11. Are they triplets? No, it's just three of *Nobody's Perfect*, otherwise known as Smiley the Dunce. There were two versions produced, one with a smile and one with a frown.
12. Compare this and #13 and you will see the paint variations can often occur. This can happen because of more than one factory being used to produce Precious Moments pieces.
13. See #12
14. E-1373 *Smile, God Loves You* has been found with a brown "black eye" as shown. There is no significance of the brown eye versus the black eye.
15. Some of the puppies on the *The Good Lord Has Blessed Us Tenfold* have unpainted eyes.
16. Notice two different inspirations on the bottom.
17. Exciting errors occasionally surface in the Precious Moments collection. The *Friendship Hits The Spot* figurine on the right is missing the table!
18. Notice the two "fake" clowns to the right of the real "thing."
19. Notice the lighter color of the figurine *Blessed Are the Peacemakers* on the right. The "Puppy" decal is also missing from the dog's dish.
20. Notice the differences between these two Birthday Train bears.
21. *I Believe In Miracles* was suspended, then reissued. The reissued figurine is pictured on the left.

The Fountain of Angels

*P*recious Moments® artist Sam Butcher stands in the midst of his fountain angels. These angels will be part of the 120, four foot angels that will make up the large fountain currently being constructed at the Chapel. These statues were cast in Thailand. This fountain, entitled *Fountain of Angels*, may be completed in 1997. In addition to the fountain, an RV park, a lake, a Victorian Home Bed & Breakfast, a restaurant and a hotel are still currently under construction.

Photo and information provided by Ron Graber of the Carthage Press

*T*he mini angel fountain at the entrance of the Chapel Complex continues to run all winter through.

Photo by Jeannie Joeseph

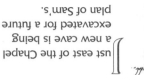

Just east of the Chapel a new cave is being excavated for a future plan of Sam's.

Although it's just bricks and mortar right now, Sam requested a heart shaped formation be built in front of the Chapel. A new flower garden, perhaps?

Uh, oh, the ice rink melted!

Photos by Jeannie Joseph and Ron Graber (Winter of '95)

Construction at The Chapel Spring 1996

528021   ***CHAPEL EXCLUSIVE - ORNAMENT***
Timmy at Chapel
"There's A Christian Welcome Here"

NM	$35	TRP	$22.50	H	$22.50
B	$25	S	$22.50		

Comments: 1992; Original Retail $22.50
Available only at the Chapel... very attractive ornament. I suggest you get one!

Personal Data: _____
____Want Mark ____ Mark _____ Purch. 19__ Pd $ _____

528072   ***NATIVITY*** **- Cart with Chicken**
"Nativity Cart"

TRP	$20	S	$18.50	H	$18.50

Comments: 1993; Original Retail $18.50
Nativity Addition.

Personal Data: _____
____Want Mark ____ Mark _____ Purch. 19__ Pd $ _____

528080   **Girl with Signboard on Back**
"Follow Your Heart"

LE 1995 - ONE YEAR OLD	TRP	$40
	S	$35

Comments: 1994; Original Retail $30.00
1995 Special Event figurine. Collector reports decal on backwards. Increase $100 for this error.

Personal Data: _____
____Want Mark ____ Mark _____ Purch. 19__ Pd $ _____

*"Papa, are you growing taller all the
time?" "No, my child, Why do you ask?"
" 'Cause the top of your head is poking
up through your hair!"*

528137   ***MINI NATIVITY*** **- African-American Boy/Scroll**
"Have I Got News For You"

TRP	$20	H	$17
S	$17		

Comments: 1994; Original Retail $16.00/$17.00
Mini Nativity addition. Retail price increased in 1995.
Collector reported decal on backwards; increase $100 for this error.

Personal Data: _____
____Want Mark ____ Mark _____ Purch. 19__ Pd $ _____

528218   ***ORNAMENT*** **- Girl Angel with Basket**
"Sending You A White Christmas"

TRP	$21	H	$16
S	$16		

Comments: 1994; Original Retail $16.00

Personal Data: _____
____Want Mark ____ Mark _____ Purch. 19__ Pd $ _____

528226   ***ORNAMENT*** **- Boy in Santa Suit**
"Bringing You A Merry Christmas"

TRP	$21	H	$16
S	$16		

Comments: 1993; Original Retail $16.00

Personal Data: _____
____Want Mark ____ Mark _____ Purch. 19__ Pd $ _____

528609   **Girl with Kite and Kitten**
"Sending My Love Your Way"

LE 1995 – ONE YEAR OLD	TRP	$45
	S	$40

Comments: 1994; Original Retail $40.00
Available only at DSR (Distinguished Service Retailers) shops for Enesco special catalog promotion. Has been reported missing the kitten and kite strings, and the stripes not painted on the kite.

Personal Data: _____
____Want Mark ____ Mark _____ Purch. 19__ Pd $ _____

528617   ***EASTER EGG* - Girl Looking at Goose**
"Make A Joyful Noise"

DATED 1993   GC $35   B $30

Comments: 1992; Original Retail $27.50

Personal Data: _____
____Want Mark _____ Mark _____ Purch. 19__ Pd $ _____

528633   **Two Girls with Kittens and Gifts**
"To A Very Special Sister"

TRP $70   H $60
S $65

Comments: 1993; Original Retail $60.00

Personal Data: _____
____Want Mark _____ Mark _____ Purch. 19__ Pd $ _____

528846   ***ORNAMENT* - Boy on Skis**
"It's So Uplifting To Have A Friend Like You"

B $22.50   S $18
TRP $18   H $17

Comments: 1992; Original Retail $16.00/$17.00
Retail price increased in 1995.

Personal Data: _____
____Want Mark _____ Mark _____ Purch. 19__ Pd $ _____

528862   **Girl Holding Up a Torch**
"America, You're Beautiful"

LE 1993 - 3 YEARS OLD   GC $50   B $45

Comments: 1992; Original Retail $35.00
1993 National Day of Prayer Figurine.

Personal Data: _____
____Want Mark _____ Mark _____ Purch. 19__ Pd $ _____

America is a great country -
if you can't make it in the rat race,
they give you free cheese.

528870   ***ORNAMENT* - Bride w/Groom in Top Hat**
"Our First Christmas Together"

DATED 1992   GC $22.50

Comments: 1992; Original Retail $17.50
Except for the date, this design is identical to the 1991 ornament.
See #28, page XIV.

Personal Data: _____
____Want Mark _____ Mark _____ Purch. 19__ Pd $ _____

529095   ***EASTER EGG* - Girl at Birdbath**
"A Reflection Of His Love"

DATED 1994   B $32.50   TRP $30

Comments: 1993; Original Retail $27.50

Personal Data: _____
____Want Mark _____ Mark _____ Purch. 19__ Pd $ _____

529206   ***ORNAMENT* - Boy/Girl Riding Reindeer**
"Our First Christmas Together"

DATED 1994   TRP $22.50

Comments: 1993; Original Retail $18.50

Personal Data: _____
____Want Mark _____ Mark _____ Purch. 19__ Pd $ _____

529648   ***ORNAMENT* - Girl Magician**
"The Magic Starts With You"

LE 1992 - 4 YEARS OLD   GC $22.50

Comments: 1992; Original Retail $16.00
Limited Edition Ornament for Distinguished Service Retailer Open
House Weekend. No demand, abundant.

Personal Data: _____
____Want Mark _____ Mark _____ Purch. 19__ Pd $ _____

Since I have no gold to give,
And love alone must make amends,
My only prayer is, while I live -
God make me worthy of my friends.
Frank Dempster Sherman

529680   *9" EASTER SEALS -*
Girl Holding Bunnies w/Dome
"Gather Your Dreams"

LE 1993 - 3 YEARS OLD   GC $575-600
                               B $550-575

Comments: 1992; Original Retail $500.
1993 9" Easter Seals Commemorative Figurine Limited to 2,000 on numbered pieces. This is shorter than other 9" pieces.

Personal Data: _____
____Want Mark ____ Mark _____ Purch. 19__ Pd $ _____

529931   **Girl Stretching to Touch a Butterfly**
"Happiness Is At Our Fingertips"

LE 1993 - 3 YEARS OLD   GC $75   B $55

Comments: 1992; Original Retail $35.00.
It was originally planned that DSR shops could only order four figurines per every 500 catalogs ordered for a special promotion. (This proved to be untrue in several cases. Extras were ordered - sales were evident at department stores.) Two variations have been reported by a collector; the girl was looking forward and had the GC mark, and on another the girl was looking upward and had the B mark.

Personal Data: _____
____Want Mark ____ Mark _____ Purch. 19__ Pd $ _____

529966   **Girl Ringing Bell**
"Ring Out The Good News"

          B $37.50   S $30
          TRP $32.50   H $30

Comments: 1992; Original Retail $27.50/$30.00
Retail price increased in 1995.

Personal Data: _____
____Want Mark ____ Mark _____ Purch. 19__ Pd $ _____

*Go often to the house of your friends,
for weeds choke up the unused paths.*

529974   *ORNAMENT - Girl in Raincoat with Puppy*
"An Event For All Seasons"

LE 1993 - 3 YEARS OLD   B $25

Comments: 1993; Original Retail $16.00.
This Second Annual Precious Moments Open House Weekend ornament was available on October 9 and 10, 1993, through local Distinguished Service Retailers. Secondary market folks tend to buy extra LEs, etc., and supply the market well. It takes 4 to 5 years to see a big jump on such pieces on the secondary market.

Personal Data: _____
____Want Mark ____ Mark _____ Purch. 19__ Pd $ _____

529982   **Girl Blowing Bubbles**
"Memories Are Made Of This"

LE 1994 - 2 YEARS OLD   B $48   TRP $40

Comments: 1993; Original Retail $30.00
Available exclusively through Distinguished Service Retailers hosting Special Events in 1994. Looks similar to girl with blue bird. Collector reports having kitty with whiskers only on one side.

Personal Data: _____
____Want Mark ____ Mark _____ Purch. 19__ Pd $ _____

530026   *EASTER SEALS* - **Girl Holding Trophy Cup**
"You're My Number One Friend"

LE 1993 - 3 YEARS OLD   GC $45   B $38

Comments: 1992; Original Retail $30.00.
1993 Easter Seals Commemorative Figurine.
A collector found this piece with a TRP signed by Sam. Does anyone else have a TRP?

Personal Data: _____
____Want Mark ____ Mark _____ Purch. 19__ Pd $ _____

530042   *NIGHT LIGHT* - **3 pc. set Noah's Ark**
"Two By Two"

          GC $135   TRP $125   H $125
          B $125   S $125

Comments: 1992; Original Retail $125.00
Two By Two Series. Three-piece set includes the Ark (a night light), Noah and his wife. Animals debut each year for this set. See complete listing in the descriptive index.

Personal Data: _____
____Want Mark ____ Mark _____ Purch. 19__ Pd $ _____

530077 **Noah's Ark**
"Sheep"

B $15   S $10
TRP $10   H $10

Comments: 1992; Original Retail $10.00
Part of *Two By Two Series.*

Personal Data: _____
____Want Mark ____ Mark _____ Purch. 19__ Pd $ _____

530085 **Noah's Ark**
"Pigs"

B $16   S $12
TRP $12   H $12

Comments: 1992; Original Retail $12.00
Part of *Two By Two Series.*

Personal Data: _____
____Want Mark ____ Mark _____ Purch. 19__ Pd $ _____

530115 **Noah's Ark**
"Giraffes"

B $20   S $16
TRP $16   H $16

Comments: 1992; Original Retail $16.00
Part of *Two By Two Series.* Giraffes are collected by many.

Personal Data: _____
____Want Mark ____ Mark _____ Purch. 19__ Pd $ _____

530123 **Noah's Ark**
"Bunnies"

B $12   S $9
TRP $9   H $9

Comments: 1992; Original Retail $9.00
Part of *Two By Two Series.*

Personal Data: _____
____Want Mark ____ Mark _____ Purch. 19__ Pd $ _____

530131 **Noah's Ark**
"Elephants"

B $22   S $18
TRP $18   H $18

Comments: 1992; Original Retail $18.00
Part of *Two By Two Series.*

Personal Data: _____
____Want Mark ____ Mark _____ Purch. 19__ Pd $ _____

530158 **Girl in Raincoat Holding Puppy**
"An Event For All Seasons"

GC $55   B $50

Comments: 1992; Original Retail $30.00
1993 "Main Event" Figurine.   Pretty piece.

Personal Data: _____
____Want Mark ____ Mark _____ Purch. 19__ Pd $ _____

530166 **Girl with Gingerbread Cookie**
"Wishing You The Sweetest Christmas"

DATED 1993   B $40

Comments: 1992; Original Retail $27.50
Recent dated pieces usually have not increased in value for 3-5 years.

Personal Data: _____
____Want Mark ____ Mark _____ Purch. 19__ Pd $ _____

530174 ***BELL* - Girl w/ Gingerbread Cookie**
"Wishing You The Sweetest Christmas"

DATED 1993   B $35

Comments: 1992; Original Retail $25.00
Last in series for this style of bell.

Personal Data: _____
____Want Mark ____ Mark _____ Purch. 19__ Pd $ _____

530182 **THIMBLE** - Girl w/ Gingerbread Cookie
"Wishing You The Sweetest Christmas"

DATED 1993   B $15

Comments: 1992; Original Retail $8.00
Last in series.

Personal Data: _____
____Want Mark ____ Mark _____ Purch. 19__ Pd $ _____

530190 **ORNAMENT** - Girl w/Gingerbread Cookie
Round Porcelain Ball/Stand
"Wishing You The Sweetest Christmas"

DATED 1993   B $35

Comments: 1992; Original Retail $30.00
Bas Relief Ornament. Many sales found below original retail.

Personal Data: _____
____Want Mark ____ Mark _____ Purch. 19__ Pd $ _____

530204 **PLATE** - Girl w/ Gingerbread Cookie
"Wishing You The Sweetest Christmas"

DATED 1993   B $55

Comments: 1992; Original Retail $50.00
Somewhat more popular than other recent dated plates, but will not increase on secondary market any faster than others.

Personal Data: _____
____Want Mark ____ Mark _____ Purch. 19__ Pd $ _____

530212 **ORNAMENT** - Girl w/Gingerbread Cookie
"Wishing You The Sweetest Christmas"

DATED 1993   B $32.50

Comments: 1992; Original Retail $15.00
I predicted this could easily be a top retail seller. It received Ornament of the Year award in '94.

Personal Data: _____
____Want Mark ____ Mark _____ Purch. 19__ Pd $ _____

530255 **ORNAMENT** - Baby Girl with Doll
Riding Stick Horse
"Baby's First Christmas"

DATED 1994   TRP $18

Comments: 1992; Original Retail $16.00

Personal Data: _____
____Want Mark ____ Mark _____ Purch. 19__ Pd $ _____

530263 **ORNAMENT** - Baby Boy with Toy Bear
Riding Stick Horse
"Baby's First Christmas"

DATED 1994   TRP $18

Comments: 1993; Original Retail $16.00

Personal Data: _____
____Want Mark ____ Mark _____ Purch. 19__ Pd $ _____

530387 **ORNAMENT** - Round Porcelain Ball/Stand
Girl in Christmas Tree Dress
"You're As Pretty As A Christmas Tree"

DATED 1994   TRP $35

Comments: 1993; Original Retail $30.00

Personal Data: _____
____Want Mark ____ Mark _____ Purch. 19__ Pd $ _____

530395 **ORNAMENT** - Girl in Christmas Tree Dress
"You're As Pretty As A Christmas Tree"

DATED 1994   TRP $25

Comments: 1993; Original Retail $16.00
More scarce than some past years' dated ornaments.

Personal Data: _____
____Want Mark ____ Mark _____ Purch. 19__ Pd $ _____

530409   *PLATE* - **Girl in Christmas Tree Dress**
"You're As Pretty As A Christmas Tree"

DATED 1994   TRP $50

Comments: 1993; Original Retail $50.00

Personal Data: _____
____Want Mark ____ Mark _____ Purch. 19___ Pd $ _____

530425   **Girl in Christmas Tree Dress**
"You're As Pretty As A Christmas Tree"

DATED 1994   TRP $35

Comments: 1993; Original Retail $27.50
It is likely that she may be found without the year decal on her star. If so, add $50 for this error. **See #15, page XIII.**

Personal Data: _____
____Want Mark ____ Mark _____ Purch. 19___ Pd $ _____

530492   **Elephant with Gift "To Jesus"**
"Happy Birthday Jesus"

     B $25   S $20
     TRP $22   H $20

Comments: 1992; Original Retail $20.00

Personal Data: _____
____Want Mark ____ Mark _____ Purch. 19___ Pd $ _____

530506   *ORNAMENT* - **Boy and Girl in Sleigh**
"Our First Christmas Together"

DATED 1993   B $25

Comments: 1992; Original Retail $17.50
Report of missing decal on side of sleigh. Add $50 to secondary market value.

Personal Data: _____
____Want Mark ____ Mark _____ Purch. 19___ Pd $ _____

*The trouble with marriage is that a fellow can't support a wife
and the government on one income.*

530697   **Girl Kneeling by Plaque**
"Serenity Prayer Girl"

     B $42.50   S $37.50
     TRP $37.50   H $37.50

Comments: 1993; Original Retail $35.00/$37.50
Still "Plentiful!" Retailers report that girls have been shipped in boys' boxes. Reported PMI (Precious Moments® Incorporated) on base. Price increase in '96.

Personal Data: _____
____Want Mark ____ Mark _____ Purch. 19___ Pd $ _____

530700   **Boy Kneeling by Plaque**
"Serenity Prayer Boy"

     B $42.50   S $37.50
     TRP $37.50   H $37.50

Comments: 1993; Original Retail $35.00/$37.50
Retail price increase in 1996.

Personal Data: _____
____Want Mark ____ Mark _____ Purch. 19___ Pd $ _____

530786   **Angel Directing Choir of Bluebirds**
"15 Happy Years Together - What A Tweet!"

LE 1993 - 3 YEARS OLD   GC $127.50   B $105

Comments: 1992; Original Retail $100.00
1993 Commemorative Figurine - Limited to 1993 production year. Easily found at these prices for now.

Personal Data: _____
____Want Mark ____ Mark _____ Purch. 19___ Pd $ _____

530840   *ORNAMENT* - **Angel w/Music and Bluebird**
"15 Years - Tweet Music Together"

LE 1993 - 3 YEARS OLD   GC $27   B $25

Comments: 1992; Original Retail $15.00.
1993 Commemorative Ornament - Limited to 1993 production year. Debuted in July 1993.

Personal Data: _____
____Want Mark ____ Mark _____ Purch. 19___ Pd $ _____

*In this confused world, some people have peace
while others go to pieces.*

● ●

530859   **_ORNAMENT_ - Baby Boy**
"Baby's First Christmas"

DATED 1993   B $22.50

Comments: 1992; Original Retail $15.00
Has been reported missing the decal.

Personal Data: _____
____Want Mark ____ Mark _____ Purch. 19__ Pd $ _____

530867   **_ORNAMENT_ - Baby Girl**
"Baby's First Christmas"

DATED 1993   B $22.50

Comments: 1992; Original Retail $15.00

Personal Data: _____
____Want Mark ____ Mark _____ Purch. 19__ Pd $ _____

530913   **_MINI NATIVITY_ - Penguins as Three Kings**
"We Have Come From Afar"

S $12.50   H   Current

Comments: 1995; Original Retail $12.00
Addition to Mini Nativity.

Personal Data: _____
____Want Mark ____ Mark _____ Purch. 19__ Pd $ _____

530948   **Noah's Ark**
           8 - Piece Collector's Set

B $205   S $190
TRP $190   H $190

Comments: 1992; Original Retail $190.00
Part of _Two By Two Series._ I do not expect "sets" to make history any
time soon on the sec. mkt. unless they're retired. The added 1995 animals were zebras (127809) and the 1996 animals are goats (163694).
1995 and 1996 saw other companies also debuting their Noah's Ark collectibles.

Personal Data: _____
____Want Mark ____ Mark _____ Purch. 19__ Pd $ _____

See Entries
530042-530131

It is Christmas in the heart that puts Christmas in the air.

530956   **_Boy and Girl Seated on Ice Block_**
"I Only Have Ice For You"

S $60   H   Current

Comments: 1995; Original Retail $55.00

Personal Data: _____
____Want Mark ____ Mark _____ Purch. 19__ Pd $ _____

530972   **_ORNAMENT_ - Bear in Heart**
"You Are Always In My Heart"

DATED 1994   TRP $20

Comments: 1993; Original Retail $16.00
Birthday Series ornament.

Personal Data: _____
____Want Mark ____ Mark _____ Purch. 19__ Pd $ _____

530999   **Girl Pointing to Ring on Finger**
"I Still Do"

B $38   S $30
TRP $32   H $30

Comments: 1993; Original Retail $30.00

Personal Data: _____
____Want Mark ____ Mark _____ Purch. 19__ Pd $ _____

_Amy Carpio from Jonesburg, MO, said that
this Christmas was the first time she was
truly able to enjoy her collection. Amy's
collection was selected as
Precious Collectibles™ January 1996
Collection of the Month. Amy is pictured here
with her neice, Ashley._

531006   Boy Pointing to Ring on Finger
"I Still Do"

B	$35	S	$30
TRP	$32	H	$30

Comments: 1993; Original Retail $30.00

Personal Data: _____
____Want Mark ____ Mark _____ Purch. 19__ Pd $ _____

531057   Dog with Hair Covering Eyes
"I Haven't Seen Much of You Lately"

S	$13.50	H	Current

Comments: 1995; Original Retail $13.50
Birthday Series addition.

Personal Data: _____
____Want Mark ____ Mark _____ Purch. 19__ Pd $ _____

531065   Angel Opening Up a Globe Full of Hearts
"What The World Needs Is Love"

TRP	$55	H	$45
S	$45		

Comments: 1994; Original Retail $45.00

Personal Data: _____
____Want Mark ____ Mark _____ Purch. 19__ Pd $ _____

531073   Boy Bandaging Tree
"Money's Not The Only Green Thing Worth Saving"

TRP	$55	S	$50	H	$50

Comments: 1994; Original Retail $50.00
A collector from PA reported she bought this figurine with the cross patch missing on the right arm. Add $100 more when insuring. How about yours?

Personal Data: _____
____Want Mark ____ Mark _____ Purch. 19__ Pd $ _____

531111   *EASTER SEALS* - Girl with Pail of Oysters
"It Is No Secret What God Can Do"

LE 1994 - 2 YEARS OLD

B	$37.50
TRP	$35

Comments: 1993; Original Retail $30.00
1994 Easter Seals Commemorative Figurine.

Personal Data: _____
____Want Mark ____ Mark _____ Purch. 19__ Pd $ _____

531146   Hispanic Girl Holding Rose
"Vaya Con Dios (To Go With God)"

TRP	$38	H	$35
S	$35		

Comments: 1994; Original Retail $32.50/$35.00
This figurine commemorates a young girl's fifteenth birthday. In the Hispanic culture, on her fifteenth birthday, a young lady is honored at a Quinceañera where she wears a lovely dress and receives gifts. This señorita figurine can be compared to the Indian in Canoe figurines with variations of dark hair and light hair. Retail increased in 1996.

Personal Data: _____
____Want Mark ____ Mark _____ Purch. 19__ Pd $ _____

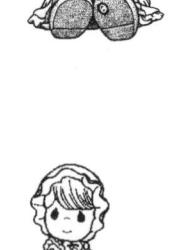

531162   Girl with Hole in Shoe
"Bless Your Sole"
"Bless Your Soul" (error)

TRP	$35	H	Current
S	$30		

Comments: 1995; Original Retail $25.00/$27.50
Enesco introduced this as *"Bless Your Sole."* To date, only *"Bless Your Soul"* has been found.

Personal Data: _____
____Want Mark ____ Mark _____ Purch. 19__ Pd $ _____

531243   *9" EASTER SEALS* - Girl w/Basket of Roses
"You Are The Rose Of His Creation"

LE 1994 - 2 YEARS OLD

		B	$500-550
		TRP	$500

Comments: 1993; 1994 Easter Seals Commemorative "9 figurine. Limited to 2,000 Numbered Pieces. ***See #25, page XIV.***

Personal Data: _____
____Want Mark ____ Mark _____ Purch. 19__ Pd $ _____

531359   *PLATE* - Girl Sharing Wordless Book
"Bring The Little Ones To Jesus"

LE 1994 - 2 YEARS OLD   B $52
                        TRP $50

Comments: 1993; Original Retail $50.00
Limited Edition. Limited to one year of production. Child Evangelism Fellowship plate. ***See #1, page XI.***

Personal Data: _____
____Want Mark ____ Mark _____ Purch. 19__ Pd $ _____

531375   **Noah's Ark**
"Llamas"

TRP $18   H $15
S $15

Comments: 1993; Original Retail $15.00
Part of *Two By Two Series.* ***See #38, page XV.***

Personal Data: _____
____Want Mark ____ Mark _____ Purch. 19__ Pd $ _____

531677   *CHAPEL EXCLUSIVE* - Girl with Wreath
"Surrounded With Joy"

NM $40   S $30
TRP $35   H $30

Comments: 1993; Original Retail $30.00
Available exclusively at the Precious Moments® Chapel. Complements the "Boy with Wreath" figurine (E-0506). Still available as of Jan., 1996.

Personal Data: _____
____Want Mark ____ Mark _____ Purch. 19__ Pd $ _____

531685   *CHAPEL EXCLUSIVE* - ORNAMENT
Girl with Wreath
"Surrounded With Joy"

NM $25   S $17.50
TRP $20   H $17.50

Comments: 1993; Original Retail $17.50
Available exclusively at the Precious Moments® Chapel. Complements the "Boy with Wreath" ornament (E-0513).

Personal Data: _____
____Want Mark ____ Mark _____ Purch. 19__ Pd $ _____

531693   **Angel Places Halo On Little Girl**
"You Deserve A Halo - Thank You"

S $55   H   Current

Comments: 1995; Original Retail $55.00
This reminds me of the new mural at the Chapel where the children are standing in line waiting to receive their halos.

Personal Data: _____
____Want Mark ____ Mark _____ Purch. 19__ Pd $ _____

531707   **Girl with Embroidery Hoop**
"The Lord Is Counting On You"

TRP $40   H $35
S $35

Comments: 1993; Original Retail $32.50/$35.00
Retail up in '96. A collector reported this figurine with the needlework decal upside down. Increase insurance by $100 with this error.

Personal Data: _____
____Want Mark ____ Mark _____ Purch. 19__ Pd $ _____

531766   *PLATE* - Girl Kneeling with Flowers
"Thinking Of You Is What I Really Like To Do"

DATED 1994   B $52
                   TRP $50

Comments: 1993; Original Retail $50.00
First Issue of the *Mother's Day Plate Series.* 8¹/₂" Dia..

Personal Data: _____
____Want Mark ____ Mark _____ Purch. 19__ Pd $ _____

531928   *CHAPEL EXCLUSIVE* -
Angel Looking At Easter Lily
"Death Can't Keep Him In The Ground"

NM $35   S $30
TRP $30   H $30

Comments: 1994; Original Retail $30.00
Available exclusively at the Precious Moments Chapel.

Personal Data: _____
____Want Mark ____ Mark _____ Purch. 19__ Pd $ _____

531952   **Angel In Eggnog Cup**
"Dropping In For The Holidays"

TRP $45   H $40
S $40

Comments: 1994; Original Retail $40.00
Decal found upside down on some pieces. Add $100 to the secondary market value when insuring.
See #15, page XIII.

Personal Data: _____
____Want Mark ____ Mark _____ Purch. 19__ Pd $ _____

532002   **Boy Holding Cross and Lily**
"Hallelujah For The Cross"

TRP $35   H $35
S $35

Comments: 1994; Original Retail $35.00
Cross is yellow instead of gold as shown on prototype. (Gold paint can easily be removed.)

Personal Data: _____
____Want Mark ____ Mark _____ Purch. 19__ Pd $ _____

532010   **Boy Holding Bottle w/ Message**
"Sending You Oceans Of Love"

TRP $40   H $37.50
S $37.50

Comments: 1994; Original Retail $35.00/$37.50
Retail raised in '96.

Personal Data: _____
____Want Mark ____ Mark _____ Purch. 19__ Pd $ _____

532037   **Cowgirl and Bear**
"I Can't Bear To Let You Go"

TRP $55   H $50
S $50

Comments: 1994; Original Retail $50.00

Personal Data: _____
____Want Mark ____ Mark _____ Purch. 19__ Pd $ _____

532088   ***CHAPEL EXCLUSIVE - ORNAMENT***
Baby Jesus in Manger/Altar
"A King Is Born"

RETIRED 1995 - ONE YEAR AGO

NM $27.50   TRP $22.50

Comments: 1994; Original Retail $17.50
Sold out at the Chapel. This ornament is only available on the secondary market now.

Personal Data: _____
____Want Mark ____ Mark _____ Purch. 19__ Pd $ _____

532096   **Boy Golfer**
"Lord Help Me To Stay On Course"

TRP $40   S $38   H $35

Comments: 1994; Original Retail $35.00

Personal Data: _____
____Want Mark ____ Mark _____ Purch. 19__ Pd $ _____

532118   **African-American Bride and Groom**
"The Lord Bless You And Keep You"

B $50   S $50
TRP $50   H $50

Comments: 1993; Original Retail $40.00/$50.00
Retail price increased in 1995 and 1996! Up $10 in two years.

Personal Data: _____
____Want Mark ____ Mark _____ Purch. 19__ Pd $ _____

532126   **African-American Graduate Girl**
"The Lord Bless You And Keep You"

B $40   S $35
TRP $35.50   H $35

Comments: 1993; Original Retail $30.00/$35.00
Retail price increased in 1995 and 1996. Up nearly 17%.

Personal Data: _____
____Want Mark ____ Mark _____ Purch. 19__ Pd $ _____

532134 **African-American Graduate Boy**
"The Lord Bless You And Keep You"

B	$40	S	$35
TRP	$35	H	$35

Comments: 1993; Original Retail $30.00/$35.00
Retail price increased in 1995 and 1996.

Personal Data: _____
____Want Mark ____ Mark _____ Purch. 19__ Pd $ _____

532916 **Shepherd Kneeling by Plaque with Lamb**
"Luke 2:10-11"

TRP	$40	H	$35
S	$35		

Comments: 1993; Original Retail $35.00

Personal Data: _____
____Want Mark ____ Mark _____ Purch. 19__ Pd $ _____

603171 **Angel on Arch**
"Ornament Enhancer"

TRP	$35	H	$30
S	$30		

Comments: 1994; Original Retail $30.00

Personal Data: _____
____Want Mark ____ Mark _____ Purch. 19__ Pd $ _____

603503 *CHAPEL EXCLUSIVE*
Two Angels with Chapel Poem Plaque
"On The Hill Overlooking The Quiet Blue Stream"

NM	$52	S	$45
TRP	$45	H	$45

Comments: 1994; Original Retail $45.00
Available exclusively at the Precious Moments Chapel.

Personal Data: _____
____Want Mark ____ Mark _____ Purch. 19__ Pd $ _____

603864 **Boy and Dog Filling Sandbag**
"Nothing Can Dampen The Spirit Of Caring"

B	$45	S	$35
TRP	$35	H	$35

Comments: 1993; Original Retail $35.00
First Issue in the *Good Samaritan Series*. Dedicated to those who aided Mississippi River flood victims in 1993. Enesco and Sam Butcher have made a donation to these agencies committed to assisting in the flood relief effort. Reportedly missing the turtle; add $100 to the secondary market value when insuring. *See #32, page XIV.*

Personal Data: _____
____Want Mark ____ Mark _____ Purch. 19__ Pd $ _____

604151 *CHAPEL EXCLUSIVE -*
Baby Jesus in Manger/Altar
"A King Is Born"

RETIRED 1995 - ONE YEAR AGO

NM	$35	TRP	$30

Comments: 1994; Original Retail $25.00
Sold out at the Chapel.

Personal Data: _____
____Want Mark ____ Mark _____ Purch. 19__ Pd $ _____

604208 **Girl Holding Flowerpot**
"A Poppy For You"

TRP	$45	H	$35
S	$35		

Comments: 1994; Original Retail $35.00
Debuted in July of 1994. Collectors were first able to order this figurine through the American Legion Auxiliary magazine. It is now available at retailers. The purchase of this figurine generated a donation to the Spirit of Youth, an Auxiliary Foundation.

Personal Data: _____
____Want Mark ____ Mark _____ Purch. 19__ Pd $ _____

604216 *BELL* - **Girl in Christmas Tree Dress**
"You're As Pretty As A Christmas Tree"

DATED 1994   TRP $27.50

Comments: 1993; Original Retail $27.50
It is likely that she may be found without the year decal on her star. If so, add $50 for this error.

Personal Data: _____
____Want Mark ____ Mark _____ Purch. 19__ Pd $ _____

617334 ♪ *ANIMATED MUSICAL*
ANGEL TREE TOPPER
"Rejoice O Earth"

FLM $130

Comments: 1989; Original Retail $125.00
Plays *Hark, The Herald Angels Sing.* Arms and wings move.

Personal Data: _____

___Want Mark ____ Mark _____ Purch. 19__ Pd $ _____

53531634S Girl in High Heels
"Who's Gonna Fill Your Shoes"

H   Current

Comments: 1995; Original Retail $37.50
Parade of Gifts catalog exclusive available at a limited number of select
retail locations. Will have a special understamp, "1996 Catalog."
See #33, page XIV.

Personal Data: _____

___Want Mark ____ Mark _____ Purch. 19__ Pd $ _____

*J*eanne Gabel has been collecting Precious Moments®
figurines since 1989, and her collection has grown to a total
of 417 pieces. "I've been able to share the joy I have gotten
from collecting. I've made many good friends."

Sammy's Circus

*Sammy's Circus is a "backyard circus" inspired by Sam Butcher's
grandchildren and their friends.*

528099   Girl on Balance Beam
"Markie"

B	$25	S	$18.50
TRP	$20	H	$18.50

Comments: 1993; Original Retail $18.50

Personal Data: _____

___Want Mark ____ Mark _____ Purch. 19__ Pd $ _____

528196   *NIGHT LIGHT*
"Circus Tent"

B	$105	S	$90
TRP	$95	H	$90

Comments: 1993; Original Retail $90.00

Personal Data: _____

___Want Mark ____ Mark _____ Purch. 19__ Pd $ _____

529168   Boy Lion Tamer and Kitty Lion
"Jordan"

B	$25	S	$20
TRP	$20	H	$20

Comments: 1994; Original Retail $20.00

Personal Data: _____

___Want Mark ____ Mark _____ Purch. 19__ Pd $ _____

529176   Boy Clown with Cannon
"Dusty"

B	$30	S	$22.50
TRP	$28	H	$22.50

Comments: 1993; Original Retail $22.50

Personal Data: _____

___Want Mark ____ Mark _____ Purch. 19__ Pd $ _____

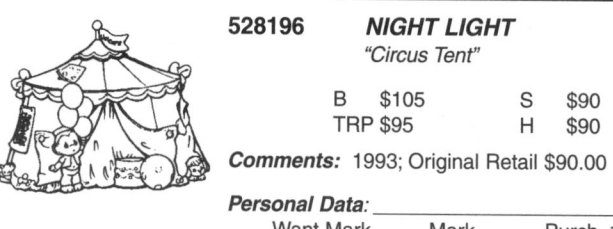

529184 **Girl Juggling Hearts**
"Katie"

| B | $22.50 | S | $18 |
| TRP | $18 | H | $17 |

Comments: 1993; Original Retail $17.00
3-¹/₂" H.

Personal Data: _____
____Want Mark ____ Mark _____ Purch. 19__ Pd $ _____

529192 **Dog Balancing Ball and Mouse**
"Tippy"

| B | $18 | S | $12 |
| TRP | $15 | H | $12 |

Comments: 1993; Original Retail $12.00
3" H.

Personal Data: _____
____Want Mark ____ Mark _____ Purch. 19__ Pd $ _____

529214 **Boy with Drum**
"Collin"

| B | $25 | S | $22 |
| TRP | $22 | H | $20 |

Comments: 1993; Original Retail $20.00
4" H.

Personal Data: _____
____Want Mark ____ Mark _____ Purch. 19__ Pd $ _____

529222 **Boy Hanging Sign**
"Sammy"

LE 1994 - 2 YEARS OLD   B $30
TRP $25

Comments: 1993; Original Retail $20.00
3" H.

Personal Data: _____
____Want Mark ____ Mark _____ Purch. 19__ Pd $ _____

163708 **Girl Clown and Teddy Bear**
"Jennifer"

H   Current

Comments: 1995; Original Retail $20.00

Personal Data: _____
____Want Mark ____ Mark _____ Purch. 19__ Pd $ _____

SUGAR TOWN

The complete 1992 Sugar Town set including the LE population sign in a GC mark has a secondary market value of $400 - $425.

1992

528684 **Decorated Evergreen Tree**
"Christmas Tree"

RETIRED 1994 - TWO YEARS AGO

GC $35   B $26   TRP $25

Comments: 1991; Original Retail $15.00
One of the original pieces for '92.

Personal Data: _____
____Want Mark ____ Mark _____ Purch. 19__ Pd $ _____

529486 **Two Women Singing**
"Aunt Ruth & Aunt Dorothy"

RETIRED 1994 - TWO YEARS AGO

GC $35   B $25   TRP $25

Comments: 1991; Original Retail $20.00

Personal Data: _____
____Want Mark ____ Mark _____ Purch. 19__ Pd $ _____

529494 **Boy Singing**
"Philip"

RETIRED 1994 - TWO YEARS AGO

GC $30   B $20   TRP $20

Comments: 1991; Original Retail $17.00

Personal Data: _____
____Want Mark ____ Mark _____ Purch. 19__ Pd $ _____

529508 **NATIVITY Scene**
"Nativity"

RETIRED 1994 - TWO YEARS AGO

GC $35   B $25   TRP $25

Comments: 1991; Original Retail $20.00

Personal Data: _____
____Want Mark ____ Mark _____ Purch. 19__ Pd $ _____

529516 **Old Man Kneeling**
"Grandfather"

RETIRED 1994 - TWO YEARS AGO

GC $25   B $20   TRP $20

Comments: 1991; Original Retail $15.00
This piece has been found with only half of the eyeglasses painted.

Personal Data: _____
_____Want Mark _____ Mark _____ Purch. 19__ Pd $ _____

529567 **Sam Standing Next to Town Sign Painting**
"Sam Butcher"

LE 1992 - 4 YEARS OLD
Population 5 and Growing!   GC $110-125

Comments: 1991; Original Retail $22.50
Limited Edition. Came with the first set which is now retired.   Sign is changed each year to "new population" figure. Most sought after of the Sugar Town pieces. This was not retired; it was a one year LE production piece.

Personal Data: _____
_____Want Mark _____ Mark _____ Purch. 19__ Pd $ _____

529621 *NIGHT LIGHT* **- Chapel with Lights**
"Chapel"

RETIRED 1994 - TWO YEARS AGO

GC $130   TRP $120
B $120

Comments: 1991; Original Retail $85.00

Personal Data: _____
_____Want Mark _____ Mark _____ Purch. 19__ Pd $ _____

Sam's house sits on a "hill" in the background as special figurines wait at the Train Station in this fun display by Millie Carey.

1993

528668 **Boy with Snowballs**
"Sammy"

B $22   S $17
TRP $17

Comments: 1992; Original Retail $17.00
Sugar Town sets were not increasing on the secondary market until the first set was retired. Most sets purchased "to keep." Extra not bought up.

Personal Data: _____
_____Want Mark _____ Mark _____ Purch. 19__ Pd $ _____

529435 **Boy with Box of Christmas Decorations**
"Dusty"

B $22   S $17
TRP $17   H $17

Comments: 1992; Original Retail $17.00

Personal Data: _____
_____Want Mark _____ Mark _____ Purch. 19__ Pd $ _____

529443 **Car with Tree on Top**
"Sam's Car"

B $26   S $22.50
TRP $22.50   H $22.50

Comments: 1992; Original Retail $22.50

Personal Data: _____
_____Want Mark _____ Mark _____ Purch. 19__ Pd $ _____

529524 **Girl with Snowman**
"Katy Lynne"

B $28   S $20
TRP $20   H $20

Comments: 1992; Original Retail $20.00
Popular piece; easily sold separately from set.

Personal Data: _____
_____Want Mark _____ Mark _____ Purch. 19__ Pd $ _____

529605 **NIGHT LIGHT - House**
"Sam's House"

B	$98	S	$85
TRP	$85	H	$85

Comments: 1992; Original Retail $80.00/$85.00
Retail price increased in 1995.

Personal Data: _____
____Want Mark ____ Mark _____ Purch. 19__ Pd $ _____

529796 **Fence**

B	$15	S	$10
TRP	$10	H	$10

Comments: 1992; Original Retail $10.00
We'd love to receive photos of your displays of the Sugar Town set.

Personal Data: _____
____Want Mark ____ Mark _____ Purch. 19__ Pd $ _____

529842 **Boy Standing by Sugar Town Sign**
"Sam Butcher"

LE 1993 - 3 years old   B $55

Comments: 1992; Original Retail $22.50
Second population sign, Population 9... and Growing! Line art reads Peppermint Lane on sign but actual piece reads Sugar Avenue. The Population sign "5" in '92 was the first sign.

Personal Data: _____
____Want Mark ____ Mark _____ Purch. 19__ Pd $ _____

530484 **ORNAMENT - Boy Standing by Chapel**
"Sugar Town Chapel"

LE 1993 - 3 years old   B $28

Comments: 1992; Original Retail $17.50

Personal Data: _____
____Want Mark ____ Mark _____ Purch. 19__ Pd $ _____

531774 **1993 Sugar Town House Collector's Set**

                                B $266

See individual listings.

Comments: 1992; Original Retail $189.00
7-piece set. Includes: 528668, 529435, 529443, 529524, 529605, 529796, 529842

Personal Data: _____
____Want Mark ____ Mark _____ Purch. 19__ Pd $ _____

1994

528064 **Three Puppies in Basket with Sign**
"Free Christmas Puppies"

TRP	$18	H	$12.50
S	$12.50		

Comments: 1993; Original Retail $12.50

Personal Data: _____
____Want Mark ____ Mark _____ Purch. 19__ Pd $ _____

529281 **Doctor's Office Collector's Set**

LE 1994 - 2 YEARS OLD   TRP $238

Comments: 1993; Original Retail $189.00
7 piece set. Includes: 529850, 529826, 529869, 529788, 529818, 533165 and 528064.

Personal Data: _____
____Want Mark ____ Mark _____ Purch. 19__ Pd $ _____

529559 **"Lamp Post"**

TRP	$10	H	$8
S	$8		

Comments: 1993; Original Retail $8.00

Personal Data: _____
____Want Mark ____ Mark _____ Purch. 19__ Pd $ _____

529788 **Stork Holding Baby Boy**
"Stork With Baby Sam"

LE 1994 - 2 YEARS OLD   TRP $30

Comments: 1993; Original Retail $22.50
"Population 13+1... and Growing."

Personal Data: _____
____Want Mark ____ Mark _____ Purch. 19__ Pd $ _____

529818 **Husband with Pregnant Wife**
"Leon And Evelyn Mae"

TRP	$25	H	$20
S	$20		

Comments: 1993; Original Retail $20.00

Personal Data: _____
____Want Mark ____ Mark _____ Purch. 19__ Pd $ _____

529826   **Nurse Holding Clipboard**
"Jan"

TRP $22   H $17
S $17

Comments: 1993; Original Retail $17.00

Personal Data: _____
____Want Mark ____ Mark _____ Purch. 19__ Pd $ _____

529850   **Doctor with Bag**
"Dr. Sam Sugar"

TRP $20   H $17
S $17

Comments: 1993; Original Retail $17.00

Personal Data: _____
____Want Mark ____ Mark _____ Purch. 19__ Pd $ _____

529869   ***NIGHT LIGHT* - Doctor's Office**
"Doctor's Office"

TRP $95   H $85
S $85

Comments: 1993; Original Retail $80.00/$85.00
Retail price increased in 1995.

Personal Data: _____
____Want Mark ____ Mark _____ Purch. 19__ Pd $ _____

530468   ***ORNAMENT* - Sam's House**

LE 1994 - 2 YEARS OLD   TRP $25
                          S $20

Comments: 1993; Original Retail $17.50
Is your Christmas Tree filled with Precious Moments® Ornaments?
Send us your photos for the "Tree of the Year" contest!

Personal Data: _____
____Want Mark ____ Mark _____ Purch. 19__ Pd $ _____

531847   *"Mailbox"*

TRP $8   H $5
S $5

Comments: 1993; Original Retail $5.00

Personal Data: _____
____Want Mark ____ Mark _____ Purch. 19__ Pd $ _____

532908   **Sugar Town Square Clock**

TRP $85   H $80
S $80

Comments: 1993; Original Retail $80.00

Personal Data: _____
____Want Mark ____ Mark _____ Purch. 19__ Pd $ _____

533149   *"Curved Road"*

TRP $12   H $10
S $10

Comments: 1993; Original Retail $10.00

Personal Data: _____
____Want Mark ____ Mark _____ Purch. 19__ Pd $ _____

533157   *"Straight Sidewalk"*

TRP $12   H $10
S $10

Comments: 1993; Original Retail $10.00

Personal Data: _____
____Want Mark ____ Mark _____ Purch. 19__ Pd $ _____

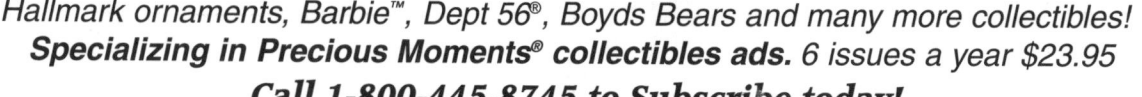

● ●

533165   **Dog and Dog House**
"Sugar And Her Dog House"

TRP $28   H $20
S $20

Comments: 1993; Original Retail $20.00
Mary E. from Ohio reported her doghouse has the "Stork" decal on the bottom.

Personal Data: _____
____Want Mark ____ Mark _____ Purch. 19__ Pd $ _____

533173   *"Single Tree"*

TRP $16   H $10
S $10

Comments: 1993; Original Retail $10.00

Personal Data: _____
____Want Mark ____ Mark _____ Purch. 19__ Pd $ _____

533181   *"Double Tree"*

TRP $14   H $10
S $10

Comments: 1993; Original Retail $10.00

Personal Data: _____
____Want Mark ____ Mark _____ Purch. 19__ Pd $ _____

533203   *"Cobblestone Bridge"*

TRP $22   H $17
S $17

Comments: 1993; Original Retail $17.00

Personal Data: _____
____Want Mark ____ Mark _____ Purch. 19__ Pd $ _____

770272   *"Sugar Town Enhancement"*

TRP $94   S $70   H $70

See individual listings.

Comments: 1993; Original Retail $70.00
Seven piece set. Includes: 529559, 531847, 533149, 533157, 533173, 533181, 533203. Send photos of your display…We may just publish them!

Personal Data: _____
____Want Mark ____ Mark _____ Purch. 19__ Pd $ _____

150150   **Ticket Booth and Waiting Room**
"Train Station Night Light"

S $100
H $100

Comments: 1994; Original Retail $100.00

Personal Data: _____
____Want Mark ____ Mark _____ Purch. 19__ Pd $ _____

150169   **Boy Train Conductor with Sign Population**
"Sam"

S $22
H $20

Comments: 1994; Original Retail $20.00
Population total = 18.

Personal Data: _____
____Want Mark ____ Mark _____ Purch. 19__ Pd $ _____

150177   **Signpost**
"Railroad Crossing Sign"

S $12
H $12

Comments: 1994; Original Retail $12.00

Personal Data: _____
____Want Mark ____ Mark _____ Purch. 19__ Pd $ _____

150185   **Cart with Suitcase and Kitten**
"Luggage Cart"

S $13
H $13

Comments: 1994; Original Retail $13.00

Personal Data: _____
____Want Mark ____ Mark _____ Purch. 19__ Pd $ _____

150193   **Train Station - Collectors' 6 piece set**

S $192
H $190

See individual listings.

Comments: 1994; Original Retail $190.00
Includes: 150150, 150169, 150177, 150185, 531812, 531871

Personal Data: _____
____Want Mark ____ Mark _____ Purch. 19__ Pd $ _____

150207   **Bus Stop with Pink Bow**
"Bus Stop Sign"

S $8.50
H $8.50

Comments: 1994; Original Retail $8.50

Personal Data: _____
____Want Mark ____ Mark _____ Purch. 19__ Pd $ _____

150215   **Fire Hydrant with Heart**
"Fire Hydrant"

S $5
H $5

Comments: 1994; Original Retail $5.00

Personal Data: _____
____Want Mark ____ Mark _____ Purch. 19__ Pd $ _____

150223   **Bird on Bird Bath**
"Bird Bath"

S $8.50
H $8.50

Comments: 1994; Original Retail $8.50

Personal Data: _____
____Want Mark ____ Mark _____ Purch. 19__ Pd $ _____

See individual listings.

152269   **"Sugar Town Enhancement"**

S $45
H $45

Comments: 1994; Original Retail $45.00
5 piece set. Includes: 150207, 150223, 529540, 531871, 532185

Personal Data: _____
____Want Mark ____ Mark _____ Purch. 19__ Pd $ _____

152595 ♪ **MUSICAL - Sugar Town Train 3-piece set**
"Sugar Town Express"

S $75   H $75

Comments: 1994; Original Retail $75.00
Includes 18 ft. of track. Light on front of engine, horn really toots. Operates forward and reverse. Plays three tunes: *Jingle Bells, Santa Claus Is Coming To Town* and *We Wish You A Merry Christmas.*

Personal Data: _____
____Want Mark ____ Mark _____ Purch. 19__ Pd $ _____

529540   **Dog and Cat on Bench**
"Park Bench"

S $13
H $13

Comments: 1994; Original Retail $13.00

Personal Data: _____
____Want Mark ____ Mark _____ Purch. 19__ Pd $ _____

530441   ***ORNAMENT*** **- Doctor's Office**
"Dr. Sugar's Office Ornament"

S $17.50
H $17.50

Comments: 1994; Original Retail $17.50

Personal Data: _____
____Want Mark ____ Mark _____ Purch. 19__ Pd $ _____

531812   **Girls with Gifts**
"Tammy And Debbie"

S $22.50
H $22.50

Comments: 1994; Original Retail $22.50

Personal Data: _____
____Want Mark ____ Mark _____ Purch. 19__ Pd $ _____

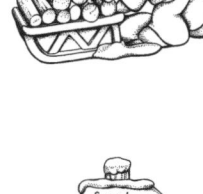

531871   **Boy with Sled/Logs**
"Donny"

S $22.50
H $22.50

Comments: 1994; Original Retail $22.50

Personal Data: _____
____Want Mark ____ Mark _____ Purch. 19__ Pd $ _____

532185   **Signpost with Street Names**
"Street Sign"

S $10   H $10

Comments: 1994; Original Retail $10.00

Personal Data: _____
____Want Mark ____ Mark _____ Purch. 19__ Pd $ _____

1996

150304   *PLATE* - Chapel Lighted Plate
"Sugar Town Chapel"

     H   Current

Comments: 1995; Original Retail $90.00
1996 Limited Edition. This lighted plate depicts three carolers and a nativity scene in front of a chapel.

Personal Data: _____
____Want Mark ____ Mark _____ Purch. 19__ Pd $ _____

184020   Ice Skating Sign
"Skating Sign"

     H   Current

Comments: 1995; Original Retail $15.00
1996 Limited Edition. The sign reads, "Ice Skating 1:00-7:00; All 22 Residents Welcome."

Personal Data: _____
____Want Mark ____ Mark _____ Purch. 19__ Pd $ _____

184039   *LIGHTED* - Lighted Tree
"Lighted Tree"

     H   Current

Comments: 1995; Original Retail $15.00

Personal Data: _____
____Want Mark ____ Mark _____ Purch. 19__ Pd $ _____

184047   Skating Pond
"Skating Pond"

     H   Current

Comments: 1995; Original Retail $40.00

Personal Data: _____
____Want Mark ____ Mark _____ Purch. 19__ Pd $ _____

184055   Girl on Ice Skates
"Mazie"

     H   Current

Comments: 1995; Original Retail $18.50

Personal Data: _____
____Want Mark ____ Mark _____ Purch. 19__ Pd $ _____

184063   Dog on Belly
"Cocoa"

     H   Current

Comments: 1995; Original Retail $7.50

Personal Data: _____
____Want Mark ____ Mark _____ Purch. 19__ Pd $ _____

184071   Boy with Hockey Gear
"Leroy"

     H   Current

Comments: 1995; Original Retail $18.50

Personal Data: _____
____Want Mark ____ Mark _____ Purch. 19__ Pd $ _____

184098   Boy and Girl on Ice Skates
"Hank And Sharon"

     H   Current

Comments: 1995; Original Retail $25.00

Personal Data: _____
____Want Mark ____ Mark _____ Purch. 19__ Pd $ _____

184101   *ORNAMENT* - Train Station
"Sugar Town Train Station"

     H   Current

Comments: 1995; Original Retail $18.50

Personal Data: _____
____Want Mark ____ Mark _____ Purch. 19__ Pd $ _____

Photo Not Available.

184128   Skating Pond (Collectors' 7-Piece Set)

     H   Current

Comments: 1995; Original Retail $184.50
Includes: 184020, 184047, 184055, 184063, 184071, 184098, 192341.

Personal Data: _____
____Want Mark ____ Mark _____ Purch. 19__ Pd $ _____

184136   **Flag Pole with Kitten on Fence**
"Flag Pole"

     H   Current

Comments: 1995; Original Retail $15.00

Personal Data: _____
____Want Mark ____ Mark _____ Purch. 19__ Pd $ _____

184144   **Barrel with Cookies and Cocoa**
"Hot Cocoa Stand"

     H   Current

Comments: 1995; Original Retail $15.00

Personal Data: _____
____Want Mark ____ Mark _____ Purch. 19__ Pd $ _____

184152   **Bunnies by Fire**
"Bonfire"

     H   Current

Comments: 1995; Original Retail $10.00

Personal Data: _____
____Want Mark ____ Mark _____ Purch. 19__ Pd $ _____

184160   **Enhancement 3-Piece Prepack**

     H   Current

See individual listings.

Comments: 1995; Original Retail $40.00
Includes: 184136, 184144, 184152.

Personal Data: _____
____Want Mark ____ Mark _____ Purch. 19__ Pd $ _____

192341   ***LIGHTED* - House with Squirrels on Roof**
"Lighted Warming Hut"

     H   Current

Comments: 1995; Original Retail $60.00

Personal Data: _____
____Want Mark ____ Mark _____ Purch. 19__ Pd $ _____

192406   **Train Car**
"Passenger Car"

     H   Current

Comments: 1995; Original Retail $27.50
1996 Limited Edition. A passenger car with people looking out the windows. A larger piece, 5" H x 12" L.

Personal Data: _____
____Want Mark ____ Mark _____ Purch. 19__ Pd $ _____

Teena Wolfe from Florida is a member of the "Fun In The Sun in Tampa Bay" club. Teena's Sugar Town display is outstanding. It took two six foot tables to set up her display!

●●●

Precious Moments Collectors' Club
Membership Pieces

Charter Membership pieces have "1981 Charter Member" written on them.

E-0001   **1981 SPECIAL CLUB WELCOME GIFT**
Boy/Girl Angels on Cloud
"But Love Goes On Forever"

NM $165-175   T $145-150   HG $150-160

Comments: 1979; Club Membership fee was $15.00
Figurine came with NM, T and HG. Less of HG mark. Charter Members' Club pieces have "Charter Member" on all subsequent years' pieces. It's my opinion fewer "Charter pieces" are being produced due to dropped memberships. These memberships have been passed on with original name remaining and a changed address. Memberships have sold as high as $100. Charter Members would "love" to see a different look to the Charter Member piece to distinguish it from the New Member piece.

Personal Data: _____
____Want Mark ____ Mark _____ Purch. 19__ Pd $ _____

E-0102   **CHARTER MEMBER –**
1982 Membership Plaque
Boy/Girl Angels on Cloud
"But Love Goes On Forever"

MM $90   T $85   HG $70

Comments: 1981; Club Membership Renewal fee was $13.50
T mark scarce. The inspiration (title) is different than the saying on the front of the plaque (*Precious Moments Last Forever*).
If a MM is found it's because the mark was left off the mold.
At one time, a mold produced approximately 75 figurines.
See #40, page XV.

Personal Data: _____
____Want Mark ____ Mark _____ Purch. 19__ Pd $ _____

E-0202   **NEW MEMBER** – 1982 Membership Plaque
Boy /Girl Angels on Cloud
"But Love Goes On Forever"

MM $90   T $80   HG $65

Canadian Error D $110-120

Comments: 1981; New Club Membership fee was $15.00
The inspiration (title) is different than the saying on the front of the plaque (*Precious Moments Last Forever*). This piece was produced by mistake in **1985** with a D mark and sent to Canada. A mad rush of collectors headed to Canada! *Precious Collectibles*™ was the first to alert the collectors of this error and we were the first to alert Enesco.

Personal Data: _____
____Want Mark ____ Mark _____ Purch. 19__ Pd $ _____

E-0103   **CHARTER MEMBER** – 1983 Membership
Boy Conducting Meeting
"Let Us Call The Club To Order"

HG $62.50   F $55   C $65

Comments: 1982; Renewal Club Membership fee was $13.50
Few C marks.

Personal Data: _____
____Want Mark ____ Mark _____ Purch. 19__ Pd $ _____

E-0303   **NEW MEMBER** – 1983 Membership
Boy Conducting Meeting
"Let Us Call The Club To Order"

HG $55   F $50   C $60

Comments: 1982; Club Membership fee was $15.00
Only a few C marks.

Personal Data: _____
____Want Mark ____ Mark _____ Purch. 19__ Pd $ _____

People who make promises off the top of their heads sometimes talk through their hats.

E-0104   **CHARTER MEMBER** – 1984 Membership
Girl with Dues Bank
"Join In On The Blessings"

F $55   C $48

Comments: 1983; Renewal Club Membership fee was $15.75
First girl in jeans. Line art is different from actual piece produced.

Personal Data: _____
____Want Mark ____ Mark _____ Purch. 19__ Pd $ _____

E-0404   **NEW MEMBER** – 1984 Membership
Girl with Dues Bank
"Join In On The Blessings"

F $50   C $45

Comments: 1983; Club Membership fee $17.50 for new members
Fewer C marks than F marks but known sales did not reflect this.
One collector reported an HG mark. Do you have an HG mark? This
mark may be very, very rare.

Personal Data: _____
____Want Mark ____ Mark _____ Purch. 19__ Pd $ _____

E-0105   **CHARTER MEMBER** – 1985 Membership
Girl with Bag
"Seek And Ye Shall Find"

C $50   D $45

Comments: 1984; Club Membership Renewal fee was $15.75
This piece has been found with a Fish mark.

Personal Data: _____
____Want Mark ____ Mark _____ Purch. 19__ Pd $ _____

E-0005   **NEW MEMBER** – 1985 Membership
Girl with Bag
"Seek And Ye Shall Find"

C $45   D $35

Comments: 1984; Club Membership fee was $17.50

Personal Data: _____
____Want Mark ____ Mark _____ Purch. 19__ Pd $ _____

E-0106   **CHARTER MEMBER** – 1986 Membership
Girl with Needlepoint
"Birds Of A Feather Collect Together"

D $50   OB $45

Comments: 1985; Club Membership renewal fee was $15.75

Personal Data: _____
____Want Mark ____ Mark _____ Purch. 19__ Pd $ _____

E-0006   **NEW MEMBER** – 1986 Membership
Girl with Needlepoint
"Birds Of A Feather Collect Together"

D $40   OB $35

Comments: 1985; Club Membership fee was $17.50

Personal Data: _____
____Want Mark ____ Mark _____ Purch. 19__ Pd $ _____

E-0107   **CHARTER MEMBER** – 1987 Membership
Girl with Wrapped Package
"Sharing Is Universal"

OB $48   CT $40

Comments: 1987; Club Membership renewal fee was $17.50

Personal Data: _____
____Want Mark ____ Mark _____ Purch. 19__ Pd $ _____

E-0007   **NEW MEMBER** – 1987 Membership
Girl with Wrapped Package
"Sharing Is Universal"

OB $40   CT $30

Comments: 1987; Club Membership fee was $17.50
CT mark easily found.

Personal Data: _____
____Want Mark ____ Mark _____ Purch. 19__ Pd $ _____

*Send us your photos of your collection
with you and your family!*

E-0108   ***CHARTER MEMBER*** – 1988 Membership
Girl with Sunflower
"A Growing Love"

CT $45   FL $40

Comments: 1987; Club Membership renewal fee was $17.50
A girl with a string of sunflowers appears as a PMC doll and on '95 Regional Ball ornaments.

Personal Data: _____
____Want Mark ____ Mark _____ Purch. 19__ Pd $ _____

E-0008   ***NEW MEMBER*** – 1988 Membership
Girl with Sunflower
"A Growing Love"

CT $40   FL $35

Comments: 1987; Club Membership fee was $18.50
Many reported that the "flat" look of the flower was a disappointment. I liked this piece. ☺

Personal Data: _____
____Want Mark ____ Mark _____ Purch. 19__ Pd $ _____

C-0109   ***CHARTER MEMBER*** – 1989 Membership
Girl Putting Puppy in Box
"Always Room For One More"

FL $45   BA $40

Comments: 1988; Club Membership renewal fee was $18.25

Personal Data: _____
____Want Mark ____ Mark _____ Purch. 19__ Pd $ _____

C-0009   ***NEW MEMBER*** – 1989 Membership
Girl Putting Puppy in Box
"Always Room For One More"

FL $45   BA $40   FLM $35

Comments: 1988; Club Membership fee was $19.50

Personal Data: _____
____Want Mark ____ Mark _____ Purch. 19__ Pd $ _____

C-0110   ***CHARTER MEMBER*** – 1990 Membership
Girl at Table with Figurine
"My Happiness"

BA $45   FLM $40

Comments: 1989; Club Membership renewal fee $21.00

Personal Data: _____
____Want Mark ____ Mark _____ Purch. 19__ Pd $ _____

C-0010   ***NEW MEMBER*** – 1990 Membership
Girl at Table with Figurine
"My Happiness"

BA $38   FLM $32

Comments: 1989; Club Membership fee $21.00
The 1990 Sharing Season Ornament (PM904) is similar to this figurine.

Personal Data: _____
____Want Mark ____ Mark _____ Purch. 19__ Pd $ _____

C-0111   **Charter Member** – 1991 Membership
Girl at Mailbox
"Sharing The Good News Together"

BA $50   FLM $38   V $38

Comments: 1990; Club Membership renewal fee $21.00
"Flat" mailbox was not popular.

Personal Data: _____
____Want Mark ____ Mark _____ Purch. 19__ Pd $ _____

C-0011   ***NEW MEMBER*** – 1991 Membership
Girl at Mailbox
"Sharing The Good News Together"

FLM $42   V $22

Comments: 1990; Club Membership fee $21.50
Found with only one eye painted - add $35 to secondary market value. Slow on secondary market for several years. Membership pieces have not continued to rise in value compared to many regular line pieces. Even most regular line pieces have been slow to rise in price since approximately 1986 except for first marks, suspended or retired pieces.

Personal Data: _____
____Want Mark ____ Mark _____ Purch. 19__ Pd $ _____

C-0112   **CHARTER MEMBER** – 1992 Membership
Girl in Space Suit
"The Club That's Out Of This World"

V $45   GC $42

Comments: 1990; Club Membership renewal fee $25.00
Came with a matching patch. Collectors received the astronaut ornament in 1992 when signing up two new members to the National Club.

Personal Data: _____
____Want Mark ____ Mark _____ Purch. 19__ Pd $ _____

Colonel Steven R. Nagle
100th Astronaut in Space

Rosie presented Steve with the Astronaut Girl Precious Moments Membership Figurine and Membership in the National Club. Steve and Rosie both claim Canton, Illinois, as their hometown. Rosie also sent the same figurine to Steve's mother.

C-0012   **NEW MEMBER** – 1992 Membership
Girl in Space Suit
"The Club That's Out Of This World"

V $42   GC $38

Comments: 1990; Club Membership fee $25.00
Came with a matching patch. I presented this piece to the 100th astronaut of the United States, Col. Steve Nagel. He is from my hometown, Canton, Illinois.

Personal Data: _____
____Want Mark ____ Mark _____ Purch. 19__ Pd $ _____

C-0113   **CHARTER MEMBER** – 1993 Membership
Girl with Satchel by Signs
"Loving, Caring And Sharing Along The Way"

GC $45   B $40

Comments: 1992; Club Membership renewal fee $25.00

Personal Data: _____
____Want Mark ____ Mark _____ Purch. 19__ Pd $ _____

C-0013   **NEW MEMBER** – 1993 Membership
Girl with Satchel by Signs
"Loving, Caring And Sharing Along The Way"

GC $40   B $35

Comments: 1993; Club Membership fee $25.00

Personal Data: _____
____Want Mark ____ Mark _____ Purch. 19__ Pd $ _____

C-0114   **CHARTER MEMBER** – 1994 Membership
Girl Sitting in Pot of Gold
"You're The End Of My Rainbow"

B $38   TRP $32

Comments: 1993; Club Membership renewal fee $25.00
Cute!

Personal Data: _____
____Want Mark ____ Mark _____ Purch. 19__ Pd $ _____

C-0014   *NEW MEMBER* – 1994 Membership
Girl Sitting in Pot of Gold
"You're The End Of My Rainbow"

        B $35   TRP $30

Comments: 1993; Club Membership fee $25.00

Personal Data: _____
____Want Mark ____ Mark _____ Purch. 19__ Pd $ _____

C-0115   *CHARTER MEMBER* – 1995 Membership
Girl w/ Heart Shaped Cookies on Tray
"You're The Sweetest Cookie In The Batch"

        TRP $32   S $28

Comments: 1994; Club Membership renewal fee $25.00
Cute!

Personal Data: _____
____Want Mark ____ Mark _____ Purch. 19__ Pd $ _____

C-0015   *NEW MEMBER* – 1995 Membership
Girl w/Heart Shaped Cookies on Tray
"You're The Sweetest Cookie In The Batch"

        TRP $30   S $30

Comments: 1994; Club Membership fee $27.00

Personal Data: _____
____Want Mark ____ Mark _____ Purch. 19__ Pd $ _____

C-0116   *CHARTER MEMBER* – 1996 Membership
Girl Holding Picture Frame
"You're As Pretty As A Picture"

        S $32   H $28

Comments: 1995; Club Membership renewal fee $25.00

Personal Data: _____
____Want Mark ____ Mark _____ Purch. 19__ Pd $ _____

C-0016   *NEW MEMBER* – 1996 Membership
Girl Holding Picture Frame
"You're As Pretty As A Picture"

        S $27   H $27

Comments: 1995; Club Membership fee $27.00

Personal Data: _____
____Want Mark ____ Mark _____ Purch. 19__ Pd $ _____

Precious Moments Collectors' Club
Club Pieces

PC112   **CLOISONNÉ Medallions**
"Loving, Caring And Sharing"

        $32

Comments: 1993; Original Retail $22.50
Set of three medallions in special gift box.

Personal Data: _____
____Want Mark ____ Mark _____ Purch. 19__ Pd $ _____

PM034   **Club Member Desk Flag**

        $4.00

Comments: 1990; Original Retail $4.00
Accessory to be placed with PM901, 1990 Club piece.

Personal Data: _____
____Want Mark ____ Mark _____ Purch. 19__ Pd $ _____

PM040   *ORNAMENT* – Girl At Signpost with Satchel
"Loving, Caring And Sharing Along The Way"

        B $35

Comments: 1992; Original Retail $12.50
1993 Club Member Appreciation ornament. This took the place of the Sharing Season ornament for 1993.

Personal Data: _____
____Want Mark ____ Mark _____ Purch. 19__ Pd $ _____

PM041　　ORNAMENT – Girl with Rainbow
"You Are The End Of My Rainbow"

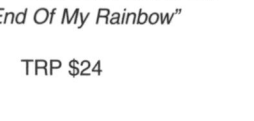

TRP $24

Comments: 1994; Original Retail $15.00
1994 Club Member Appreciation ornament.

Personal Data: _____
____Want Mark ____ Mark _____ Purch. 19__ Pd $ _____

CHAPEL WINDOW ORNAMENTS

Insignificant amount of sales reported to establish a price.

Comments:　　1990; Original Retail $15.00　　$18-$20

PM190　　*"Blessed Are The Poor In Spirit,
　　　　　　For Theirs Is The Kingdom Of God"*

PM290　　*"Blessed Are They That Mourn,
　　　　　　For They Shall Be Comforted"*

PM390　　*"Blessed Are The Meek,
　　　　　　For They Shall Inherit The Earth"*

PM490　　*"Blessed Are They That Hunger And Thirst
　　　　　　For Righteousness, For They Shall Be Filled"*

PM590　　*"Blessed Are The Merciful,
　　　　　　For They Shall Obtain Mercy"*

PM690　　*"Blessed Are The Pure In Heart,
　　　　　　For They Shall See God"*

PM790　　*"Blessed Are The Peacemakers,
　　　　　　For They Shall Be Called Sons Of God"*

PM890　　7 Piece Assortment

Comments: 1990; Original Retail $105.00 set.
Try several as wind chimes! Available to Club Members Only. Do not look for a secondary market on these for another year or more.

Personal Data: _____
____Want Mark ____ Mark _____ Purch. 19__ Pd $ _____

PM811　　Boy On Telephone
"Hello, Lord, It's Me Again"

T　$425　　　　HG　$425

Comments: 1981; Original Retail $25.00
1981 Club piece. A popular Club piece. More T than HG marks. Excellent to display with Girl on Telephone (521477). Sam designed this for his son, Jon, who received a "Dear Jon" note. Price down from '95 on T Mark. As old as this piece is new collectors will pay the same to own. Insure T mark at $450.

Personal Data: _____
____Want Mark ____ Mark _____ Purch. 19__ Pd $ _____

PM821　　Girl in Curlers with Mirror
"Smile, God Loves You"

HG　$195　　　　F　$185

Comments: 1982; Original Retail $25.00
1982 Club piece. HG mark can easily be found at above price of $195 or less. Do not over insure! 1981 and 1982 Club pieces are high in value mainly because members never thought to get extra memberships.

Personal Data: _____
____Want Mark ____ Mark _____ Purch. 19__ Pd $ _____

PM822　　Clown with Mask
"Put On A Happy Face"

HG　$190-200　　F　$150-160　　C　$140-145

Comments: 1981; Original Retail $25.00
1983 Club piece. Bottoms of bases had differences also; no real significance on the secondary market. This piece has been found with color variations in the clown's outfit. First two Club pieces higher on secondary market due to "popular pieces" as well as less production until 1983. 1983-1984 were the "over produced" years. Have seen gray hearts instead of pink on this piece.

Personal Data: _____
____Want Mark ____ Mark _____ Purch. 19__ Pd $ _____

PM831　　Girl Looking Under Blanket
"Dawn's Early Light"

F　$75　　　　C　$70

Comments: 1983; Original Retail $27.50
1983 Club piece. "Dawn" is Sam's sister.

Personal Data: _____
____Want Mark ____ Mark _____ Purch. 19__ Pd $ _____

PM841   **Boy with Flashlight**
"God's Ray Of Mercy"

F $75   C $50   D $40

Comments: 1983; Original Retail $25.00
1984 Special Edition. Sam's tribute to his brother, Ray Butcher. Cute piece!

Personal Data: _____
____Want Mark ____ Mark _____ Purch. 19__ Pd $ _____

PM842   **Race Car Driver**
"Trust In The Lord To The Finish"

C $58   D $55

Comments: 1984; Original Retail $25.00
1984 Club piece. Sam's tribute to his younger brother, Hank Butcher. Most club pieces can be found at *Precious Collectibles™* swap meets. Remember our shows on March 16 and October 26, 1996, in Westmont IL. Usually 150 to 200 tables of collectibles. A great time to meet other collectors represented from over 16 states.

Personal Data: _____
____Want Mark ____ Mark _____ Purch. 19__ Pd $ _____

PM843   *NEEDLECRAFT* **- Race Car Driver**
"Trust In The Lord To The Finish"

$15

Comments: 1984; Original Retail $11.00

Personal Data: _____
____Want Mark ____ Mark _____ Purch. 19__ Pd $ _____

PM851   **Girl with Lambs**
"The Lord Is My Shepherd"

C $75   D $70   OB $80

Comments: 1984; Original Retail $25.00.
1985 Club piece. (We've heard two reports of MM pieces.) Occurs on most pieces. OB mark is scarce. Check out today's classified ads. Club pieces tend to be slow in trading the last four years!

Personal Data: _____
____Want Mark ____ Mark _____ Purch. 19__ Pd $ _____

PM852   **Boy Lying on Stomach with Lamb**
"I Love To Tell The Story"

D $60   OB $55

Comments: 1984; Original Retail $27.50.
1985 Club piece. A popular piece. This figurine was a tribute to Pastor Blue who led Sam to the Lord. He is a man in whom we can see Jesus. Pastor Blue writes an article in each issue of *Precious Collectibles.™* This is a very special piece; a favorite of many.

Personal Data: _____
____Want Mark ____ Mark _____ Purch. 19__ Pd $ _____

PM853   **Needlecraft - Girl with Lambs**
"The Lord Is My Shepherd"

$18

Comments: 1984; Original Retail $11.00.

Personal Data: _____
____Want Mark ____ Mark _____ Purch. 19__ Pd $ _____

PM861   **Grandma Praying**
"Grandma's Prayer"

D $80   OB $65   CT $80

Comments: 1986; Original Retail $25.00.
1986 Club piece. Less of CT mark than other marks. More OB than others.

Personal Data: _____
____Want Mark ____ Mark _____ Purch. 19__ Pd $ _____

PM862   **Boy in Car**
"I'm Following Jesus"

OB $70   CT $75   FL $75

Comments: 1986; Original Retail $25.00
1986 Club piece. Our research indicates this 1986 piece was produced with the CT mark and the FL mark. May eventually prove to be scarce marks. Lots of OB trading found.

Personal Data: _____
____Want Mark ____ Mark _____ Purch. 19__ Pd $ _____

PM863   ***MUGS* - Boy in Car**
"I'm Following Jesus"

$18

Comments: 1986; Original Retail $17.50
Set of four mugs.

Personal Data: _____
____Want Mark ____ Mark _____ Purch. 19__ Pd $ _____

PM871   **Girl with Lamb**
"Feed My Sheep"

CT $55   FL $50

Comments: 1986; Original Retail $25.00
1987 Club piece. A very popular piece! This piece is becoming harder to find on the secondary market. Collectors are saying that "Club" pieces should be "different" from the regular line. Most trading found on CT mark in '95 & '96. Reported OB mark found.

Personal Data: _____
____Want Mark ____ Mark _____ Purch. 19__ Pd $ _____

PM872   **Boy Watching Seeds**
"In His Time"

OB $50   CT $45   FL $35

Comments: 1987; Original Retail $25.00
1987 Club piece. 1986 license date on box; 1987 on figurines. Two other figurines in the regular line are very similar. Notice price compared to other Club pieces because of this similarity.

Personal Data: _____
____Want Mark ____ Mark _____ Purch. 19__ Pd $ _____

PM873   **Boy Drawing Valentine**
"Loving You Dear Valentine"

OB $40   CT $38   FL $35

Comments: 1986; Original Retail $25.00
1987 Club piece.

Personal Data: _____
____Want Mark ____ Mark _____ Purch. 19__ Pd $ _____

PM874   **Girl Drawing Valentine**
"Loving You Dear Valentine"

OB $40   CT $38   FL $35

Comments: 1986; Original Retail $25.00
1987 Club piece.

Personal Data: _____
____Want Mark ____ Mark _____ Purch. 19__ Pd $ _____

PM881   **Girl Painting Butterfly**
"God Bless You For Touching My Life"

CT $50   FL $45   BA $45

Comments: 1988; Original Retail $27.50
1988 Club piece. This is a pretty piece.

Personal Data: _____
____Want Mark ____ Mark _____ Purch. 19__ Pd $ _____

PM882   **Boy with Dog in Trash Can**
"You Just Cannot Chuck A Good Friendship"

FL $45   BA $40

Comments: 1988; Original Retail $27.50
1988 Club piece. A tribute to "Chuck," Sam's brother.

Personal Data: _____
____Want Mark ____ Mark _____ Purch. 19__ Pd $ _____

PM891   **Girl at Ballot Box**
"You Will Always Be My Choice"

BA $40   FLM $35

Comments: 1989; Original Retail $27.50
1989 Club piece.

Personal Data: _____
____Want Mark ____ Mark _____ Purch. 19__ Pd $ _____

PM892   **Boy with Push Mower**
"Mow Power To Ya!"

BA $50   FLM $45

Comments: 1989; Original Retail $27.50
1989 Club piece. Cute piece!

Personal Data: _____
____Want Mark ____ Mark _____ Purch. 19__ Pd $ _____

PM901   **Girl in Race Car**
"Ten Years And Still Going Strong"

FLM $55   V $45

Comments: 1990; Original Retail $30.00
1990 Club piece. A *"desk flag"* (PM034) was sold separately to be displayed with this piece. This is a popular figurine!

Personal Data: _____
____Want Mark ____ Mark _____ Purch. 19__ Pd $ _____

PM902   **Girl Patching Teddy Bear**
"You Are A Blessing To Me"

FLM $52.50   V $48

Comments: 1990; Original Retail $27.50
1990 Club piece. Fewer V marks. Teddy bear lovers want this piece!

Personal Data: _____
____Want Mark ____ Mark _____ Purch. 19__ Pd $ _____

PM911   **Girl Helping Baby Walk**
"One Step At A Time"

V $42.50   GC $38

Comments: 1990; Original Retail $33.00
1991 Club piece. Was not popular for a Club piece. Collectors voiced their opinion – "Resembles *Baby's First Series*." So why not display this piece with that series?

Personal Data: _____
____Want Mark ____ Mark _____ Purch. 19__ Pd $ _____

PM912   **Indian Boy Eating Spinach**
"Lord Keep Me In TeePee-Top Shape"

V $48   GC $45

Comments: 1990; Original Retail $27.50
1991 Club piece.

Personal Data: _____
____Want Mark ____ Mark _____ Purch. 19__ Pd $ _____

PM921   **Mr. Webb Building a Bird House**
"Only Love Can Make A Home"

GC $48   B $45

Comments: 1992; Original Retail $30.00
Dedicated to Mr. Webb, a friend of Sam's, who made homes for blue birds in Missouri.

Personal Data: _____
____Want Mark ____ Mark _____ Purch. 19__ Pd $ _____

PM922   **Girl Kneeling in Garden**
"Sowing The Seeds Of Love"

GC $38   B $38

Comments: 1992; Original Retail $30.00
1992 Club piece.

Personal Data: _____
____Want Mark ____ Mark _____ Purch. 19__ Pd $ _____

For the latest news in Precious Moments® Collecting, subscribe to
Precious Collectibles™ and the Weekly Collectors' Gazette™!
Call Today! 1-800-445-8745

PM931   **Girl Kneeling by Sand Pail**
"His Little Treasure"

| | B | $40 | | TRP $35 |

Comments: 1992; Original Retail $30.00
1993 Club piece.

Personal Data: _____
____Want Mark ____ Mark ____ Purch. 19__ Pd $ _____

PM932   **Girl Holding Teddy Bear**
"Loving"

| | B | $45 | | TRP $40 |

Comments: 1992; Original Retail $30.00
1993 Club piece. Great for Precious Moments® collectors as well as teddy bear collectors.

Personal Data: _____
____Want Mark ____ Mark ____ Purch. 19__ Pd $ _____

PM941   **Girl Bandaging Teddy Bear**
"Caring"

| | TRP $45 | | S | $40 |

Comments: 1992; Original Retail $35.00
1994 Club piece.

Personal Data: _____
____Want Mark ____ Mark ____ Purch. 19__ Pd $ _____

PM942   **Girl Feeding Teddy Bear**
"Sharing"

| | TRP $45 | | S | $40 |

Comments: 1992; Original Retail $35.00
1994 Club piece. PM932, PM941 and PM942, together, form the theme of the Precious Moments® collection - *Loving, Caring and Sharing.*

Personal Data: _____
____Want Mark ____ Mark ____ Purch. 19__ Pd $ _____

PMB034   **Girl with Book**
"You Fill The Pages Of My Life"
LE 1994
Error – *You Fill The Page Of My Life*   TRP $95

Corrected   TRP $75

Comments: 1994; Original Retail $67.50
Available in the Members Only package containing the Club edition of the hardcover book *Precious Moments Last Forever* and figurine (530980). This figurine's earliest production pieces have been known to contain an error which has since been corrected. The inscription was incorrectly printed as *You Fill The Page Of My Life.*

Personal Data: _____
____Want Mark ____ Mark ____ Purch. 19__ Pd $ _____

PM951   **Girl Panning for Gold**
"You're One In A Million To Me"

| | S | $35 |

Comments: 1994; Original Retail $35.00
1995 Club piece.

Personal Data: _____
____Want Mark ____ Mark ____ Purch. 19__ Pd $ _____

PM952   **Girl Peeling Potatoes**
"Always Take Time To Pray"

| | S | $35 |

Comments: 1995; Original Retail $35.00
1995 Club piece.

Personal Data: _____
____Want Mark ____ Mark ____ Purch. 19__ Pd $ _____

PM961   **Girl Standing at Blackboard**
"Teach Us To Love One Another"

| | H | $40 |

Comments: 1995; Original Retail $40.00
1996 Club piece. May debut with the Ship mark. **See #33, page XIV.**

Personal Data: _____
____Want Mark ____ Mark ____ Purch. 19__ Pd $ _____

PM962   **Boy and Girl**
"Our Club Is Soda-licious"

H $35

Comments: 1995; Original Retail $35.00
1996 Club piece.

Personal Data: _____
____Want Mark ____ Mark _____ Purch. 19__ Pd $ _____

12440   **Commemorative Edition 5th Anniversary**
"God Bless Our Years Together"

D $260

Comments: 1984; Original Retail $175.00
Extra large pieces haven't risen on the secondary market proportionally to regular pieces. Easily found at these prices.

Personal Data: _____
____Want Mark ____ Mark _____ Purch. 19__ Pd $ _____

127817   **Girl Standing by Curio Cabinet**
"A Perfect Display Of Fifteen Happy Years"

S $100

Comments: 1994; Original Retail $100.00
Special commemorative figurine of the Fifteenth Anniversary of the Enesco Precious Moments Collectors' Club.

Personal Data: _____
____Want Mark ____ Mark _____ Purch. 19__ Pd $ _____

227986   ***ORNAMENT***
"Celebrating A Decade Of Loving, Caring And Sharing"

DATED 1990 $10

Comments: 1984; Original Retail $7.00
Special Ten-Year Anniversary Ornament. Flat porcelain ornament.

Personal Data: _____
____Want Mark ____ Mark _____ Purch. 19__ Pd $ _____

527386   **Columbus in Large Ship**
"This Land Is Our Land"

LE 1992 - 4 YEARS OLD   V $350-425   GC $350-400

Comments: 1991; Original Retail $350.00
1992 Limited Edition Commemorative available to Club Members only.
Production problems with paint chipping off of Columbus' hat.

Personal Data: _____
____Want Mark ____ Mark _____ Purch. 19__ Pd $ _____

Club Fun!

Precious Moments Local Collectors' Clubs keep busy throughout the year with appearances by the life-size figures and fund-raisers for Easter Seals and other charities.

Above: *Precious Moments Give You Showers Of Blessings Precious Moments Collectors' Club*

Right: *Love Reigns In Portland PMCC,* Portland, OR, and *Precious Moments Fill Our World PMCC* of Vancouver, WA, teamed up for the Oregon 24 Hour Easter Seals Relay. The 40 teams involved in the relay raised $100,893 for Easter Seals.

Left: *Purr-fect Friends* of Glenview, IL, raised $1300 through the Lou Skender raffle for his favorite charity, the Telephone Pioneers of America. This charity is made up of volunteers who create and donate items to children with special needs. Pictured with club members is Eugene Freedman.

Sharing Season Gifts

Gift from Enesco for signing up new Club Members

12246   **MEDALLION – 1984**
"Precious Moments Last Forever"

C $98

Comments: 1984 Sharing Season Gift

Personal Data: _____
____Want Mark ____ Mark _____ Purch. 19__ Pd $ _____

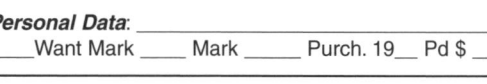

MAGNET – 1985
B/G on Cloud Precious Moments Logo

$25

Comments: 1985 Sharing Season Gift

Personal Data: _____
____Want Mark ____ Mark _____ Purch. 19__ Pd $ _____

PM864   **ORNAMENT – 1986**
"Birds Of A Feather Collect Together"

OB $155-165

Comments: 1986 Sharing Season Gift
Very little trading found on this ornament in research the past few years.
Could be the value is trading down.

Personal Data: _____
____Want Mark ____ Mark _____ Purch. 19__ Pd $ _____

PM009   **ORNAMENT – 1987**
Brass Filigree Bell-Shaped

$45

Comments: 1987 Sharing Season Gift

Personal Data: _____
____Want Mark ____ Mark _____ Purch. 19__ Pd $ _____

520349   **ORNAMENT – 1988**
"A Growing Love"

FL $70

Comments: 1988 Sharing Season Gift

Personal Data: _____
____Want Mark ____ Mark _____ Purch. 19__ Pd $ _____

522961   **ORNAMENT – 1989**
"Always Room For One More"

BA $88

Comments: 1989 Sharing Season Gift

Personal Data: _____
____Want Mark ____ Mark _____ Purch. 19__ Pd $ _____

PM904   **ORNAMENT – 1990**
"My Happiness"

FLM $80

Comments: 1990 Sharing Season Gift

Personal Data: _____
____Want Mark ____ Mark _____ Purch. 19__ Pd $ _____

PM037   **ORNAMENT – 1991**
"Sharing The Good News Together"

V $70

Comments: 1991 Sharing Season Gift

Personal Data: _____
____Want Mark ____ Mark _____ Purch. 19__ Pd $ _____

PM038   **ORNAMENT – 1992**
"The Club That's Out Of This World"

GC $65

Comments: 1992 Sharing Season Gift

Personal Data: _____
____Want Mark ____ Mark _____ Purch. 19__ Pd $ _____

Special Orient Medallion

PM030   *MEDALLION*
Goose Girl

$375

Comments: Gift by the factory to those who went on the Annual Tour of The Orient and visited the factory. Less than 150 are in the hands of collectors now. Around 25 per year were given to the group of visitors who traveled on the Enesco Orient Tour. If more have been given I am not aware of them. A great trip! You're treated like royalty! Go if you can should this trip be offered again by Enesco. Plan to shop in Hong Kong! Don't plan on sleeping or eating foods with sugar! Walk and exercise before you go! Jet lag will be something else! Memories will last forever. If this medallion has only a $375 value, then don't insure the Enesco Cruise medallions for any more! There are approximately 800 of those and they can be found on the secondary market. See page 18 for Orient photos.

Personal Data: _____
____Want Mark ____ Mark _____ Purch. 19__ Pd $ _____

Some vacation this is...
not one Precious Moments shop in sight!

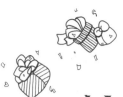

Birthday Club
Membership Pieces

The following membership pieces came with the purchase of the Birthday Club Membership Kit. Club pieces are purchased using redemption forms after you receive the Membership Kit.
Hint: Join on January 1 in order to get the prior year's mark on your Club pieces!

B-0001   **1986 Charter Membership**
Clown Beating Drum
"Our Club Can't Be Beat"

HG	$100	OB	$70
D	$85	CT	$65

Comments: 1985; Club Membership fee was $10.00.
Has "Charter Member" on base. New in 1986. HG very rare but it is out there!

Personal Data: _____
____Want Mark ____ Mark _____ Purch. 19__ Pd $ _____

B-0102   *1987 Charter Membership*
Clown with Cymbals
"A Smile's The Cymbal Of Joy"

A Smile's The Symbol Of Joy (error)	OB	$95
	CT	$90

A Smile's The Cymbal Of Joy (corrected)	OB	$70
	CT	$65
	FL	$60

Comments: 1987; Club Membership fee was $10.00
Has "Charter Member" on base.
Personal Data: _____
____Want Mark ____ Mark _____ Purch. 19__ Pd $ _____

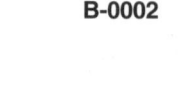

B-0002 *1987 New Member*
Clown with Cymbals
"A Smile's The Cymbal Of Joy"

A Smile's The Symbol Of Joy (error)	OB	$70
	CT	$65
A Smile's The Cymbal Of Joy (corrected)	FL	$50

Comments: 1987; Club Membership fee was $10.00
No "Charter Member" on base. Several sales found at these prices!

Personal Data: _____
____Want Mark _____ Mark _____ Purch. 19__ Pd $ _____

B-0103 *1988 Charter Membership*
Clown with Birthday Cake
"The Sweetest Club Around"

FL $42   BA $40

Comments: 1988; Club Membership fee was $11.50
Has "Charter Member" on base. Those who signed up in 1986 were "Charter Members," first in the club. Each year's Charter Member piece will state "Charter Member" on it (omitted in 1990). Notice two different numerals for the same piece; one for Charter Members, one for Club Members who did not join the first year.

Personal Data: _____
____Want Mark _____ Mark _____ Purch. 19__ Pd $ _____

B-0003 *1988 New Member*
Clown with Birthday Cake
"The Sweetest Club Around"

FL $35   BA $38

Comments: 1988; Club Membership fee was $11.50
1988 Membership Renewal Gift.

Personal Data: _____
____Want Mark _____ Mark _____ Purch. 19__ Pd $ _____

B-0104 *1989 Charter Membership*
Bear Holding Balloons
"Have A Beary Special Birthday"

FL $45   BA $35   FLM $30

Comments: 1988; Club Membership fee was $11.50

Personal Data: _____
____Want Mark _____ Mark _____ Purch. 19__ Pd $ _____

B-0004 *1989 New Member*
Bear Holding Balloons
"Have A Beary Special Birthday"

BA $28   FLM $25

Comments: 1988; Club Membership fee was $11.50
Very little trading found on this piece.

Personal Data: _____
____Want Mark _____ Mark _____ Purch. 19__ Pd $ _____

B-0105 *1990 Charter Member*
Clown with Dog Jumping Through Hoop
"Our Club Is A Tough Act To Follow"

BA $40	V $25
FLM $28	

Comments: 1988; Club Membership fee was $13.50.
Prices down from last year.

Personal Data: _____
____Want Mark _____ Mark _____ Purch. 19__ Pd $ _____

B-0005 *1990 New Member*
Clown with Dog Jumping Through Hoop
"Our Club Is A Tough Act To Follow"

BA $30	V $25
FLM $25	

Comments: 1988; Club Membership fee was $13.50.
One collector has reported no white dots in the eyes of the clown and the dog... add $25 to the secondary market value.

Personal Data: _____
____Want Mark _____ Mark _____ Purch. 19__ Pd $ _____

B-0106 *1991 Charter Member*
Clown Jack-in-the-Box
"Jest To Let You Know You're Tops"

V $28   GC $22

Comments: 1990; Club Renewal fee was $13.50
Prices down.

Personal Data: _____
____Want Mark _____ Mark _____ Purch. 19__ Pd $ _____

B-0006   *1991 New Member*
Clown Jack-in-the-Box
"Jest To Let You Know You're Tops"

V $25   GC $20

Comments: 1990; Club Membership fee was $15.00

Personal Data: _____
____Want Mark _____ Mark _____ Purch. 19__ Pd $ _____

B-0107   **1992 Charter Member**
Clown Riding a Train
"All Aboard For Birthday Club Fun"

GC $30   B $25

Comments: 1992; Club Renewal fee was $16.00
Wow! Don't you just love this piece!?

Personal Data: _____
____Want Mark _____ Mark _____ Purch. 19__ Pd $ _____

B-0007   **1992 New Member**
Clown Riding a Train
"All Aboard For Birthday Club Fun"

GC $28   B $25

Comments: 1992; Club Membership fee was $16.00

Personal Data: _____
____Want Mark _____ Mark _____ Purch. 19__ Pd $ _____

B-0108   **1993 Charter Member**
Clown with Heart-Shaped Balloon
"Happiness Is Belonging"

B $25   TRP $22

Comments: 1992; Club Renewal fee was $16.00

Personal Data: _____
____Want Mark _____ Mark _____ Purch. 19__ Pd $ _____

B-0008   **1993 New Member**
Clown with Heart-Shaped Balloon
"Happiness Is Belonging"

B $20   TRP $18

Comments: 1992; Club Membership fee $16.00

Personal Data: _____
____Want Mark _____ Mark _____ Purch. 19__ Pd $ _____

B-0109   **1994 Charter Member**
Girl Clown Feeding Doll
"Can't Get Enough Of Our Club"

TRP $25   S $22

Comments: 1994; Club Renewal fee was $19.00

Personal Data: _____
____Want Mark _____ Mark _____ Purch. 19__ Pd $ _____

B-0009   **1994 New Member**
Girl Clown Feeding Doll
"Can't Get Enough Of Our Club"

TRP $22   S $20

Comments: 1994; Club Membership fee $19.00

Personal Data: _____
____Want Mark _____ Mark _____ Purch. 19__ Pd $ _____

B-0110   **1995 Charter Member**
Frog on Birthday Cake
"Hoppy Birthday"

S $20   H $20

Comments: 1995, Club Renewal fee was $20.00

Personal Data: _____
____Want Mark _____ Mark _____ Purch. 19__ Pd $ _____

B-0010   **1995 New Member**
Frog on Birthday Cake
"Hoppy Birthday"

S $20   H $20

Comments: 1995, Club Membership fee was $20.00
Personal Data: _____
____Want Mark _____ Mark _____ Purch. 19__ Pd $ _____

Birthday Club
Club Pieces

Birthday Club Pieces are available only to Birthday Club Members. Also known as "Members Only" pieces, these are purchased with a redemption certificate included in the Membership Kit. Membership pieces may carry marks for several years.

BC861   **1986 Members Only**
              Raccoon
              "Fishing For Friends"

D $160   OB $130   CT $125

Comments: 1986; Original Retail $10.00
Miniature figurine. First Club Piece, 1986. Many reported the "fish" had been broken from this piece (watch for "glued on" fish). Sellers, be sure to tell your buyer that a piece is *"glued."* Although Club pieces are designated for a specific year, earlier years' marks and following years' marks have also appeared on pieces. Easily found at OB prices.

Personal Data: _____
____Want Mark ____ Mark _____ Purch. 19__ Pd $ _____

BC871   **1987 Members Only**
              Mouse in Sugar Bowl
              "Hi, Sugar"

CT $100   FL $90   BA $85

Comments: 1987; Original Retail $11.00
Second Club Piece, 1987. A great little collectible. He's special!

Personal Data: _____
____Want Mark ____ Mark _____ Purch. 19__ Pd $ _____

BC881   **1988 Members Only**
              Baby Bunny with Patched Carrot
              "Somebunny Cares"

FL $55   BA $50

Comments: 1988; Original Retail $13.50
Third Club Piece, 1988.

Personal Data: _____
____Want Mark ____ Mark _____ Purch. 19__ Pd $ _____

BC891   **1989 Members Only**
              Bear with Bee Hive
              "Can't Bee Hive Myself Without You"

BA $45   FLM $40   V $35

Comments: 1989; Original Retail $13.50
Fourth Club Piece, 1989. Cute piece! Found prices even lower. Insure at these prices.

Personal Data: _____
____Want Mark ____ Mark _____ Purch. 19__ Pd $ _____

BC901   **1990 Members Only**
              Skunk with Bouquet of Flowers
              "Collecting Makes Good Scents"

FLM $35   V $30

Comments: 1990; Original Retail $15.00
Fifth Club Piece, 1990. He's precious!

Personal Data: _____
____Want Mark ____ Mark _____ Purch. 19__ Pd $ _____

BC902   **1990 Members Only**
              Squirrel with Bag of Nuts
              "I'm Nuts Over My Collection"

FLM $38   V $32.50

Comments: 1990; Original Retail $15.00
Sixth Club Piece, 1990. These Club Pieces get sweeter every year!

Personal Data: _____
____Want Mark ____ Mark _____ Purch. 19__ Pd $ _____

BC911   **1991 Members Only**
              Girl Monkey with Pacifier
              "Love Pacifies"

V $28   GC $22

Comments: 1990; Original Retail $15.00
Seventh Club Piece, 1991. A favorite for many!

Personal Data: _____
____Want Mark ____ Mark _____ Purch. 19__ Pd $ _____

BC912   **1991 Members Only**
              Cat and Dog Holding a Paint Brush
              "True Blue Friends"

                        V $30   GC $27.50

Comments: 1990; Original Retail $15.00
Eighth Club Piece, 1991.

Personal Data: _____
____Want Mark ____ Mark _____ Purch. 19__ Pd $ _____

BC921   **1992 Members Only**
              Beaver Building House From Twigs
              "Every Man's House Is His Castle"

                        GC $32   B $28

Comments: 1991; Original Retail $16.50
Ninth Club Piece, 1992. Popular! We have received one report of this
piece having a TRP. Mm, very unusual.

Personal Data: _____
____Want Mark ____ Mark _____ Purch. 19__ Pd $ _____

BC922   **1992 Members Only**
              Dog with Sheep Skin
              "I've Got You Under My Skin"

                        GC $30   B $28

Comments: 1991; Original Retail $16.50
Tenth Club Piece, 1992. The actual figurine shows a sheep's "face."

Personal Data: _____
____Want Mark ____ Mark _____ Purch. 19__ Pd $ _____

BC931   **1993 Members Only**
              Kangaroo with Boxing Gloves
              "Put A Little Punch In Your Birthday"

                        B $22   TRP $18

Comments: 1991; Original Retail $16.00
Eleventh Club Piece, 1993.

Personal Data: _____
____Want Mark ____ Mark _____ Purch. 19__ Pd $ _____

BC932   **1993 Members Only**
              Owls Sitting on Branch
              "Owl Always Be Your Friend"

                        B $22   TRP $20

Comments: 1991; Original Retail $16.00
Twelfth Club Piece, 1993.

Personal Data: _____
____Want Mark ____ Mark _____ Purch. 19__ Pd $ _____

BC941   **1994 Members Only**
              Turtle with Mouse On Back
              "God Bless Our Home"

                        TRP $18   S $18

Comments: 1993; Original Retail $16.00
Thirteenth Club Piece, 1994.

Personal Data: _____
____Want Mark ____ Mark _____ Purch. 19__ Pd $ _____

BC942   **1994 Members Only**
              Penguin and Pelican
              "You're A Pel-I-Can Count On"

                        TRP $22   S $18

Comments: 1994; Original Retail $16.00
Fourteenth Club Piece, 1994-95.

Personal Data: _____
____Want Mark ____ Mark _____ Purch. 19__ Pd $ _____

BC951   **1995 Members Only**
              Porcupine
              "Making A Point To Say You're Special"

                        S $15

Comments: 1994; Original Retail $15.00
Fifteenth Club Piece, 1995.

Personal Data: _____
____Want Mark ____ Mark _____ Purch. 19__ Pd $ _____

BC952 **1995 Members Only**
Clown with Birthday Cake
"10 Wonderful Years Of Wishes"

S $50

Comments: 1995; Original Retail $50.00
Sixteenth Club Piece, 1995.

Personal Data: _____
____Want Mark ____ Mark _____ Purch. 19__ Pd $ _____

Precious Moments creator Sam Butcher was presented with the Missouri Travel and Tourism Hall of Fame Award by Governor Mel Carnahan and Director of the Missouri Division of Tourism Marjorie Beenders at the Missouri Conference on Tourism in Jefferson City.

Sam Butcher also received the Richard M. Webster Citizen of the Year Award at the annual Carthage, MO, Chamber of Commerce Banquet January 12, 1995. The award was a Bill Snow Sculpture and was presented by Janet Webster (pictured). State Representative Bubs Hohulin presented Sam with a proclamation from the Missouri House of Representatives and a state manual.

Photos and information by Ron Graber, The Carthage Press, Carthage, MO.

Birthday Train

It is not necessary to join the Birthday Club in order to get "Birthday Train" pieces. The animals with numerals may be purchased from retailers; no redemption forms are necessary. Ages Nine and Ten debuted in the Spring of 1992. Collectors are hoping these will go to age sixteen in years to come, but today retailers are happy just to get delivery on pieces one through ten. This is especially so for ages one, two, three and four due to their popularity for young children. The Birthday Train cars are designed to hook together starting with the Clown, then Age 10, Age 9, etc., ending with the Baby Teddy on the Caboose.

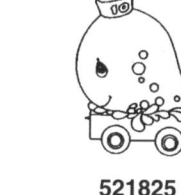

16004
Clown Pulling Train
See page 56

521825
Age 10 - Whale
See page 103

521833
Age 9 - Horse
See page 103

109460
Age 8 - Ostrich
See page 71

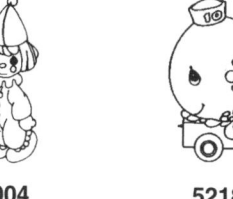

109479
Age 7 - Leopard
See page 71

15997
Age 6 - Giraffe
See page 56

15989
Age 5 - Lion
See page 56

15970
Age 4 - Elephant
See page 55

15954
Age 3 - Pig
See page 55

15962
Age 2 -Seal
See page 55

15946
Age 1 - Lamb
See page 55

15938
Baby - Teddy/
Caboose
See page 55

Numerals one through four are the hardest to find at retailers as these are the most popular for "gift" buyers. This set is planned to go only to age ten until further notice. Numeral decals have been found to be missing on each of these pieces. Add $50-75 to the regular secondary market value of these "missing numeral" pieces.

Birthday Series Figurines

The Birthday Series, a unique collection of charming little animals, is a delightful way to celebrate a child's special day (many adults are also captivated by this collection). It is not required that you be a Birthday Club member to acquire these figurines and ornaments.

524506
Pig with Gift
See page 118

527769
Octopus
See page 126

526924
Elephant with
String Around Trunk
See page 121

105953
Skunk and Mouse
See page 69

522260
Giraffe with
Baby in Mouth
See page 106

521671
Camel with Monkey
on Back
See page 102

105945
Elephant
Showering Mouse
See page 69

527343
Chick with
Birthday Cake
See page 124

527270
Two Dogs
Hugging
See page 123

521175
Kangaroo with
Baby in Pouch
See page 99

524492
Cat with Bird
in Cage
See page 117

521043
Gorilla with Fan
See page 99

104418
Rhino with Bird
See page 68

520659
Bear with Cake
See page 96

128686
Rabbits with Cake
See page 79

183792
Bunny on Snowball
See page 87

531057
Dog with
Hair in Eyes
See page 134

Sammy's Circus Superstars gather together to have fun and support Easter Seals .

Page 165

Birthday Series Ornaments

1986
102466
ORNAMENT
Reindeer
See page 65

1987
104515
ORNAMENT
Bear in Tub/Skis
See page 68

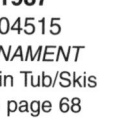

1988
520292
ORNAMENT
Kitten on Wreath
See page 93

1989
520462
ORNAMENT
Dog/Gift Box
See page 94

1990
520497
ORNAMENT
Kitten with Ornament
See page 95

1991
520438
ORNAMENT
Bunny with Ice
Skates
See page 94

1992
520411
ORNAMENT
Squirrel on
Dated Log
See page 94

1993
520489
ORNAMENT
Turtle with Gift
See page 94

1994
530972
ORNAMENT
Bear in Heart
See page 133

1995
520403
ORNAMENT
Hippo
See page 94

1996
128708
ORNAMENT
Owl
See page 80

Event Figurines

1988
115231
Girl Carrying
Bag/Balloons
See page 78

1989
520861
Girl with Slate
See page 98

1990
523526
Girl with Fan
See page 111

1991
527122
Girl with Puppy
in Blanket
See page 122

1992
527319
Girl Wading
with Duck
See page 123

1993
530158
Girl in Raincoat
with Dog
See page 130

1994
529982
Girl Blowing
Bubbles
See page 129

1995
528080
Girl with
Signboard
See page 127

1996
136836
Girl with Guitar
See page 82

Open House Ornaments

1990
525057
Bundles Of Joy
See page 119

1992
529648
*The Magic Starts
With You*
See page 127

1993
529974
*An Event For
All Seasons*
See page 141

1994
520470
*Take A Bow
Cuz You're My
Christmas Star*
See page 94

1995
150134
*Merry
Chrismoose*
See page 83

Easter Seals Figurines

Easter Seals ®

9" Easter Seals Figurines
"Announced Each July"

1987
107999
Girl on Crutches
See page 71

1988
115479
Boy with
Arm Braces/Dog
See page 79

1989
522376
Girl with Easter
Lily in Hands
See page 106

1990
524522
Girl with Chick
in Egg
See page 118

1988
104531
Girl with Bunny
See page 68

1989
520322
Girl with
Goose
See page 93

1990
523283
Girl with
String of Hearts
See page 110

1991
527114
Girl with
Bluebird
See page 122

1992
527173
Girl Hand-Signing
"I Love You"
See page 123

1993
530026
Girl with
Trophy Cup
See page 129

1994
531111
Girl with Pail
of Oysters
See page 134

1991
523879
Girl with Butterfly
See page 114

1992
526010
Girl Holding
Kitten
See page 120

1993
529680
Girl Kneeling with
Bunnies in Lap
See page 128

1995
524387
Girl with Roses
See page 117

1996
526827
Girl with
Piggy Bank
See page 121

1997
192368
Boy with basketball in
wheelchair
See page 89.

1994
531243
Girl with Basket
of Roses
See page 134

1995
526886
Angel with
World in Hands
See page 121

1996
152277
Girl with Daisy
See page 84.

Easter Seals Ornaments

1990
225290
ORNAMENT
Girl with
Chick in Egg
See page 89

1991
233196
ORNAMENT
Girl with Dove
See page 89

1992
238899
ORNAMENT
Girl Signing
"I Love You"
See page 90

1993
250112
ORNAMENT
Girl with
Trophy Cup
See page 90

1994
244570
ORNAMENT
Girl with Pail
of Oysters
See page 90

1995
128899
ORNAMENT
Girl with Roses
See page 80

1996
152579
ORNAMENT
Girl with
Piggy Bank
See page 84

1997
192384
ORNAMENT
Boy with basketball in
wheelchair
See page 89

Wreaths

Bea Butler's Christmas Wreaths

111465   1987 Christmas Wreath w/8 Ornaments

See Photo Above.

With "Heaven Bound" error upside down
on plane ornament. $245-250

                                                       CT $195-200

Comments: 1986; Original Retail $150.00

Personal Data: _____
____Want Mark ____ Mark _____ Purch. 19__ Pd $ _____

**112348   Porcelain Bell
            from the '87 Christmas Wreath**

Photo Not Available.

With Hook   CT $75-80
Without Hook   CT $60-62

Comments: 1986 Many bells were broken off the wreath, leaving no
hook on the bell. Most bells for sale by collectors have a broken hook.

Personal Data: _____
____Want Mark ____ Mark _____ Purch. 19__ Pd $ _____

1988 Christmas Wreath with Ornaments

See Photo Above.

                                    FL $115-120
                    Bell alone   FL $50-55

Comments: 1987; Original Retail $100.00

Personal Data: _____
____Want Mark ____ Mark _____ Purch. 19__ Pd $ _____

CHAPEL LITHOGRAPHS

Chapel Masterpieces, Set One

The Life Of Christ

A Collector's Set of Seven
16" x 20"
Limited Edition Lithographs
750 Numbered Sets,
75 Artist Proof Sets.
Original Retail $420

Chapel Masterpieces, Set Two

Heroes Of The Old Testament

A Collector's Set of Seven 16" x 20"
Limited Edition Lithographs - 1990
1,950 Numbered Sets,
150 Artist Proof Sets.
Original Retail $550

RETIRED 12/31/93
All lithos unsold as of 12/31/93
were burned at the Chapel
in February, 1994.
See the May '94 issue of
Precious Collectibles™ for
press coverage. Rosie and Dave
were personally invited
to attend this special event.

Samuel and his mother stand
before the Temple of Shiloh.

Esther pleas to the King for her
people, Israel.

Chapel Masterpieces, Volume Three

Hallelujah Square

An Exclusive 22" x 28"
Limited Edition Lithograph -1991
2,500 Numbered Sets,
200 Artist Proof Sets.
Original Retail $150

*Artist Proof Sets are signed by
Sam and are "hand picked" as to
the "best productions"
from the presses.*

Chapel Masterpieces, Set Four

The Seven Days Of The Creation

A Collector's Set of Seven Limited Edition Lithographs
Each lithograph has an image area of 10" x 18½" on a 13" x 21½" sheet.

RETIRED 12/31/93
All unsold lithos were burned
at the Chapel in February, 1994.
Each print includes a certificate
of authenticity signed by Sam
and his son Jon Butcher, which were
hand-numbered and embossed
with the artist's signature.
**3,000 Numbered Sets,
250 Artist Proof Sets.
Original Retail
$295/set of 7**

Chapel Masterpieces, Set Five
Phil's Mural

This print is 23" x 23," signed by Sam Butcher,
and presented in a white leather portfolio.
RETIRED 12/31/93.
All unsold lithos were burned at the Chapel in
February, 1994.

Each print includes a certificate
of authenticity signed by Jon Butcher.
Limited to 2,250 prints.   Original Retail $175

Chapel Masterpieces, Set Six
Jonathan & David Mural

Size: 25" x 15"
Each print includes a Certificate of Authenticity
Exclusively Limited to 1,000 prints
875 numbered prints, 125 Artist Proofs.
Original Retail $175

*"I know it's a club meeting
but you have to leave your
club outside."*

Precious Moments® Paraphernalia

Dealers' Plaque - Girl/Boy on Stump - Shiny Glass $120
Dealers' Plaque - Girl At Oven $100
Crewel Pictures on Brown Velvet ....$45 ea.
Avon Figs. (5) w/Precious Moments® inscription, see pg.XV $95
Old J&D Buttons ....$50 ea.
Christmas Embroidered Stockings $10
Cardboard Display Cards:
    "Hello Lord" $40
    "Curler Girl" $40
    "Five Year Piece" $20
    Others $10
Old J&D Cards $10
British PM Cards $10
J&D Puzzles...$20
Cloisonné pin – Enesco gift pin (tie-tack back) $25
Dear Customer – J&D Retailer Poster – mint in frame $200
Spanish Posters $75
5 year Enesco Pin $18
7 year Enesco Tac-pin $10
Magnet Gift from Enesco for signing up new Members $2
Keychain $1
J&D Posters $25-40
1983 Enesco Round Blue Angel Pin $50
J&D Cloisonné Pins ....$25 ea.
J&D Bicentennial Greeting Cards...$20-25
Reg. Capiz Ornaments (Many appear to be coming apart) $25
Capiz Plaque Displays $45
Enesco's Birthday Club Animal Cloisonné Pin......................$15
Cheerleader Pin for collection of 200 or more $5
J&D Clown Dolls..$60
1990 Porcelain Egg (NM; more orders than production) $35
Medallion received from 1993 Convention $50
Medallion received from 1993 Enesco Cruise ....$200 up
PM008 - 1987 Wreath Filigree Medallion $50
PM030 - Goose Girl Medallion
     (Received from Orient Tour)......................................$350 up

I received the Orient medallion, #495301, in a lavender gift box when I took the Orient Tour. The inscription was "A Special Gift Commemorating My Trip to the Precious Moments® Facility, April 1990." Several feel this medallion should be insured for at least $500. (I received one offer of $350 from an ad in 1993.) Has anyone sold theirs? How much did you receive?

J&D PEWTER

Until 1990 the J&D pewter was rising steadily on the secondary market as it was no longer available on the retail market. Collectors were disappointed to see it reissued and once again available in the summer of 1990. It is now being produced by the Fort Company for Precious Moments Company. It appears the "same molds" are being used. Prices seem to remain stable, but there's much less trading now on the J&D Pewter than in previous years. Let us know if you are buying or selling the pewter in 1994. It's my opinion less than 20 avid Precious Moments collectors have "all" the pewter... if that many. Not being traded as in the mid '80s!

(Painted pewter by Enesco NOT being sought after as a collectible on the secondary market to date.)

Pewter by the Jonathan & David Company

Insure for replacement cost

BABY CUPS

JY227	'82 Dated Angel/Boy	$20	$45.00
JY228	'82 Dated Angel/Girl	$20	$40.00
JY237	'83 Dated Angel/Girl	$20	$40.00
JY238	'83 Dated Angel/Boy	$20	$40.00

BELLS

JY202	Jesus Loves Me/Girl	$15	$50.00
JY203	Jesus Loves Me/Boy	$15	$50.00
JY205	Graduate Boy	$15	$50.00
JY206	Graduate Girl	$15	$50.00
JY208	Angels On a Cloud	$15	$50.00
JY219	'82 Dated Drummer Boy	$15	$50.00
JY225	Angel/Trumpet	$15	$40.00
JY239	'83 Dated Boy/Wreath	$15	$50.00
JY402	'84 Dated Choir Girl	$15	$45.00
JY405	'83 Dated Angel/Heart (Hardest to find)	$15	$65.00

BRACELETS

JY119	Jesus Loves Me/Girl	$13	$25.00
JY120	Jesus Loves Me/Boy	$13	$25.00
JY121	Girl/Goose	$13	$38.00
JY122	Graduate Girl	$13	$25.00
JY123	Graduate Boy	$13	$25.00
JY124	Girl/Candle and Doll	$13	$28.00

CHARMS

JY101	Jesus Loves Me/Girl	$10	$25.00
JY102	Jesus Loves Me/Boy	$10	$25.00
JY103	Girl/Goose	$10	$30.00
JY104	Graduate Girl	$10	$35.00

(The Girl Graduate is hardest to find, probably because it was given as gift.)

JY105	Graduate Boy	$10	$25.00
JY106	Girl/Candle and Doll	$10	$25.00
JY151	Bride and Groom	$14	$28.00
JY152	Boy and Girl On Cloud	$14	$35.00
JY153	Boy and Girl on Tree Stump	$14	$40.00
JY154	Boy and Girl/Baby	$14	$25.00

FIGURINES

JY200	Nativity Set	$100	$200.00
JY231	Graduate Girl	$30	$110.00
JY232	Graduate Boy	$30	$100.00
JY233	Girl/Candle and Doll	$30	$90.00
JY234	Girl/Goose	$30	$130.00
JY235	Jesus Loves Me/Girl	$30	$100.00
JY236	Jesus Loves Me/Boy	$30	$100.00
JY243	Drummer Boy	$30	$130.00
JY244	Angel/Trumpet	$30	$150.00
JY245	Wise Men (set of 3)	$90	$350.00
JY303	Boy/Ice Cream Cone	$40	$90.00
JY304	Girl/Puppies	$40	$150.00
JY305	Grandma in Rocker	$40	$90.00
JY306	Mother Sew Dear	$40	$90.00
JY307	Bride and Groom	$45	$100.00

KEY CHAINS

JY125	Bride and Groom	$17	$40.00
JY126	Boy and Girl on Cloud	$17	$40.00
JY127	Boy and Girl on Tree Stump	$17	$35.00
JY128	Boy and Girl/Baby	$17	$35.00

NECKLACES

JY113	Jesus Loves Me/Girl	$12	$40.00
JY114	Jesus Loves Me/Boy	$12	$40.00
JY115	Girl/Goose	$12	$40.00
JY116	Graduate Girl	$12	$30.00
JY117	Graduate Boy	$12	$28.00
JY118	Girl/Candle and Doll	$12	$30.00

PLATES

JY230	Nativity	$15	$38.00
JY242	Two Boys at Manger	$15	$35.00
JY300	Mother Sew Dear	$15	$40.00
JY404	Boy at Manger/Butterfly	$15	$40.00

SPOONS

JY212	Jesus Loves Me/Boy	$12	$40.00
JY213	Jesus Loves Me/Girl	$12	$40.00
JY214	Girl/Goose	$12	$40.00
JY215	Graduate Boy	$12	$40.00
JY216	Graduate Girl	$12	$40.00
JY217	Girl/Candle and Doll	$12	$40.00
JY220	'82 Dated Drummer Boy	$12	$60.00
JY226	Angel/Trumpet	$12	$40.00
JY240	'83 Dated Boy/Wreath	$12	$50.00
JY301	Mother Sew Dear	$12	$60.00
JY401	'84 Dated Choir Girl	$12	$38.00
JY407	'85 Dated Angel/Heart (Hard to Find)	$12	$70.00

If Sold Individually $558
If Sold as a Complete Set $465-510

THIMBLES

JY201	Mother Sew Dear	$16	$40.00
JY218	'82 Dated Drummer Boy	$16	$55.00
JY224	Angel/Trumpet	$16	$45.00
JY241	'83 Dated Boy/Wreath	$16	$45.00
JY246	Girl/Pie	$16	$55.00
JY302	Grandma	$16	$45.00
JY403	'84 Dated Choir Girl	$16	$45.00
JY406	'85 Dated Angel/Heart (Hard to Find)	$16	$60.00

**PAINTED PEWTER LICENSED BY SAMUEL J. BUTCHER COMPANY
PRODUCED BY ENESCO IMPORTS CORP.**

Because there is no secondary market increase on painted pewter and the numerous new productions by Precious Moments Company, we do not list this category. Should these pieces enter the secondary market, then we will once again include painted pewter in this guide as well as the Precious Moments Company pewter.

Left: Donna Pierce expresses her feelings on her Precious Moments collection, "I look at my Precious Moments figurines and wonder if, when Sam was creating them, he felt the same way I do about the joy children bring into our lives. My collection adds up to over 400 pieces. As with my granddaughters, I could not pick a favorite."

Pictured are club members and their club coordinator. Sharing Precious Moments Club is sponsored by Altemueller Jewelry Store. (Photo reprinted with permission from Missourian Publishing Co.)

The Sharing Precious Moments Club in Washington, Missouri, donated 30 hand-made bears to the children hurt in the Oklahoma City bombing. The bears were mailed to the fire chief there, for distribution.

Above: Together, Jack and Treva Jennings enjoy a large collection of Precious Moments "kids." Jack and Treva's collection was named Precious Collectibles™ collection of the month for August 1995.

Left: Doreen Wixson and her husband both share the love of collecting Precious Moments figurines. Doreen's husband even built a special 16 x 18 room just for Doreen's beloved collection. Wow!

Left: The Tulsa Precious Moments Club of Tulsa, OK, gave $250 to the Oklahoma City Bombing Victims Scholarship Fund. The club also donated 19 Precious Moments® figurines entitled Safe In The Arms Of Jesus, to be given to family members who lost loved ones in this tragedy.
Diana H., Collinsville, OK

Right: The My Favorite Fan Precious Moments Club actively participates in community projects. For the past several years during the holiday season, this club has collected food and toys for distribution through their local food pantry. The club also sold hand made craft items to raise money for local charities.

Diana Anderson has over 600 Precious Moments figurines and 51 PMC dolls. In the picture (right) she proudly displays her newly acquired McCoon's County collection. She credits the Weekly Collectors' Gazette™ with helping her acquire these charming figurines.

Left: Cathy Robbins received her first Precious Moments piece as a birthday gift in 1980. She became a serious collector in 1988 and her collection has grown to 273 figurines. Cathy's husband shares her enthusiasm for collecting and often surprises her with rare or retired pieces. Her most memorable experience was meeting Sam Butcher and having him sign her 200th piece!

The Stories...

PM-811 **Hello, Lord, It's Me Again** p.152

Jon, Sam's oldest son, inspired this figurine after a romantic setback.

E-2823 **To God Be The Glory** p. 16

The figurine depicts Sam's life. Sam feels that the Lord has blessed him with the ability to draw children, but believes it is not his gift but the Lord's. The gift is only on loan to him. This may be Sam's favorite piece.

PM-851 **The Lord Is My Shepherd** p.153

This figurine was inspired by the warm and sensitive spirit of Sam's second daughter Debbie.

E-1378 **God Loveth A Cheerful Giver** p. 7

Debbie, Sam's daughter, inspired this piece. Sam will probably never forget Debbie, with her box full of puppies, asking him if any of his friends needed a pet.

PM-842 **Trust In The Lord To The Finish** p. 153

Sam began the painting for this figurine on his way to the Philippines. His youngest brother Hank always loved driving race cars. After a successful racing career the crowds' roar eventually died down. Sam realized that trust in the Lord would lead to the finish line.

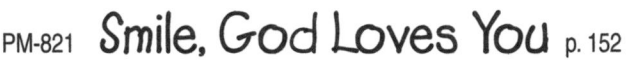

PM-821 **Smile, God Loves You** p. 152

Sam believes that outward appearances don't matter and that "you can't judge a book by its cover."

100110 **Lord, I'm Coming Home** p. 58

This design was inspired by a collector who was an Idea Contest winner. Her brother, who loved to play ball, died at the young age of 19. Sam was moved by the collector's story and her idea for a figurine, so he created this piece.

PM - 831 **Dawn's Early Light** p.152

Sam created this figurine as a tribute to his memories of his sister Dawn guarding over him as a child.

E-1376 **Love One Another** p. 7

This was the first Precious Moments art. Tammy sat by "Uncle Bill" on a stool back to back and the love she portrayed for Uncle Bill was the inspiration for the first Precious Moments figurine. The original art was stolen from the Jonathan & David Company.

100145 **God Bless The Day We Found You** p. 58

Heather was adopted by Sam and Katie in 1974. This figurine was created as a token of love for her.

PM-822 Put On A Happy Face p. 152

Sam created this figurine because he believes that laughter and happiness are contagious. This figurine received the 1983 Figurine of the Year award from The National Association of Limited Edition Dealers.

PM-862 I'm Following Jesus p. 154

After encountering a jobless Filipino friend, Carlito, Sam was inspired to create this figurine. Carlito and his family trusted the Lord to take care of their needs. Eventually, Carlito got his own cab which has a sign in the window which reads, "I'm Following Jesus."

12149 Part Of Me Wants To Be Good p.47

Albern Cuidad of the Philippines was always in trouble. He would make one mistake after another and then ask you to forgive him; he meant to be good.

PM-841 God's Ray Of Mercy p. 153

Sam was inspired to create this angel because of his older brother, Ray Butcher. Sam feels the figurine depicts his brother's warm and sensitive spirit.

E-2829 I'm Sending You A White Christmas p. 17

Sam's mother was born in Michigan, but was moved to Florida at an early age. After the death of her father, her mother moved the family back to Michigan. Sam's mother was only five years old and had never seen snow. Upon the first snow his mother was found packing snowballs in a box to be mailed to her relatives in Florida.

E-1374B Praise The Lord Anyhow p. 6

Philip, Sam's second son, was the inspiration for this figurine. Sam said you couldn't spend much time with him before you threw up your hands lovingly and said, Praise The Lord Anyhow!

100226 The Lord Giveth And The Lord Taketh Away p. 59

After returning home from the Philippines, Sam found the house in total chaos. When he saw the empty, tipped-over canary cage, Sam realized that the family cat had eaten the canary.

E-3108 The Hand That Rocks The Future p. 22

This was designed for Katie, the mother of Sam's children. Once, when Katie was upset after a disagreement with Sam, she sat down to feed Jon. Sam noticed as she fed Jon each bite she would smile. He asked her why she smiled even though she was crying. She told him that the baby would digest his food better.

E-7156 I Believe In Miracles p.36

Sam's former partner, Bill, was given no hope for his eyesight, but through prayer Bill's sight was restored. This figurine also became the official gift of Child's Wish, an organization for terminally ill children.

PM-852 I Love To Tell The Story p. 153

Inspired by the old Christian song, this piece was dedicated to Pastor Royal Blue. Pastor Blue led Sam to the Lord Jesus. "The child is speaking to a lamb, which symbolizes a pastor feeding God's flock with the bread of life, which is the word of God."

Samuel J. Butcher.....

Reprinted from Precious Collectibles' 1995 Secondary Market Price Guide.

Turn Your Eyes Upon Jesus

Unto Us A Child Is Born

Samuel John Butcher, born on January 1, 1939, in Jackson, Michigan, was the third child born to Leon Donald Butcher, a mechanic of English-Irish descent, and Evelyn Mae (Curry) Butcher, of Lebanese and Syrian ancestry.

Safe In The Arms Of Jesus

Sam received many *Blessings From Above*. He was described as being a different child, alone most of the time, and would spend hours under the kitchen table, writing and illustrating his own stories. His parents recognized his gift at an early age. *Have I Got News For You,* by the time he was in kindergarten, Sam knew he would be an artist. His teachers recognized his gift and gave him much encouragement. While in kindergarten Sam illustrated "Little Black Sambo."

When he was 10 years old, Sam's family moved to a small, mountainous community in Northern California. Sam spent many hours by himself, drawing and painting the scenery around him. It may have been there that he learned *We Are God's Workmanship.*

Guess who? It's Sam!

Lord Help Me Make The Grade

Sam loved music and played the accordion and piano. He was popular in high school; he drew pictures and gave of his talents freely to *Brighten Someone's Day*. Sam was elected president of the sophomore class and vice-president of the student body. He worked on the school yearbook staff and the track team but, as *It's What's Inside That Counts,* nothing could take the place of art.

Sam's art teacher, Mr. Moravec, is the person he credits with teaching him how to put life into his paintings. Because of Mr. Moravec's

Sam's first art at age 7.

instruction, Sam was awarded a scholarship to one of the finest private art schools in the country, the College of Arts and Crafts in Berkeley, California.

With This Ring I

Sam and Katie Cushman were married in 1959. After Jon and Philip were born, Sam and Katie began attending North Valley Baptist Church in Redding, California, near their home to *Worship The Lord.* Pastor Royal Blue was God's instrument to lead Sam to the Lord. After Sam became a Christian the Lord was able to give him direction and a place to channel his ability, *To God Be The Glory!* Sam painted "his tallest picture ever" on the baptismal wall at the North Valley Baptist church. Sam worked and studied the Bible with fervor. Shortly after becoming a Christian he was offered a job in the shipping department at the international office of Child Evangelism Fellowship (CEF) in Grand Rapids, Michigan. *Walking By Faith,* Sam moved his family to Michigan and was quickly promoted to the art department.

As Sam's talent and ability grew, so did his family. More *Bundles Of Joy,* Tammy, Debbie and Timmy, followed Philip. When the work load for CEF grew to be too much, a new artist, Bill Biel, was brought in to work with Sam. Bill and Sam became *Friends To The End*. When Katie became ill, Sam and his young family returned to California to be near her parents.

Bringing God's Blessing To You

After Donny was born, Sam received a phone call from CEF asking him to come back to Grand Rapids. About one year after his return to Michigan, Sam became the storyteller for the CEF national television program, "The Tree House Club," first telling *The Story Of God's Love,* then illustrating it. While watching a film one day, Bill and Sam realized the need for visual aids in the Christian

Rev. Blue led Sam to the Lord

Sam Butcher and Bill Biel look on as Yasuhei Fujioka's special talent transforms Sam's original drawings into delicate three-dimensional art.

teaching field. With a bit of poster paint and God-given talent, they began the Jonathan & David Company.

The J&D Company first designed buttons and Bible flannelgraph backgrounds for Sunday schools and did free lance work for other companies. Mott Media persuaded Sam and Bill to attend the Christian Booksellers Convention in California. When they were told they could have a booth of their own, Sam quickly began preparing greeting cards; Bill thought of the name Precious Moments® for these products.

Believe The Impossible

The Lord's hand in Sam's life and work is evident. Eugene Freedman (president and chief executive of Enesco Imports Corp.) wanted to produce Sam's art work in three-dimensional figurines. Master sculptor Yasuhei Fujioka of Nagoya, Japan, was sensitive in soul and could comprehend what Sam wanted to accomplish even though they didn't speak the same language. With unequaled skill he recreated Sam's work, with all of its intricate detail, in figural form.

Sam Butcher and Bill Biel

I Love To Tell The Story

Today, Sam travels throughout the world spreading the message of Precious Moments® but his message doesn't stop with the drawings he has created. He tells collectors everywhere that God is waiting to help us in every part of our lives and that *There Is Joy In Serving Jesus*. Sam cares deeply about those who have been wounded in life and he shares the hope we have in Christ.

Make Me A Blessing

Another avenue through which Sam proclaims that *God Is Love* is the Precious Moments Chapel located near Carthage, Missouri. "The Chapel is my gift of thanksgiving to the Lord for all that He has given me," said Sam. "It also is my gift to all the people who appreciate Precious Moments, so that they might come and see my expression of love for the Lord."

Sam is currently working on an exciting "angelic" fountain which, when completed, will be a spectacular addition to the Chapel grounds. This Fountain of the Angels will feature dozens of sculpted bronze angels in many different poses. You will want to take a trip to the Chapel when this projected is completed and *Join In On The Blessings.*

Blessed Are The Humble

The work of this humble, talented man speaks for itself. Sam has been blessed by God, not only with his artistry, but with the message of Christ which he so readily and naturally shares with everyone he meets all over the world as *Sharing Is Universal.* Through his special gift, Sam offers a continual witness of the love and the Glory of God. *Precious Moments Last Forever!*

... A Lifetime of Loving, Caring, And Sharing Along The Way

Plate Series
Limited Edition Plates

Inspired Thoughts
1 ......E-5215 ......1981 ....*Love One Another*
2 ......E-7174 ......1982 ....*Make A Joyful Noise*
3 ......E-9257 ......1983 ....*I Believe In Miracles*
4 ......E-2847 ......1984 ....*Love Is Kind*

Mother's Love
1 ......E-5217 ......1981 ....*Mother Sew Dear*
2 ......E-7173 ......1982 ....*The Purr-fect Grandma*
3 ......E-9256 ......1983 ....*The Hand That Rocks The Future*
4 ......E-2848 ......1984 ....*Loving Thy Neighbor*

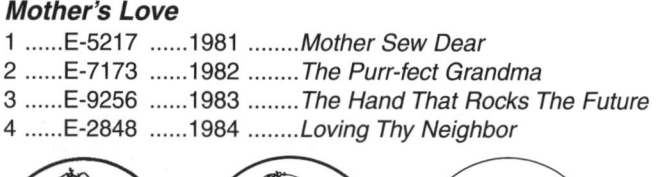

Christmas Collection
1 ......E-5646 ......1981 ....*Come Let Us Adore Him*
2 ......E-2347 ......1982 ....*Let Heaven And Nature Sing*
3 ......E-0538 ......1983 ....*Wee Three Kings*
4 ......E-5395 ......1984 ....*Unto Us A Child Is Born*

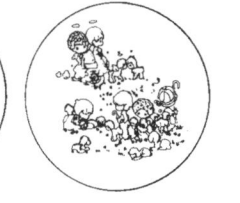

Limited Edition Plates

Mother's Day
1 ......531766 ......1994 ....*Thinking Of You Is What I Really Like To Do*
2 ......129151 ......1995 ....*He Hath Made Everything Beautiful In His Time*
3 ......163716 ......1996 ....*Of All The Mothers I Have Known, There's None as Precious As My Own*

Annual Dated Plates

Joy Of Christmas
1 ......E-2357 ......1982 ....*I'll Play My Drum For Him*
2 ......E-0505 ......1983 ....*Christmastime Is For Sharing*
3 ......E-5396 ......1984 ....*The Wonder Of Christmas*
4 ......15237 ....1985 ....*Tell Me The Story Of Jesus*

Christmas Love
1 ......101834 ......1986 ....*I'm Sending You A White Christmas*
2 ......102954 ......1987 ....*My Peace I Give Unto Thee*
3 ......520284 ......1988 ....*Merry Christmas Deer*
4 ......523003 ......1989 ....*May Your Christmas Be A Happy Home*

●●

Christmas Blessing

1 .....523801 .....1990 ....*Wishing You A Yummy Christmas*
2 .....523860 .....1991 ....*Blessings From Me To Thee*
3 .....527742 .....1992 ....*But The Greatest Of These Is Love*
4 .....530204 .....1993 ....*Wishing You The Sweetest Christmas*

The Beauty of Christmas

1 ......530409 ......1994 ....*You're As Pretty As A Christmas Tree*
2 ......142670 ......1995 ....*He Covers The Earth With His Beauty*

Figurine Series

Baby's First

1 ....E-2840..........*Baby's First Step*
2 ....E-2841..........*Baby's First Picture*
3 .... 12211 ....*Baby's First Haircut*
4 .... 16012 ....*Baby's First Trip*
5 ....520705 ......*Baby's First Pet*
6 ....524077 ......*Baby's First Meal*
7 ....527238 ......*Baby's First Word*
8 ....524069 ....*Baby's First Birthday*

Bridal Party

1 ....E-2831 ....*Bridesmaid*
2 ....E-2836 ....*Groomsman*
3 ....E-2835 ....*Flower Girl*
4 ....E-2833 ....*Ringbearer*
5 ....E-2845 ....*Junior Bridesmaid*
6 ....E-2837 ....*Groom*
7 ....E-2846 ....*Bride*
8 ....E-2838 ....*This Is The Day Which The Lord Hath Made*

Calendar Girl

1 ....109983 ....January	7 ....110051 ....July
2 ....109991 ....February	8 ....110078 ....August
3 ....110019 ....March	9 ....110086 ....September
4 ....110027 ....April	10 ..110094 ....October
5 ....110035 ....May	11 ..110108 ....November
6 ....110043 ....June	12 ..110116 ....December

Clown

1 .... 12262 ......*I Get A Bang Out Of You*
2 .... 12459 ......*Waddle I Do Without You*
3 .... 12467 ......*The Lord Will Carry You Through*
4 .... 12270 ......*Lord, Keep Me On The Ball*
5 ....520632 ....*A Friend Is Someone Who Cares*

(For more clowns not in series see Alphabetical Listing by Description)

Family Christmas Scene All Suspended 1992

1 .... 15776 ....*May You Have The Sweetest Christmas*
2 .... 15784 ....*The Story Of God's Love*
3 .... 15792 ....*Tell Me A Story*
4 .... 15806 ....*God Gave His Best*
5 .... 15814 ....*Silent Night*
6 ....522856 ....*Have A Beary Merry Christmas*
7 ....524883 ....*Christmas Fireplace*

Growing In Grace Series

136204 ....*Infant Angel With Newspaper*
136190 ....*Age 1* - Baby with Cake
136212 ....*Age 2* - Girl with Blocks
136220 ....*Age 3* - Girl with Flowers
136239 ....*Age 4* - Girl with Doll
136247 ....*Age 5* - Girl with Lunch Box
136255 ....*Age 6* - Girl on Bicycle
163740 ....*Age 7* - Girl Nursing Sick Pet
163759 ....*Age 8* - Girl Puppies/Marbles
183865 ....*Age 9* - Girl with Bird
183873 ....*Age 10* - Girl with Bowling Ball
136263 ....*Sweet Sixteen* - Girl Holding Sixteen Roses

Rejoice In The Lord Band Series

12165 ....*Lord, Keep My Life In Tune*
12173 ....*There's A Song In My Heart*
12378 ....*Happiness Is The Lord*
12386 ....*Lord Give Me A Song*
12394 ....*He Is My Song*
12580 ....*Lord, Keep My Life In Tune*

Heavenly Halo Angel Series

This *Series* was so named by collectors who had seen the "Heavenly Halo" Angel Cards. Enesco does not show a *Series* by this name.

E-9260 ......*God's Promises Are Sure*
E-9274 ......*Taste And See That The Lord Is Good*
E-9288 ......*Sending You A Rainbow*
E-9289 ......*Trust In The Lord*

Annual Issues

Child Evangelism Fellowship Pieces

1992 ....527556 ....*Bring The Little Ones To Jesus*
1993 ....521922 ....*Safe In The Arms Of Jesus*
1994 ....531359 ....*Bring The Little Ones To Jesus* - Plate

National Day of Prayer Figurines

1992 ....527564 ....*God Bless The USA*
1993 ....528862 ....*America, You're Beautiful*
1994 ....524158 ....*Lord Teach Us To Pray*

Dated Porcelain Easter Eggs

1991 ....523534 ....*I Will Cherish The Old Rugged Cross*
1992 ....525960 ....*We Are God's Workmanship*
1993 ....528617 ....*Make A Joyful Noise*
1994 ....529095 ....*A Reflection Of His Love*

Cross Series Figurines

1995 ....127019 ....*Love Blooms Eternal*
1996 ....163732 ....*Standing In The Presence Of The Lord*

Masterpiece Series
Porcelain Ball Ornaments

1	523062	1989	*Peace On Earth*
2	523704	1990	*May Your Christmas Be A Happy Home*
3	526940	1991	*May Your Christmas Be Merry*
4	527734	1992	*But The Greatest Of These Is Love*
5	530190	1993	*Wishing You The Sweetest Christmas*
6	530387	1994	*You're As Pretty As A Christmas Tree*
7	142689	1995	*He Covers The Earth With His Beauty*
8	183350	1996	*Peace On Earth... Anyway*

Only the first four Porcelain Ball Ornaments are listed as Masterpiece Series, however, we have included the 1993, 1994, 1995 and 1996 ornaments with this listing.

Four Seasons Series

FIGURINES

1 .....12068 ....1985 ....*The Voice Of Spring* (most sought after)
2 .....12076 ....1985 ....*Summer's Joy*
3 .....12084 ....1986 ....*Autumn's Praise*
4 .....12092 ....1986 ....*Winter's Song*

PLATES

1 .....12106 ....1985 ....*The Voice Of Spring*
2 .....12114 ....1985 ....*Summer's Joy*
3 .....12122 ....1986 ....*Autumn's Praise*
4 .....12130 ....1986 ....*Winter's Song*

THIMBLES

100641 ....Set of Four/Four Seasons

DOLLS

Limited to Two Years Production 1990-1991

1 .....408786 ....*The Voice Of Spring*
2 .....408743 ....*Summer's Joy*
3 .....408808 ....*Autumn's Praise*
4 .....408816 ....*Winter's Song*

JACK-IN-THE BOX

Limited to Two Years Production 1990-1991

1 .....408735 ....*The Voice Of Spring*
2 .....408743 ....*Summer's Joy*
3 .....408751 ....*Autumn's Praise*
4 .....408778 ....*Winter's Song*

REGULAR-SIZED NATIVITY AND ADDITIONS

104000 ...*O Come Let Us Adore Him*
           9-pc w/Cassette (form. E2800)
E-0511 ....*Tubby's First Christmas*
E-0512 ....*It's A Perfect Boy*
E-2360 ....*I'll Play My Drum For Him*
E-2363 ....*Camel*
E-2364 ....*Goat*
E-2365 ....*The First Noel* (boy)
E-2366 ....*The First Noel* (girl)
E-2800 ....*Come Let Us Adore Him* (9-Pc Set)
E-5378 ....*Joy To The World*
E-5379 ....*Isn't He Precious*
E-5621 ....*Donkey*
E-5624 ....*They Followed The Star* (3-Pc Set)
E-5635 ....*Wee Three Kings* (2-Pc Set)
E-5636 ....*Rejoice O Earth*
E-5637 ....*The Heavenly Light*

E-5638 ....*Cow*
E-5639 ....*Isn't He Wonderful* (boy)
E-5640 ....*Isn't He Wonderful* (girl)
E-5644 .....*Nativity Walls* (2-Pc Set)
15490 ......*Honk If You Love Jesus*
102962 ....*It's The Birthday Of A King*
105635 ....*Have I Got News For You*
111333 ....*Come Let Us Adore Him* (4-Pc Set)
115274 ....*Some Bunny's Sleeping*
520357 ....*Jesus The Savior Is Born*
523097 ....*Jesus Is The Sweetest Name I Know*
524875 ....*Happy Birthday Dear Jesus*
526959 ....*We Have Come From Afar*
527750 ....*Wishing You A Comfy Christmas*
529966 ....*Ring Out The Good News*
528072 ....*Nativity Cart*
142751 ....*Making A Trail To Bethlehem*
183954 ....*Shepherd With Lambs*

MINIATURE NATIVITY AND ADDITIONS

E-2395 ...*Come Let Us Adore Him*
............11-Pc Set
E-2387 ...*Three Houses and Palm Tree*
.... 4-Pc Set
E-5384 ...*I'll Play My Drum For Him*
E-5385 ...*Oh Worship The Lord* (boy)
E-5386 ...*Oh Worship The Lord* (girl)
102261 ..*Shepherd Of Love*
102296 ..*Turtle, Rabbit & Lamb*
216624 ..*Wee Three Kings*

108243 ...*They Followed The Star*
520268 ...*Rejoice O Earth*
522988 ...*Isn't He Precious*
522996 ...*Some Bunny's Sleeping*
525286 ...*It's A Perfect Boy*
525278 ...*Tubby's First Christmas*
530492 ...*Happy Birthday Jesus*
528137 ...*Have I Got News For You*
530913 ...*We Have Come Form Afar*
184004 ...*Making A Trail To Bethlehem*

BELLS

E-5620
Shepherd/Lamb
See page 31

E-7179
Bride/Groom
See page 39

E-7175
Boy Graduate
See page 39

E-7176
Girl Graduate
See page 39

E-7181
Mother Sew Dear
See page 39

E-5623
Shepherd
See page 32

E-7183
Grandma
See page 40

E-5208
Boy w/Teddy
See page 26

E-5209
Girl w/Bunny
See page 26

E-5211
Boy/Report Card
See page 27

E-5210
Praying Girl
See page 26

Dated Annual Bells

E-5622
1981 Annual
See page 32

E-2358
1982 Annual
See page 11

E-0522
1983 Annual
See page 3

E-5393
1984 Annual
See page 30

15873
1984 Annual
See page 54

102318
1986 Annual
See page 63

109835
1987 Annual
See page 73

115304
1988 Annual
See page 78

522821
1989 Annual
See page 107

523828
1990 Annual
See page 113

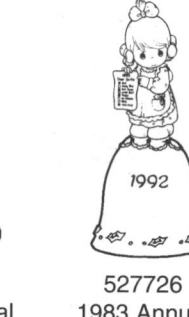

524182
1982 Annual
See page 115

527726
1983 Annual
See page 126

530074
1984 Annual
See page 130

604216
Girl/Christmas
Tree Skirt
See page 137

Dated Annual Ornaments

E-5629
1981 Annual
See page 32

E-2359
1982 Annual
See page 11

E-0513
1983 Annual
See page 2

E-5387
1984 Annual
See page 29

15768
1985 Annual
See page 53

102326
1986 Annual
See page 63

109770
1987 Annual
See page 72

115320
1988 Annual
See page 78

522848
1989 Annual
See page 97

523852
1990 Annual
See page 107

524174
1991 Annual
See page 115

527696
1992 Annual
See page 126

530212
1993 Annual
See page 131

530395
1994 Annual
See page 131

142662
1995 Annual
See page 82

183369
1996 Annual
See page 87

Retired Pieces

ITEM #   NAME ....STYLE ....YR

_____ Retired 1981 _____

| E-1378 | GOD LOVETH A CHEERFUL GIVER | FIGURINE | 1981 |
| E-2011 | COME LET US ADORE HIM | FIGURINE | 1981 |

_____ Retired 1982 _____

| E-1374B | PRAISE THE LORD ANYHOW | FIGURINE | 1982 |

_____ Retired 1983 _____

| E-3112 | GOD'S SPEED | FIGURINE | 1983 |
| E-3118 | EGGS OVER EASY | FIGURINE | 1983 |

_____ Retired 1984 _____

E-1373B	SMILE, GOD LOVES YOU	FIGURINE	1984
E-1380B	O, HOW I LOVE JESUS	FIGURINE	1984
E-1380G	HIS BURDEN IS LIGHT	FIGURINE	1984
E-2368	THE FIRST NOEL	ORNAMENT	1984
E-2806	CHRISTMAS IS A TIME TO SHARE	MUSICAL	1984
E-5211	GOD UNDERSTANDS	BELL	1984
E-6120	WE HAVE SEEN HIS STAR	ORNAMENT	1984

_____ Retired 1985 _____

E-2376	DROPPING OVER FOR CHRISTMAS	ORNAMENT	1985
E-2805	WISHING YOU A SEASON FILLED WITH JOY	FIGURINE	1985
E-2850	MOTHER SEW DEAR	DOLL	1985
E-3107	BLESSED ARE THE PEACEMAKERS	FIGURINE	1985
E-3111	BE NOT WEARY IN WELL DOING	FIGURINE	1985
E-7185	LOVE IS SHARING	MUSICAL	1985

_____ Retired 1986 _____

E-0519	SHARING OUR SEASON TOGETHER	MUSICAL	1986
E-0532	LET HEAVEN AND NATURE SING	ORNAMENT	1986
E-2353	O COME ALL YE FAITHFUL	FIGURINE	1986
E-2369	DROPPING OVER FOR CHRISTMAS	ORNAMENT	1986
E-2841	BABY'S FIRST PICTURE	FIGURINE	1986
E-7157	THERE IS JOY IN SERVING JESUS	FIGURINE	1986
E-9274	TASTE AND SEE THAT THE LORD IS GOOD	FIGURINE	1986

_____ Retired 1987 _____

E-0530	HIS EYE IS ON THE SPARROW	FIGURINE	1987
E-2351	HOLY SMOKES	FIGURINE	1987
E-5377	LOVE IS KIND	FIGURINE	1987
E-5388	JOY TO THE WORLD	ORNAMENT	1987
E-9273	LET LOVE REIGN	FIGURINE	1987

_____ Retired 1988 _____

E-1373G	JESUS IS THE LIGHT	FIGURINE	1988
E-2371	UNICORN	ORNAMENT	1988
E-2822	THIS IS YOUR DAY TO SHINE	FIGURINE	1988
E-5645	REJOICE O EARTH	MUSICAL	1988
12467	THE LORD WILL CARRY YOU THROUGH	FIGURINE	1988
100129	LORD KEEP ME ON MY TOES	FIGURINE	1988

_____ Retired 1989 _____

E-0506	SURROUNDED WITH JOY	FIGURINE	1989
E-0525	YOU CAN'T RUN AWAY FROM GOD	FIGURINE	1989
E-0534	TO THEE WITH LOVE	ORNAMENT	1989
12459	WADDLE I DO WITHOUT YOU	FIGURINE	1989
15504	GOD SENT YOU JUST IN TIME	MUSICAL	1989

_____ Retired 1990 _____

E-0504	CHRISTMASTIME IS FOR SHARING	FIGURINE	1990
E-9268	NOBODY'S PERFECT	FIGURINE	1990
100269	HELP, LORD, I'M IN A SPOT	FIGURINE	1990
100102	MAKE ME A BLESSING	FIGURINE	1990
102423	LORD KEEP ME ON MY TOES	ORNAMENT	1990
520772	MANY MOONS IN SAME CANOE, BLESS-UM YOU...	FIGURINE	1990

_____ Retired 1991 _____

E- 2375	DROPPING OVER FOR CHRISTMAS	FIGURINE	1991
100196	THE SPIRIT IS WILLING BUT THE FLESH IS WEAK	FIGURINE	1991
100528	SCENT FROM ABOVE	FIGURINE	1991
101842	SMILE ALONG THE WAY	FIGURINE	1991
113980	REJOICE O EARTH	ORNAMENT	1991
520640	I'M SO GLAD YOU FLUTTERED INTO MY LIFE	FIGURINE	1991

_____ Retired 1992 _____

E-7156R	I BELIEVE IN MIRACLES	FIGURINE	1/1992
101850	LORD, HELP US KEEP OUR ACT TOGETHER	FIGURINE	1/1992
101702	OUR FIRST CHRISTMAS TOGETHER	MUSICAL	8/1992
109584	HAPPINESS DIVINE	FIGURINE	8/1992
520683	SENDING YOU SHOWERS OF BLESSINGS	FIGURINE	8/1992
520799	SOMEDAY MY LOVE	FIGURINE	8/1992
521566	GLIDE THROUGH THE HOLIDAYS	ORNAMENT	8/1992

Retired 1993

E-1375A	LOVE LIFTED ME	FIGURINE	5/1993
E-3110B	LOVING IS SHARING	FIGURINE	5/1993
105945	SHOWERS OF BLESSINGS	FIGURINE	5/1993
521396	FAITH IS A VICTORY	FIGURINE	5/1993
E-2374	BUNDLES OF JOY	FIGURINE	10/1993
100188	I'M A POSSIBILITY	FIGURINE	10/1993
112402	I'M SENDING YOU A WHITE CHRISTMAS	MUSICAL	10/1993
522112	DON'T LET THE HOLIDAYS GET YOU DOWN	FIGURINE	10/1993

Retired 1994

E-3116	THEE I LOVE	FIGURINE	6/1994
E-9254	PRAISE THE LORD ANYHOW	FIGURINE	6/1994
521590	DON'T LET THE HOLIDAYS GET YOU DOWN	ORNAMENT	6/1994
522260	TO BE WITH YOU IS UPLIFTING	FIGURINE	6/1994
523747	BLESSINGS FROM ABOVE	FIGURINE	6/1994
524271	FRIENDSHIP GROWS WHEN YOU PLANT A SEED	FIGURINE	6/1994
528684	EVERGREEN TREE	FIGURINE	11/1994
529486	AUNT RUTH AND AUNT DOROTHY	FIGURINE	11/1994
529494	PHILIP	FIGURINE	11/1994
529508	NATIVITY	FIGURINE	11/1994
529516	GRANDFATHER	FIGURINE	11/1994
529621	LIGHTED CHAPEL	FIGURINE	11/1994

Retired 1995

100226	THE LORD GIVETH AND THE LORD TAKETH AWAY	FIGURINE	6/1995
106798	PUPPY LOVE IS FROM ABOVE	FIGURINE	6/1995
520632	A FRIEND IS SOMEONE WHO CARES	FIGURINE	6/1995
523623	I'M SO GLAD THAT GOD BLESSED ME WITH A FRIEND LIKE YOU	FIGURINE	6/1995
109762	WE GATHER TOGETHER TO ASK THE LORD'S BLESSING	FIGURINE	11/1995
521299	HUG ONE ANOTHER	FIGURINE	11/1995
522937	FRIENDS NEVER DRIFT APART	ORNAMENT	11/1995
527599	BRINGING YOU A MERRY CHRISTMAS	FIGURINE	11/1995

CHAPEL ONLY

RETIRED 1995:

532088	A KING IS BORN	ORNAMENT	11/1995
604151	A KING IS BORN	FIGURINE	11/1995

SUSPENDED 1995:

523011	THERE'S A CHRISTIAN WELCOME HERE (CHAPEL)	FIGURINE	11/1995

Suspended 1984

ITEM #	NAME	STYLE
E-1375B	PRAYER CHANGES THINGS	FIGURINE
E-1377A	HE LEADETH ME	FIGURINE
E-1377B	HE CARETH FOR YOU	FIGURINE
E-1379A	LOVE IS KIND	FIGURINE
E-1379B	GOD UNDERSTANDS	FIGURINE
E-1381	JESUS IS THE ANSWER	FIGURINE
E-2010	WE HAVE SEEN HIS STAR	FIGURINE
E-2012	JESUS IS BORN	FIGURINE
E-2013	UNTO US A CHILD IS BORN	FIGURINE
E-2345	MAY YOUR CHRISTMAS BE COZY	FIGURINE
E-2350	DROPPING IN FOR CHRISTMAS	FIGURINE
E-2352	O COME ALL YE FAITHFUL	MUSICAL
E-2355	I'LL PLAY MY DRUM FOR HIM	MUSICAL
E-2365	THE FIRST NOEL	FIGURINE
E-2366	THE FIRST NOEL	FIGURINE
E-2367	THE FIRST NOEL	ORNAMENT
E-2381	MOUSE WITH CHEESE	ORNAMENT
E-2386	CAMEL, DONKEY, COW	ORNAMENT
E-2801	JESUS IS BORN	FIGURINE
E-2802	CHRISTMAS IS A TIME TO SHARE	FIGURINE
E-2803	CROWN HIM LORD OF ALL	FIGURINE
E-2804	PEACE ON EARTH	FIGURINE
E-2807	CROWN HIM LORD OF ALL	MUSICAL
E-2808	UNTO US A CHILD IS BORN	MUSICAL
E-3105	HE WATCHES OVER US ALL	FIGURINE
E-3108	THE HAND THAT ROCKS THE FUTURE	FIGURINE
E-3119	IT'S WHAT'S INSIDE THAT COUNTS	FIGURINE
E-4723	PEACE AMID THE STORM	FIGURINE
E-4725	PEACE ON EARTH	FIGURINE
E-4726	PEACE ON EARTH	MUSICAL
E-5200	BEAR YE ONE ANOTHER'S BURDENS	FIGURINE
E-5201	LOVE LIFTED ME	FIGURINE
E-5202	THANK YOU FOR COMING TO MY ADE	FIGURINE
E-5203	LET NOT THE SUN GO DOWN UPON YOUR WRATH	FIGURINE
E-5207	MY GUARDIAN ANGEL	NIGHT LIGHT
E-5210	PRAYER CHANGES THINGS	BELL
E-5214	PRAYER CHANGES THINGS	FIGURINE
E-5623	JESUS IS BORN	BELL
E-5633	COME LET US ADORE HIM	ORNAMENT
E-5634	WEE THREE KINGS	ORNAMENT
E-7155	THANKING HIM FOR YOU	FIGURINE
E-7161	HIS SHEEP AM I	FIGURINE
E-7162	LOVE IS SHARING	FIGURINE
E-7163	GOD IS WATCHING OVER YOU	FIGURINE
E-7164	BLESS THIS HOUSE	FIGURINE
E-7168	MY GUARDIAN ANGEL	FRAME
E-7169	MY GUARDIAN ANGEL	FRAME
E-9283	FOREVER FRIENDS	CONTAINER

Suspended 1985

ITEM #	NAME	STYLE
E-0526	HE UPHOLDETH THOSE WHO CALL	FIGURINE
E-0537	JESUS IS THE LIGHT THAT SHINES	ORNAMENT
E-2344	JOY TO THE WORLD	CANDLE CLIMBERS
E-2349	TELL ME THE STORY OF JESUS	FIGURINE
E-2356	I'LL PLAY MY DRUM FOR HIM	FIGURINE
E-2372	BABY'S FIRST CHRISTMAS	ORNAMENT
E-2377	OUR FIRST CHRISTMAS TOGETHER	FIGURINE
E-2378	OUR FIRST CHRISTMAS TOGETHER	PLATE
E-2809	JESUS IS BORN	MUSICAL
E-4722	LOVE CANNOT BREAK A TRUE FRIENDSHIP	FIGURINE
E-5205	MY GUARDIAN ANGEL	MUSICAL
E-5208	JESUS LOVES ME	BELL
E-5209	JESUS LOVES ME	BELL
E-5619	COME LET US ADORE HIM	FIGURINE
E-5620	WE HAVE SEEN HIS STAR	BELL
E-5627	BUT LOVE GOES ON FOREVER	ORNAMENT
E-5628	BUT LOVE GOES ON FOREVER	ORNAMENT
E-5630	UNTO US A CHILD IS BORN	ORNAMENT
E-5631	BABY'S FIRST CHRISTMAS	ORNAMENT
E-5632	BABY'S FIRST CHRISTMAS	ORNAMENT
E-5639	ISN'T HE WONDERFUL?	FIGURINE
E-5640	ISN'T HE WONDERFUL?	FIGURINE
E-5641	THEY FOLLOWED THE STAR	FIGURINE
E-5642	SILENT KNIGHT	MUSICAL
E-6214B	MIKEY	DOLL
E-6214G	DEBBIE	DOLL
E-7156	I BELIEVE IN MIRACLES	FIGURINE
E-7159	LORD GIVE ME PATIENCE	FIGURINE
E-7167	THE LORD BLESS YOU AND KEEP YOU	CONTAINER
E-7170	JESUS LOVES ME	FRAME
E-7171	JESUS LOVES ME	FRAME
E-7172	REJOICING WITH YOU	PLATE
E-7175	THE LORD BLESS YOU AND KEEP YOU	BELL
E-7176	THE LORD BLESS YOU AND KEEP YOU	BELL
E-9251	LOVE IS PATIENT	FIGURINE
E-9253	THE END IS IN SIGHT	FIGURINE
E-9263	HOW CAN TWO WALK TOGETHER EXCEPT THEY AGREE	FIGURINE
E-9275	JESUS LOVES ME	PLATE
E-9276	JESUS LOVES ME	PLATE
E-9280	JESUS LOVES ME	CONTAINER
E-9281	JESUS LOVES ME	CONTAINER
E-9285	IF GOD BE FOR US, WHO CAN BE AGAINST US	FIGURINE

Suspended 1986

ITEM #	NAME	STYLE
E-0501	SHARING OUR SEASON TOGETHER	FIGURINE
E-0502	JESUS IS THE LIGHT THAT SHINES	FIGURINE
E-0503	BLESSINGS FROM MY HOUSE TO YOURS	FIGURINE
E-0508	PREPARE YE THE WAY OF THE LORD	FIGURINE
E-0520	WEE THREE KINGS	MUSICAL
E-0531	O COME ALL YE FAITHFUL	ORNAMENT
E-0535	LOVE IS PATIENT	ORNAMENT
E-0536	LOVE IS PATIENT	ORNAMENT
E-2361	CHRISTMAS JOY FROM HEAD TO TOE	FIGURINE
E-2826	MAY YOUR BIRTHDAY BE A BLESSING	FIGURINE
E-2827	I GET A KICK OUT OF YOU	FIGURINE
E-3120	TO THEE WITH LOVE	FIGURINE
E-5376	MAY YOUR CHRISTMAS BE BLESSED	FIGURINE
E-5380	A MONARCH IS BORN	FIGURINE
E-5382	FOR GOD SO LOVED THE WORLD	FIGURINE
E-5385	O WORSHIP THE LORD	FIGURINE
E-5386	O WORSHIP THE LORD	FIGURINE
E-5389	PEACE ON EARTH	ORNAMENT
E-5394	WISHING YOU A MERRY CHRISTMAS	MUSICAL
E-6901	PRECIOUS MOMENTS LAST FOREVER	PLAQUE
E-7153	GOD IS LOVE, DEAR VALENTINE	FIGURINE
E-7154	GOD IS LOVE, DEAR VALENTINE	FIGURINE
E-7160	THE PERFECT GRANDPA	FIGURINE
E-7186	LET THE WHOLE WORLD KNOW	MUSICAL
E-7241	MOTHER SEW DEAR	FRAME
E-9261	SEEK YE THE LORD	FIGURINE
E-9262	SEEK YE THE LORD	FIGURINE
E-9287	PEACE ON EARTH	FIGURINE
E-9288	SENDING YOU A RAINBOW	FIGURINE
12203	GET INTO THE HABIT OF PRAYER	FIGURINE
12343	JESUS IS COMING SOON	FIGURINE
12424	AARON	DOLL
12432	BETHANY	DOLL
12475	P.D	DOLL
12483	TRISH	DOLL

Suspended 1987

ITEM #	NAME	STYLE
E-0507	GOD SENT HIS SON	FIGURINE
E-0509	BRINGING GOD'S BLESSING TO YOU	FIGURINE
E-0521	BLESSED ARE THE PURE IN HEART	FRAME
E-2823	TO GOD BE THE GLORY	FIGURINE
E-4720	THE LORD BLESS YOU AND KEEP YOU	FIGURINE
E-5216	THE LORD BLESS YOU AND KEEP YOU	PLATE
E-5381	HIS NAME IS JESUS	FIGURINE
E-6613	GOD SENDS THE GIFT OF HIS LOVE	FIGURINE
E-7165	LET THE WHOLE WORLD KNOW	FIGURINE
E-7177	THE LORD BLESS YOU AND KEEP YOU	FRAME
E-7178	THE LORD BLESS YOU AND KEEP YOU	FRAME
E-9260	GOD'S PROMISES ARE SURE	FIGURINE
E-9289	TRUST IN THE LORD	FIGURINE
12017	LOVING YOU	FRAME
12025	LOVING YOU	FRAME
12033	GOD'S PRECIOUS GIFT	FRAME
12211	BABY'S FIRST HAIRCUT	FIGURINE
12297	IT IS BETTER TO GIVE THAN TO RECEIVE	FIGURINE
12408	WE SAW A STAR	MUSICAL

Suspended 1988

ITEM #	NAME	STYLE
E-0515	TO A SPECIAL DAD	ORNAMENT
E-0533	TELL ME THE STORY OF JESUS	ORNAMENT
E-0539	KATIE LYNNE	DOLL
E-2343	JOY TO THE WORLD	ORNAMENT
E-2348	MAY YOUR CHRISTMAS BE WARM	FIGURINE
E-2362	BABY'S FIRST CHRISTMAS	ORNAMENT
E-2840	BABY'S FIRST STEP	FIGURINE
E-5206	MY GUARDIAN ANGEL	MUSICAL
E-6118	BUT LOVE GOES ON FOREVER	CANDLE CLIMBERS
E-7181	MOTHER SEW DEAR	BELL
E-7183	THE PURR-FECT GRANDMA	BELL
E-7242	THE PURR-FECT GRANDMA	FRAME
E-9266	OUR LOVE IS HEAVEN SCENT	CONTAINER
	I'M FALLING FOR SOME BUNNY AND IT HAPPENS TO BE YOU	CONTAINER
12335	YOU CAN FLY	FIGURINE
12351	HALO, AND MERRY CHRISTMAS	FIGURINE
100021	TO MY FAVORITE PAW	FIGURINE
100668	THIMBLES -- CLOWNS	THIMBLES
102431	SERVE WITH A SMILE	ORNAMENT
102458	SERVE WITH A SMILE	ORNAMENT
102490	SHARING OUR CHRISTMAS TOGETHER	FIGURINE

Suspended 1989

ITEM #	NAME	STYLE
E-2346	LET HEAVEN AND NATURE SING	MUSICAL
E-2364	GOAT	FIGURINE
E-2851	KRISTY DOLL	DOLL
E-5213	GOD IS LOVE	FIGURINE
E-5378	JOY TO THE WORLD	FIGURINE
E-5390	MAY GOD BLESS YOU WITH A PERFECT HOLIDAY SEASON	ORNAMENT
E-5391	LOVE IS KIND	ORNAMENT
E-9252	FORGIVING IS FORGETTING	FIGURINE
12149	PART OF ME WANTS TO BE GOOD	FIGURINE
12165	LORD KEEP MY LIFE IN TUNE	MUSICAL
15822	MAY YOUR CHRISTMAS BE HAPPY	ORNAMENT
15830	HAPPINESS IS THE LORD	ORNAMENT
16012	BABY'S FIRST TRIP	FIGURINE
16020	GOD BLESS YOU WITH RAINBOWS	NIGHT LIGHT
100544	BROTHERLY LOVE	FIGURINE
100625	GOD IS LOVE, DEAR VALENTINE	THIMBLE
102415	IT'S A PERFECT BOY	ORNAMENT
102962	IT'S THE BIRTHDAY OF A KING	FIGURINE

Suspended 1990

ITEM #	NAME	STYLE
E-0512	IT'S A PERFECT BOY	FIGURINE
E-0517	THE PERFECT GRANDPA	ORNAMENT
E-9259	WE'RE IN IT TOGETHER	FIGURINE
E-9282A	TO SOME BUNNY SPECIAL	FIGURINE
E-9282B	YOU'RE WORTH YOUR WEIGHT IN GOLD	FIGURINE
E-9282C	ESPECIALLY FOR EWE	FIGURINE
12157	THIS IS THE DAY THE LORD HAS MADE	FIGURINE
12173	THERE'S A SONG IN MY HEART	FIGURINE
12254	LOVE COVERS ALL	THIMBLE
12378	HAPPINESS IS THE LORD	FIGURINE
12386	LORD GIVE ME A SONG	FIGURINE
12394	HE IS MY SONG	FIGURINE
12580	LORD, KEEP MY LIFE IN TUNE	MUSICAL
100145	GOD BLESS THE DAY WE FOUND YOU	FIGURINE
100153	GOD BLESS THE DAY WE FOUND YOU	FIGURINE
100161	SERVING THE LORD	FIGURINE
100293	SERVING THE LORD	FIGURINE
104027	LOVE IS THE GLUE THAT MENDS	FIGURINE
104396	HAPPY DAYS ARE HERE AGAIN	FIGURINE
104825	SITTING PRETTY	FIGURINE
105813	TO TELL THE TOOTH YOU'RE SPECIAL	FIGURINE
106216	LORD HELP ME MAKE THE GRADE	FIGURINE
111120	I'M A POSSIBILITY	ORNAMENT

Suspended 1991

ITEM #	NAME	STYLE
E-2385	OUR FIRST CHRISTMAS TOGETHER	ORNAMENT
E-2834	SHARING OUR JOY TOGETHER	FIGURINE
E-3104	BLESSED ARE THE PURE IN HEART	FIGURINE
E-5397	TIMMY	DOLL
E-9267A	TEDDY BEAR	FIGURINE
E-9267B	DOG WITH SLIPPER	FIGURINE
E-9267C	BUNNY WITH CARROT	FIGURINE
E-9267D	CAT	FIGURINE
E-9267E	LAMB	FIGURINE
E-9267F	PIG	FIGURINE
12009	LOVE COVERS ALL	FIGURINE
100056	SENDING MY LOVE	FIGURINE
100633	THE LORD BLESS YOU AND KEEP YOU	THIMBLE
102474	ROCKING HORSE	ORNAMENT
105635	HAVE I GOT NEWS FOR YOU	FIGURINE
105643	SOMETHING'S MISSING WHEN YOU'RE NOT AROUND	FIGURINE
106151	WE'RE PULLING FOR YOU	FIGURINE
109487	BELIEVE THE IMPOSSIBLE	FIGURINE
111333	O COME LET US ADORE HIM	FIGURINE
113972	GOD SENT YOU JUST IN TIME	ORNAMENT
113999	CHEERS TO THE LEADER	ORNAMENT
114006	MY LOVE WILL NEVER LET YOU GO	ORNAMENT
115290	OUR FIRST CHRISTMAS TOGETHER	FIGURINE
520802	MY DAYS ARE BLUE WITHOUT YOU	FIGURINE
520810	WE NEED A GOOD FRIEND THROUGH THE RUFF TIMES	FIGURINE
520853	I BELONG TO THE LORD	FIGURINE
521868	THE GREATEST OF THESE IS LOVE	FIGURINE

Suspended 1992

ITEM #	NAME	STYLE
12041	GOD'S PRECIOUS GIFT	FRAME
15776	MAY YOU HAVE THE SWEETEST CHRISTMAS	FIGURINE
15784	THE STORY OF GOD'S LOVE	FIGURINE
15792	TELL ME A STORY	FIGURINE
15806	GOD GAVE HIS BEST	FIGURINE
15814	SILENT NIGHT	MUSICAL
102296	SHEEP, BUNNY, TURTLE (3 PC. SET)	FIGURINE
102369	WEDDING ARCH FOR BRIDAL PARTY	ARCH
112372	I'M SENDING YOU A WHITE CHRISTMAS	ORNAMENT
522856	HAVE A BEARY MERRY CHRISTMAS	FIGURINE
524883	FIREPLACE FOR FAMILY CHRISTMAS SCENE	FIGURINE
526568	BLESS THOSE WHO SERVE THEIR COUNTRY (NAVY)	FIGURINE
526576	BLESS THOSE WHO SERVE THEIR COUNTRY (ARMY)	FIGURINE
526584	BLESS THOSE WHO SERVE THEIR COUNTRY (AIR FORCE)	FIGURINE
527289	BLESS THOSE WHO SERVE THEIR COUNTRY (GIRL SOLDIER)	FIGURINE
527297	BLESS THOSE WHO SERVE THEIR COUNTRY (AFRICAN AMERICAN)	FIGURINE
527521	BLESS THOSE WHO SERVE THEIR COUNTRY (MARINE)	FIGURINE

Suspended 1993

ITEM #	NAME	STYLE
E-0511	TUBBY'S FIRST CHRISTMAS	FIGURINE
E-2810	COME LET US ADORE HIM	MUSICAL
E-7166	THE LORD BLESS YOU AND KEEP YOU	FRAME
E-7179	THE LORD BLESS YOU AND KEEP YOU	BELL
E-7184	THE PURR-FECT GRANDMA	MUSICAL
15849	MAY YOUR CHRISTMAS BE DELIGHTFUL	ORNAMENT
15857	HONK IF YOU LOVE JESUS	ORNAMENT
100285	HEAVEN BLESS YOU	MUSICAL
102288	SHEPHERD OF LOVE	ORNAMENT
104418	FRIENDS TO THE END	FIGURINE
105953	BRIGHTEN SOMEONE'S DAY	FIGURINE
106836	HAPPY BIRTHDAY POPPY	FIGURINE
109746	PEACE ON EARTH	MUSICAL
113964	SMILE ALONG THE WAY	ORNAMENT
520357	JESUS THE SAVIOR IS BORN	FIGURINE
520691	LORD, KEEP MY LIFE IN BALANCE	MUSICAL
520756	JESUS IS THE ONLY WAY	FIGURINE
521043	TO MY FAVORITE FAN	FIGURINE
521205	HOPE YOU'RE UP AND ON THE TRAIL AGAIN	FIGURINE
521310	YIELD NOT TO TEMPTATION	FIGURINE
521434	TO A VERY SPECIAL MOM AND DAD	FIGURINE
521949	WISHING YOU A COZY SEASON	FIGURINE
521957	HIGH HOPES	FIGURINE
522031	THANK YOU LORD FOR EVERYTHING	FIGURINE
522252	HE IS THE STAR OF THE MORNING	FIGURINE
522988	ISN'T HE PRECIOUS	FIGURINE
522996	SOME BUNNY'S SLEEPING	FIGURINE
523097	JESUS IS THE SWEETEST NAME I KNOW	FIGURINE
524875	HAPPY BIRTHDAY DEAR JESUS	FIGURINE
527165	THE GOOD LORD ALWAYS DELIVERS	ORNAMENT

Suspended 1994

ITEM #	NAME	STYLE
15482	MAY YOUR CHRISTMAS BE DELIGHTFUL	FIGURINE
109754	WISHING YOU A YUMMY CHRISTMAS	FIGURINE
429570	THE EYES OF THE LORD ARE UPON YOU	MUSICAL
429589	THE EYES OF THE LORD ARE UPON YOU	MUSICAL
520705	BABY'S FIRST PET	FIGURINE
521272	TAKE HEED WHEN YOU STAND	FIGURINE
521280	HAPPY TRIP	FIGURINE
521302	MAY ALL YOUR CHRISTMASES BE WHITE	ORNAMENT
521574	DASHING THROUGH THE SNOW	ORNAMENT
522104	IT'S NO YOLK WHEN I SAY I LOVE YOU	FIGURINE
522244	DO NOT OPEN TIL CHRISTMAS	FIGURINE
522953	I BELIEVE IN THE OLD RUGGED CROSS	ORNAMENT
523224	HAPPY TRAILS IS TRUSTING JESUS	ORNAMENT
523763	I CAN'T SPELL SUCCESS WITHOUT YOU	FIGURINE
524484	NOT A CREATURE WAS STIRRING	FIGURINE
526959	WE HAVE COME FROM AFAR	FIGURINE

Suspended 1995 – No pieces were Suspended from The Enesco Precious Moments Collection in 1995.

Alphabetical Listing by Description©

Item	Number	Type	Page
Angel with Animals Caroling	E-2347	Plate	10
Angel with Announcement	136204	Figurine	81
Angel with Butterfly	520640	Figurine	96
Angel with Flashlight	E-5637	Nativity	33
Angel with Flute	153338	Ornament	84
Angel with Lamb	102261	Mini Nativity	63
Angel with Lamb	102288	Ornament	63
Angel with Newspaper and dog	520357	Figurine	94
Angel with Trumpet	E-2343	Ornament	9
Angel with Trumpet	E-5636	Nativity	33
Angel with Trumpet	113980	Ornament	77
Angel with Trumpet (Miniature)	520268	Figurine	93
Angel with Trumpet, pair	E-2344	Candle Climbers	9
Angel with Water Can	176958	Figurine	87
Angel with World in Hands	5268869	Figurine	121
Angel/Rainbow	E-9260	Figurine	42
Angels in Chariot	E-2801	Figurine	14
Angels in Chariot	E-5395	Plate	30
Angels Making Star (3-pc. set)	12408	Musical	50
Angels Preparing Manger	E-0508	Figurine	1
Boy Angel	E-7168	Frame	38
Boy Angel	12424	Doll	50
Boy Angel on Cloud	E-5205	Musical	26
Boy Angel on Cloud	E-5627	Ornament	32
Boy Angel on Cloud	12335	Figurine	49
Boy Angel w/Candle and Teddy Bear	129267	Figurine	80
Boy Angel w/Candle and Teddy Bear	129275	Ornament	80
Boy Angel with Candle	E-2365	Figurine	12
Boy Angel with Candle	E-2367	Ornament	12
Boy Angel with Doctor's Bag	525286	Figurine	119
Boy Angel with Red Cross Bag	E-0512	Figurine	2
Boy Angel/Birthday Cake	102962	Figurine	66
Boy /Girl Angels on Cloud	E-0202	Plaque	147
Boy Hitching a Ride with Angel	525979	Figurine	120
Boy Making Snow Angels	183776	Figurine	87
Boy Pilot Angel	E-9289	Figurine	45
Boy/Girl Angels	E-6118	Candle Climbers	35
Boy/Girl Angels Cloud	E-5207	Night Light	26
Boy/Girl Angels on Cloud	E-0001	Figurine	147
Boy/Girl Angels on Cloud	E-0102	Plaque	147
Clown Angel/Bouquet	109584	Figurine	72
Follow Me Angel with Three Kings	E-5641	Figurine	34
Girl Angel	E-7169	Frame	38
Girl Angel	12432	Doll	51
Girl Angel in Bonnet Praying	E-2366	Figurine	12
Girl Angel on Cloud	E-5206	Musical	26
Girl Angel on Cloud	E-5628	Ornament	32
Girl Angel Pushing Jesus in Cart	E-0509	Figurine	2
Girl Angel with Basket	528218	Ornament	127
Girl Angel with Book	523097	Figurine	109
Girl Angel with Sprinkling Can	E-9288	Figurine	45
Girl Angel/Bonnet Praying	E-2368	Ornament	12
Girl Making Angel Food	E-9274	Figurine	43
Girl with Angel Jack-in-Box	523755	Figurine	112
Kneeling Girl Angel with Harp	E-5640	Figurine	34
Miniature Boy Angel with Candle	E-5385	Figurine	29
Miniature Girl Angel Praying	E-5386	Figurine	29
Oval Shaped w/Boy Angel	E-6901	Plaque	35
Praying Angel	526835	Figurine	121
Sleeping Knight with Angel	E-5642	Musical	34
Two Angels Making Snowman	12351	Figurine	50
Two Angels on Stool	524921	Figurine	118
Two Angels Ringing a Bell	525898	Figurine	119
Two Angels with Candles	E-2351	Figurine	10
Two Angels with Chapel Poem Plaque	603503	Figurine	137
Animals (Set of 3 Camel, donkey, Cow)	E-2386	Ornament	14
Animals (Set of 3-Mini)	102296	Mini Nativity	63

ANNIVERSARY:

Item	Number	Type	Page
5-Year Club Anniversary	12440	Figurine	51
10-Year Collection Anniversary	114022	Figurine	78
10-Year Club Anniversary	227986	Ornament	157
10th Anniversary Figurine	E-2856	Figurine	21
15-Year Club Anniversary	127817	Figurine	157
15-Year Collection Anniversary	530786	Figurine	132
15-Year Collection Anniversary	530840	Ornament	132
1st Anniversary Figurine	E-2854	Figurine	20
5th Anniversary Figurine	E-2855	Figurine	21
25th Anniversary Figurine	E-2857	Figurine	21
40th Anniversary Figurine	E-2859	Figurine	21
50th Anniversary Figurine	E-2860	Figurine	21
Anniversary Boy/Girl Holding Plate	E-2853	Figurine	20
Anniversary Couple - General	129097	Figurine	80
Anniversary Couple with Cake - 1st	163783	Figurine	86
Anniversary Couple with Clock - 5th	163791	Figurine	86
Anniversary Couple with Heart Pillow - 10th	163805	Figurine	86
Anniversary Couple with Gift - 40th	163821	Figurine	86
Anniversary Couple with Photo Album - 50th	163848	Figurine	86
Anniversary Couple with Puppy	106798	Figurine	70
Commemorative 5th Anniversary	12440	Figurine	157

ASTRONAUT:

Item	Number	Type	Page
Girl in Space Suit	C-0112	Figurine	150
Girl in Space Suit	C-0012	Figurine	150
Girl in Space Suit	PM038	Ornament	158

BABY:

Item	Number	Type	Page
Angel Helping Baby Walk	E-2840	Figurine	19
Baby Assortment Set (6 styles)	E-2852	Figurine	20
Baby Boy	12033	Frame	46
Baby Boy	12475	Doll	51
Baby Boy	530859	Ornament	133
Baby Boy Holding Bottle	15539	Figurine	52
Baby Boy in Sleigh with Bear	523194	Ornament	109
Baby Boy in Stocking	183946	Ornament	88
Baby Boy on Candy Cane	527483	Ornament	124
Baby Boy w/Bear Riding Stick Horse	530263	Ornament	131

Boy with Basketball in Wheelchair	192384	Ornament	89
Boy with Basketball in Wheelchair	192368	Figurine	89
Boy with Bear in Sleigh	115282	Ornament	78
Boy with Bell	524468	Figurine	117
Boy with Block	E-2372	Ornament	13
Boy with Box of Valentine Candy	526487	Figurine	121
Boy with Broken Heart	114014	Figurine	77
Boy with Candle/Bedtime Stories	522058	Figurine	105
Boy with Candy Cane	102512	Ornament	66
Boy with Christmas Tree	521590	Ornament	102
Boy with Christmas Tree Across Lap	522112	Figurine	105
Boy with Crutches	E-3105	Figurine	21
Boy with Dog in Trash Can	PM882	Figurine	154
Boy with Dog Ripping Britches	E-9253	Figurine	41
Boy with Donkey	106151	Figurine	69
Boy with Drum	527084	Ornament	122
Boy with Drum	529214	Figurine	139
Boy with Duck	526150	Figurine	120
Boy with Fish	103497	Figurine	67
Boy with Flashlight	PM841	Figurine	153
Boy with Flower	109975	Figurine	73
Boy with Flower and Mom	100536	Figurine	61
Boy with Football	100188	Figurine	59
Boy with Gold Crown/Jeweled Ring	526037	Figurine	120
Boy with Hockey Gear	184071	Figurine	145
Boy with Ice Bag	E-7163	Figurine	37
Boy with Kite	521957	Figurine	104
Boy with Lawnmower/Fence	163899	Figurine	86
Boy with Paper Over Head	520683	Figurine	96
Boy with Pie	523798	Ornament	113
Boy with Potted Flower	521965	Figurine	104
Boy with Push Mower	PM892	Figurine	155
Boy with Report Card	E-5211	Bell	27
Boy with Scroll	105635	Figurine	69
Boy with Slate	E-0535	Ornament	4
Boy with Sled/Logs	531871	Figurine	144
Boy with Snowballs	528668	Figurine	140
Boy with Teacher	E-9251	Figurine	41
Boy with Teddy	E-0505	Plate	1
Boy with Teddy	E-5208	Bell	26
Boy with Teddy	E-5631	Ornament	33
Boy with Teddy	E-7170	Frame	38
Boy with Teddy	E-9275	Plate	43
Boy with Teddy	E-9280	Container	44
Boy with Wreath	E-0506	Figurine	1
Boy with X-Ray Machine	520624	Figurine	95
Boy/Apple/Books	E-3119	Figurine	24
Boy/Arm Braces/Dog	115479	Figurine	79
Boy/Basket with Chick	109924	Figurine	73
Boy/Dog/Fishing Pole	520721	Figurine	96
Boy/Gift Box with Dog, Ball and Bat	522120	Figurine	105
Boy/Hobby Horse	104027	Figurine	67
Boy/Ink Spot	100269	Figurine	60
Boy/Piano (2 pc. set)	12165	Musical	48
Boy/Rocking Horse	109428	Ornament	71
Boy/Trumpet/Dog (2 pc.)	12394	Figurine	50
Choir Boy	E-5389	Ornament	29
Choir Boys	E-4725	Figurine	25
Choir Boys	E-4726	Musical	25
Dentist with Boy's Tooth	105813	Figurine	69
Drummer Boy	E-2360	Nativity	11
Drummer Boy at Manger	E-2355	Musical	10
Drummer Boy at Manger	E-2356	Figurine	11
Dunce Boy	E-9268	Figurine	43
Indian Boy Eating Spinach	PM912	Figurine	155
Little Boy Sitting	15792	Figurine	53
Mini figurine Boy Holding Teddy	E-9278	Figurine	44
Miniature Boy Angel with Candle	E-5385	Figurine	29
Miniature Drummer Boy	E-5384	Figurine	29
Orphan Boy with Flowers	520853	Figurine	98
Sad Boy/Teddy	E-5200	Figurine	25
Shepherd Boy on Stick Horse	142751	Nativity	83
Stork Holding Baby Boy	529788	Figurine	141
Tennis Boy	102431	Ornament	65

BOY/GIRL:

Boy/Girl Angels	E-6118	Candle Climbers	35
Boy/Girl Angels Cloud	E-5207	Night Light	26
Boy/Girl Angels on Cloud	E-0001	Figurine	147
Boy/Girl Angels on Cloud	E-0102	Plaque	147
Boy/Girl in Gift Box	102350	Ornament	64
Boy/Girl in Horse Costume	E-9263	Figurine	42
Boy/Girl in Package	112399	Ornament	76
Boy/Girl in Tub	E-7165	Figurine	37
Boy/Girl in Tub	E-7186	Musical	40
Boy/Girl Indians in Canoe	520772	Figurine	97
Boy/Girl Making Up	E-9252	Figurine	41
Boy/Girl Moving with Cart	E-3117	Figurine	23
Boy/Girl on Cloud	E-3115	Figurine	23
Boy/Girl on Swing	E-2847	Plate	19
Boy/Girl Painting Dog House	E-7164	Figurine	37
Boy/Girl Praying at Table	E-5214	Figurine	27
Boy/Girl Riding Reindeer	529206	Ornament	128
Boy/Girl/Baby Christening	E-4724	Figurine	25
Boy/Girl/Sled	E-5396	Plate	30
Boy and Girl	PM962	Figurine	157
Boy and Girl Hugging	521299	Figurine	100
Boy and Girl in Boat	100250	Figurine	59
Boy and Girl in Boat	522937	Ornament	108
Boy and Girl in Box	101702	Musical	62
Boy and Girl in School Play	E-2809	Musical	15
Boy and Girl in Sleigh	530506	Ornament	132
Boy and Girl Kissing	524441	Figurine	117
Boy and Girl Kissing Under Mistletoe	523747	Figurine	112
Boy and Girl on Ice Skates	184098	Figurine	145
Boy and Girl on Motorcycle	522201	Figurine	105
Boy and Girl on Skis	183911	Ornament	88
Boy and Girl on Stump	E-1376	Figurine	7

Page 198

Mouse in Sugar Bowl .... BC871 .... Figurine 162
Mouse with Cheese .... E-2381 .... Ornament 13
Skunk and Mouse .... 105953 .... Figurine 69
Turtle with Mouse On Back .... BC941 .... Figurine 163

Magnet
Mugs, Boy in Car .... PM863 .... Mugs 139

MUSICALS:
Angel with Animals Caroling .... E-2346 .... Musical 9
Angel with Trumpet .... E-5645 .... Musical 34
Angels Making Star (3-pc. set) .... 12408 .... Musical 50
Baby with Toys .... 100285 .... Musical 60
Ballerina on Base .... 520691 .... Musical 96
Boy and Girl in Box .... 101702 .... Musical 62
Boy and Girl in School Play .... E-2809 .... Musical 15
Boy and Girl Reading Book .... E-2808 .... Musical 15
Boy Angel on Cloud .... E-5205 .... Musical 26
Boy Caroling/Lamp Post .... E-2352 .... Musical 10
Boy Giving Toy Lamb to Jesus .... E-2806 .... Musical 15
Boy Kneeling Manger/Crown .... E-2807 .... Musical 15
Boy Looking in Package .... 522244 .... Musical 106
Boy Pushing Girl on Sled .... E-0519 .... Musical 3
Boy/Girl in Tub .... E-7186 .... Musical 40
Boy/Piano (2 pc. set) .... 12165 .... Musical 48
Bride and Groom/Cake .... E-7180 .... Musical 39
Choir Boys .... E-4726 .... Musical 25
Clown on Elephant .... 102520 .... Musical 66
Drummer Boy at Manger .... E-2355 .... Musical 10
Girl Angel on Cloud .... E-5206 .... Musical 26
Girl at School Desk .... E-7185 .... Musical 40
Girl by Lamppost .... 521507 .... Musical 101
Girl by Wishing Well .... 526916 .... Musical 121
Girl Mailing Snowball .... 112402 .... Musical 76
Girl with Bible and Cross .... 523682 .... Musical 112
Girl with Piano (2 pc. set) .... 12580 .... Musical 51
Girl with String of Hearts .... 112577 .... Musical 77
Girl/Cradle .... E-5204 .... Musical 26
Girls with Puppy .... E-5394 .... Musical 30
Grandma in Rocker .... E-7184 .... Musical 40
Jack in the Box .... 15504 .... Musical 52
Jack-In-Box Four Seasons Autumn .... 408751 .... Musical 90
Jack-In-Box Four Seasons Spring .... 408735 .... Musical 90
Jack-In-Box Four Seasons Summer .... 408743 .... Musical 90
Jack-In-Box - Girl w/Hearts .... 422282 .... Musical 91
Jack-In-The-Box Christmas Girl .... 417777 .... Musical 91
Kids Caroling .... 109746 .... Musical 72
Mother Needlepointing .... E-7182 .... Musical 39
Nativity .... E-2810 .... Musical 15
Sleeping Knight with Angel .... E-5642 .... Musical 34
Sugar Town Train 3 - piece .... 152595 .... Musical 144
Three Kings on Base .... E-0520 .... Musical 3
Tree .... 15814 .... Musical 53

NATIONAL DAY OF PRAYER:
Girl Holding Up a Torch .... 528862 .... Figurine 128
Girl Kneeling at Altar with Bible .... 524158 .... Figurine 115
Uncle Sam Kneeling .... 527564 .... Figurine 125

NATIVITY:
See listings of regular and miniature Nativity and Additions on page181.

NEEDLECRAFT:
Girl with Lambs .... PM853 .... Needlecraft 153
Race Car Driver .... PM843 .... Needlecraft 153

NIGHT LIGHT:
3 pc. set Noah's Ark .... 530042 .... Night Light 129
Angel Behind Rainbow .... 16020 .... Night Light 56
Boy/Girl Angels Cloud .... E-5207 .... Night Light 26
Chapel with Lights .... 529621 .... Night Light 140
Circus Tent .... 528196 .... Night Light 138
Doctor's Office Night Light .... 529869 .... Night Light 142
House .... 529605 .... Night Light 141

NOAH'S ARK:
3 pc. set Noah's Ark .... 530042 .... Night Light 129
Bunnies - Noah's Ark .... 530123 .... Figurine 130
Elephants - Noah's Ark .... 530131 .... Figurine 130
Giraffes - Noah's Ark .... 530115 .... Figurine 130
Llamas - Noah's Ark .... 531375 .... Figurine 135
Pigs - Noah's Ark .... 530085 .... Figurine 130
Sheep - Noah's Ark .... 530077 .... Figurine 130
Zebras - Noah's Ark .... 127809 .... Figurine 79

Nun Figurine .... 12203 .... Figurine 48

NURSE:
Nurse .... 12491 .... Doll 51
Nurse .... 102407 .... Ornament 64
Nurse Holding Clipboard .... 529826 .... Figurine 142
Nurse with Alarm Clock .... 523739 .... Figurine 112
Nurse with Bear .... E-7158 .... Figurine 36
Nurse with Flower .... 102482 .... Figurine 65

Octopus with Fish - Birthday Series .... 527769 .... Figurine 126
Orphan Boy with Flowers .... 520853 .... Figurine 98
Ostrich - Age 8 .... 109460 .... Figurine 76
Owls on Branch .... BC932 .... Figurine 148

PENGUIN:
Penguin and Pelican .... BC942 .... Figurine 163
Penguins as Three Kings .... 530913 .... Mini Nativity 133
Three Penguin Kings .... 526959 .... Nativity 122

PIGS:
Age 3 - Pig .... 15954 .... Figurine 55
Boy and Pig in Mud .... E-9259 .... Figurine 42

Pig - Animal Figurine	E-9267F	Figurine	43
Pig on Heart-Shaped Base	E-9282B	Figurine	44
Pig with Chicken on Back	525278	Figurine	119
Pig with Gift	524506	Figurine	118
Pig with Hen on Back	E-0511	Figurine	2
Pigs	530085	Figurine	130
Pilgrim and Indian with Turkey Leg	100544	Figurine	61
Plaque-Oval Shaped W/Boy Angel	E-6901	Plaque	35
Plaque - The Enesco PM Collection	230448	Plaque	81

PLATES: See plates beginning on page 178

Policeman	102377	Ornament	63
Policeman	12297	Figurine	49
Raccoon	BC861	Figurine	162
Race car Driver	PM842	Figurine	153
Race Car Driver Needlecraft	PM843	Needlecraft	153

REINDEER

Boy/Girl Riding Reindeer	529206	Ornament	128
Girl with Reindeer	520284	Plate	93
Reindeer	102466	Ornament	65
Rhino with Bird	104418	Figurine	68
Ring Bearer	E-2833	Figurine	17

ROCKING HORSE:

Boy on Rocking Horse	521272	Figurine	99
Rocking Horse	102474	Ornament	65
Sam's House	529605	Night Light	142

SHARING SEASON:

See entries on page158

SAMMY'S CIRCUS:

See entries on page 138

Seal - Age 2	15962	Figurine	55
Secretary	E-9254	Figurine	41
Secretary - Girl at Typewriter	523542	Figurine	111
Serenity Prayer Boy	530700	Figurine	132
Serenity Prayer Girl	530697	Figurine	132

SHEPHERD:

Shepherd	E-5630	Ornament	32
Shepherd at Manger/Butterfly	E-5380	Figurine	28
Shepherd Boy on Stick Horse	142751	Nativity	83
Shepherd Kneeling by Plaque w/ Lamb	532916	Figurine	137
Shepherd Playing Harp	E-5378	Figurine	28
Shepherd Playing Harp	E-5388	Ornament	29

Shepherd with Lambs (3 pc)	183954	Nativity	88
Shepherd with Staff	E-5623	Bell	32
Two Shepherds at Manger	E-5381	Figurine	28
Shepherd	E-5620	Bell	31
Sister - Girl Putting Bows in Sister's Hair	E-2825	Figurine	16

SKUNK:

Lamb/Skunk	E-9266	Container	43
Girl with Skunk	100528	Figurine	61
Skunk and Mouse	105953	Figurine	69
Skunk with Bouquet of Flowers	BC901	Figurine	162
Snowman: Girl with Melting Snowman	100528	Figurine	60
Snowman: Two Angels Making Snowman	12351	Figurine	108
Soldier Driving Car	136271	Figurine	80

SPECIAL EVENT FIGURINES:

See Special Event listings on page166.

SPORTS:

Baseball Player with Bat	100110	Figurine	58
Boy Golfer	532096	Figurine	136
Boy Jogger	E-3112	Figurine	22
Boy on Skis	524905	Figurine	118
Boy Tennis Player	100293	Figurine	60
Boy with Barbells	109487	Figurine	71
Boy with Football	100188	Figurine	59
Cheerleader	113999	Ornament	77
Football Player	111120	Ornament	75
Football Player Among Leaves	522023	Figurine	104
Girl Cheerleader	104035	Figurine	68
Girl Tennis Player	100161	Figurine	59
Girl with Boxing Gloves	521396	Figurine	100
Tennis Boy	102431	Ornament	65
Tennis Girl	102458	Ornament	65

SQUIRREL:

House with Squirrels on Roof	192341	Lighted	146
Squirrel on Log	520411	Ornament	94
Squirrel with Bag of Nuts	BC902	Figurine	162
Statue of Liberty - 1993 National Day of Prayer	528862	Figurine	128

SUGAR TOWN:

1993 Sugar Town House Collector's Set	531774	Figurine	141
Boy Singing	529494	Figurine	139
Boy Standing by Chapel	530484	Ornament	141
Boy Standing by Sugar Town Sign	529842	Figurine	141
Boy Train Conductor w/Sign Pop.	150169	Figurine	143
Boy w/ Box of Christmas Decorations	529435	Figurine	140
Boy with Snowballs	528668	Figurine	140

Alphabetical Listing by Inspiration

A

ELEPHANTS - NOAH'S ARK	FIGURINE	530131	130
ESPECIALLY FOR EWE	FIGURINE	E-9282C	45
EVERGREEN TREE - SUGAR TOWN	FIGURINE	528684	139
EVERY MAN'S HOUSE IS HIS CASTLE	FIGURINE	BC921	163

F

FAITH IS A VICTORY	FIGURINE	521396	100
FAITH TAKES THE PLUNGE	FIGURINE	111155	75
FEBRUARY - CALENDAR GIRL	FIGURINE	109991	73
FEED MY SHEEP	FIGURINE	PM871	154
FENCE - SUGAR TOWN	FIGURINE	529796	141
FIRE HYDRANT	FIGURINE	150215	144
FISHING FOR FRIENDS - BIRTHDAY CLUB	FIGURINE	BC861	162
FLAG POLE	FIGURINE	184136	146
FOLLOW YOUR HEART	FIGURINE	528080	127
FOR GOD SO LOVED THE WORLD	NATIVITY	E-5382	28
FOREVER FRIENDS	CONTAINERS	E-9283	45
FOREVER FRIENDS	CONTAINERS	E-9283	45
FORGIVING IS FORGETTING	FIGURINE	E-9252	41
FREE CHRISTMAS PUPPIES	FIGURINE	528064	141
FRIENDS NEVER DRIFT APART	FIGURINE	100250	59
FRIENDS NEVER DRIFT APART	ORNAMENT	522937	108
FRIENDS TO THE END - BIRTHDAY SERIES	FIGURINE	104418	68
FRIENDS TO THE VERY END	FIGURINE	526150	120
FRIENDSHIP GROWS WHEN YOU PLANT A SEED	FIGURINE	524271	116
FRIENDSHIP HITS THE SPOT	FIGURINE	520748	97

G

GATHER YOUR DREAMS - 9"	FIGURINE	5296809	129
GET INTO THE HABIT OF PRAYER	FIGURINE	12203	48
GIRAFFES - NOAH'S ARK	FIGURINE	530115	130
GIVE ABILITY A CHANCE	ORNAMENT	192384	89
GIVE ABILITY A CHANCE	FIGURINE	192368	89
GLIDE THROUGH THE HOLIDAYS	ORNAMENT	521566	101
GOAT	FIGURINE	E-2364	12
GOD BLESS AMERICA	FIGURINE	102938	66
GOD BLESS OUR FAMILY - GROOM	FIGURINE	100498	60
GOD BLESS OUR FAMILY - BRIDE	FIGURINE	100501	61
GOD BLESS OUR HOME	FIGURINE	12319	49
GOD BLESS OUR HOME	FIGURINE	BC941	163
GOD BLESS OUR YEARS TOGETHER	FIGURINE	12440	51
GOD BLESS OUR YEARS TOGETHER	FIGURINE	12440	157
GOD BLESS THE BRIDE	FIGURINE	E-2832	17
GOD BLESS THE DAY WE FOUND YOU - GIRL	FIGURINE	100145	58
GOD BLESS THE DAY WE FOUND YOU - GIRL	FIGURINE	100145R	58
GOD BLESS THE DAY WE FOUND YOU - BOY	FIGURINE	100153	59
GOD BLESS THE DAY WE FOUND YOU - BOY	FIGURINE	100153R	59
GOD BLESS THE USA	FIGURINE	527564	125
GOD BLESS YOU FOR TOUCHING MY LIFE	FIGURINE	PM881	154

GOD BLESS YOU GRADUATE	FIGURINE	106194	70
GOD BLESS YOU ON YOUR BIRTHDAY - BIRTHDAY SERIES	FIGURINE	15962	55
GOD BLESS YOU WITH RAINBOWS	NIGHT LIGHT	16020	56

GOD BLESSED OUR YEARS TOGETHER WITH SO MUCH LOVE AND HAPPINESS - ANNIVERSARY FIGURINES

GOD BLESSED OUR YEAR TOGETHER WITH SO MUCH LOVE AND HAPPINESS	FIGURINE	E-2854	20
GOD BLESSED OUR YEARS TOGETHER WITH SO MUCH LOVE AND HAPPINESS (1)	FIGURINE	E-2853	20
GOD BLESSED OUR YEARS TOGETHER WITH SO MUCH LOVE AND HAPPINESS (5)	FIGURINE	E-2855	21
GOD BLESSED OUR YEARS TOGETHER WITH SO MUCH LOVE AND HAPPINESS (10)	FIGURINE	E-2856	21
GOD BLESSED OUR YEARS TOGETHER WITH SO MUCH LOVE AND HAPPINESS (25)	FIGURINE	E-2857	21
GOD BLESSED OUR YEARS TOGETHER WITH SO MUCH LOVE AND HAPPINESS (40)	FIGURINE	E-2859	21
GOD BLESSED OUR YEARS TOGETHER WITH SO MUCH LOVE AND HAPPINESS (50)	FIGURINE	E-2860	21

GOD CARED ENOUGH TO SEND HIS BEST	FIGURINE	524476	117
GOD GAVE HIS BEST	FIGURINE	15806	53
GOD IS LOVE	FIGURINE	E-5213	27
GOD IS LOVE, DEAR VALENTINE/BOY	FIGURINE	E-7153	35
GOD IS LOVE, DEAR VALENTINE/GIRL	FIGURINE	E-7154	36
GOD IS LOVE, DEAR VALENTINE/GIRL	THIMBLE	100625	61
GOD IS LOVE DEAR VALENTINE/GIRL - HEART BEHIND BACK	FIGURINE	523518	111
GOD IS WATCHING OVER YOU	FIGURINE	E-7163	37
GOD LOVETH A CHEERFUL GIVER	FIGURINE	E-1378	7
GOD SENDS THE GIFT OF HIS LOVE	FIGURINE	E-6613	35

GOD SENT HIS LOVE - 1985 DATED ANNUAL

GOD SENT HIS LOVE	ORNAMENT	15768	53
GOD SENT HIS LOVE	THIMBLE	15865	54
GOD SENT HIS LOVE	BELL	15873	54
GOD SENT HIS LOVE	FIGURINE	15881	54

GOD SENT HIS SON	FIGURINE	E-0507	1
GOD SENT YOU JUST IN TIME	MUSICAL	15504	52
GOD SENT YOU JUST IN TIME	ORNAMENT	113972	77
GOD UNDERSTANDS	FIGURINE	E-1379B	7
GOD UNDERSTANDS	BELL	E-5211	27
GOD'S LOVE IS REFLECTED IN YOU - CENTURY CIRCLE	FIGURINE	175277	87
GOD'S PRECIOUS GIFT/BOY	FRAME	12033	46
GOD'S PRECIOUS GIFT/GIRL	FRAME	12041	46
GOD'S PRECIOUS GIFT	ORNAMENT	183881	88
GOD'S PROMISES ARE SURE	FIGURINE	E-9260	42
GOD'S RAY OF MERCY	FIGURINE	PM841	153
GOD'S SPEED	FIGURINE	E-3112	22
GOING HOME	FIGURINE	525979	120
GOOD FRIENDS ARE FOR ALWAYS	FIGURINE	524123	114
GOOD FRIENDS ARE FOR ALWAYS	ORNAMENT	524131	114
GOOD FRIENDS ARE FOREVER	FIGURINE	521817	102

GOOD FRIENDS ARE FOREVER	FIGURINE	525049	118
GOOD NEWS IS SO UPLIFTING	FIGURINE	523615	112
GRANDFATHER - SUGAR TOWN	FIGURINE	529516	140
GRANDMA'S PRAYER	FIGURINE	PM861	153
GRANDPA'S ISLAND	FIGURINE	129259	80
GROOM	FIGURINE	E-2837	19

H

HALLELUJAH COUNTRY	FIGURINE	105821	69
HALLELUJAH FOR THE CROSS	FIGURINE	532002	136
HALLELUJAH HOEDOWN	FIGURINE	136836	82
HALO, AND MERRY CHRISTMAS	FIGURINE	12351	50
HANG ON FOR THE HOLLY DAYS	ORNAMENT	520292	93
HANK AND SHARON	FIGURINE	184098	145
HAPPINESS DIVINE	FIGURINE	109584	72
HAPPINESS IS AT OUR FINGERTIPS	FIGURINE	529931	129
HAPPINESS IS BELONGING	FIGURINE	B-0108	161
HAPPINESS IS BELONGING	FIGURINE	B-0008	161
HAPPINESS IS THE LORD	FIGURINE	12378	50
HAPPINESS IS THE LORD	ORNAMENT	15830	54
HAPPY BIRDIE - BIRTHDAY SERIES	FIGURINE	527343	124
HAPPY BIRTHDAY DEAR JESUS	FIGURINE	524875	118
HAPPY BIRTHDAY JESUS	FIGURINE	530492	132
HAPPY BIRTHDAY LITTLE LAMB - BIRTHDAY SERIES	FIGURINE	15946	55
HAPPY BIRTHDAY POPPY	FIGURINE	106836	70
HAPPY DAYS ARE HERE AGAIN	FIGURINE	104396	68
HAPPY HULA DAYS	FIGURINE	128694	80
HAPPY TRAILS IS TRUSTING JESUS	ORNAMENT	523224	110
HAPPY TRIP	FIGURINE	521280	100
HAVE A BEARY MERRY CHRISTMAS	FIGURINE	522856	107
HAVE A BEARY SPECIAL BIRTHDAY	FIGURINE	B-0104	160
HAVE A BEARY SPECIAL BIRTHDAY	FIGURINE	B-0004	160
HAVE A HEAVENLY CHRISTMAS	ORNAMENT	12416	50
HAVE I GOT NEWS FOR YOU	FIGURINE	105635	69
HAVE I GOT NEWS FOR YOU	FIGURINE	528137	127
HAVE I TOAD YOU LATELY THAT I LOVE YOU	FIGURINE	521329	100
HE CARETH FOR YOU	FIGURINE	E-1377B	7
HE CLEANSED MY SOUL	FIGURINE	100277	60
HE CLEANSED MY SOUL	ORNAMENT	112380	76
HE COVERS THE EARTH WITH HIS BEAUTY	FIGURINE	142654	82
HE COVERS THE EARTH WITH HIS BEAUTY	ORNAMENT	142662	82
HE COVERS THE EARTH WITH HIS BEAUTY	PLATE	142670	82
HE COVERS THE EARTH WITH HIS BEAUTY	ORNAMENT	142689	82
HE HATH MADE EVERYTHING BEAUTIFUL IN HIS TIME	PLATE	129151	80
HE IS MY INSPIRATION	FIGURINE	523038	109
HE IS MY SONG	FIGURINE	12394	50
HE IS NOT HERE FOR HE IS RISEN AS HE SAID	FIGURINE	527106	122
HE IS THE STAR OF THE MORNING	FIGURINE	522252	106
HE LEADETH ME	FIGURINE	E-1377A	7
HE LOVES ME	FIGURINE	1522779	84
HE LOVES ME	FIGURINE	524263	115

HE UPHOLDETH THOSE WHO FALL	FIGURINE	E-0526	4
HE WALKS WITH ME	FIGURINE	107999	71
HE WATCHES OVER US ALL	FIGURINE	E-3105	21
HE'S GOT THE WHOLE WORLD IN HIS HANDS	FIGURINE	5268869	121
HE'S THE HEALER OF BROKEN HEARTS	FIGURINE	100080	58
HEAVEN BLESS YOU	MUSICAL	100285	60
HEAVEN BLESS YOU	FIGURINE	520934	98
HEAVEN BLESS YOUR SPECIAL DAY - BIRTHDAY SERIES	FIGURINE	15954	55
HEAVEN BLESS YOUR TOGETHERNESS	FIGURINE	106755	70
HELLO, LORD, IT'S ME AGAIN	FIGURINE	PM811	152
HELLO WORLD! - BIRTHDAY SERIES	FIGURINE	521175	99
HELP, LORD I'M IN A SPOT	FIGURINE	100269	60
HI, SUGAR - BIRTHDAY CLUB	FIGURINE	BC871	162
HIGH HOPES	FIGURINE	521957	104
HIPPO HOLIDAYS - BIRTHDAY CLUB	ORNAMENT	520403	94
HIS BURDEN IS LIGHT	FIGURINE	E-1380G	8
HIS EYE IS ON THE SPARROW	FIGURINE	E-0530	4
HIS LITTLE TREASURE	FIGURINE	PM931	156
HIS LOVE WILL SHINE ON YOU	FIGURINE	522376	106
HIS NAME IS JESUS	FIGURINE	E-5381	28
HIS SHEEP AM I	FIGURINE	E-7161	37
HOLY SMOKES	FIGURINE	E-2351	10
HONK IF YOU LOVE JESUS (2 PIECE SET)	FIGURINE	15490	52
HONK IF YOU LOVE JESUS	ORNAMENT	15857	54
HOPE YOU'RE OVER THE HUMP - BIRTHDAY SERIES	FIGURINE	521671	102
HOPE YOU'RE UP AND ON THE TRAIL AGAIN	FIGURINE	521205	99
HOPPY BIRTHDAY	FIGURINE	B-0110	161
HOPPY BIRTHDAY	FIGURINE	B-0010	161
HOPPY EASTER, FRIEND	FIGURINE	521906	103
HOT COCOA STAND - SUGAR TOWN	FIGURINE	184144	146
HOW CAN I EVER FORGET YOU	FIGURINE	526924	121
HOW CAN TWO WALK TOGETHER EXCEPT THEY AGREE	FIGURINE	E-9263	42
HUG ONE ANOTHER	FIGURINE	521299	100

I

I BELIEVE IN MIRACLES	FIGURINE	E-7156	36
I BELIEVE IN MIRACLES	FIGURINE	E-7156R	36
I BELIEVE IN MIRACLES	PLATE	E-9257	42
I BELIEVE IN THE OLD RUGGED CROSS	FIGURINE	103632	67
I BELIEVE IN THE OLD RUGGED CROSS	ORNAMENT	522953	108
I BELONG TO THE LORD	FIGURINE	520853	98
I CAN'T BEAR TO LET YOU GO	FIGURINE	532037	136
I CAN'T SPELL SUCCESS WITHOUT YOU	FIGURINE	523763	113
I GET A BANG OUT OF YOU	FIGURINE	12262	48
I GET A KICK OUT OF YOU	FIGURINE	E-2827	16
I GIVE YOU MY LOVE FOREVER TRUE	FIGURINE	129100	80
I HAVEN'T SEEN MUCH OF YOU LATELY	FIGURINE	531057	134
I LOVE TO TELL THE STORY	FIGURINE	PM852	153
I ONLY HAVE ARMS FOR YOU	FIGURINE	527769	126
I ONLY HAVE ICE FOR YOU - BIRTHDAY SERIES	FIGURINE	530956	133
I PICKED A VERY SPECIAL MOM	FIGURINE	100536	61

J

WATCH FOR ROCKS

Notes

This Guide Belongs To:

Name_____

Address _____

Phone_____

If you find this lost guide...
please return to Desperate Collector above.

"Let us protect you!"

Introducing *RL&G Collection Protection*[SM]*

Patty Rickey
RL&G Collection Protection Specialist 1-800-962-0431

Let's face it...your ENESCO®** Precious Moments®, Cherished Teddies®, and other collectibles are valuable members of your family...and yet, the coverage you may have for these items on your existing homeowner's insurance policy may be limited. RL&G can make sure these buddies of yours are protected against theft or breakage...at very reasonable rates!

- **Worldwide protection.**
  From the Midwest to the Far East, your collectibles are covered anywhere and everywhere.

- **24-hour toll-free claim hotline.**
  Claims may be reported 24 hours a day, 365 days a year, at no charge.

- **From big city, small town, to out in the country.**
  RL&G Collection Protection is available to you.

- **Coverage for small or LARGE collections.**
  Unlike many homeowner policies, *RL&G Collection Protection* can provide coverage on virtually any size collection.

- **Replacement at secondary market prices.**
  No need to get appraisals — claims are paid on qualified secondary market values.

- **Installment billing available.**
  Aetna's flexible billing system allows you to pay for your protection with "easy on the budget" installments.

- **Breakage coverage available — without a deductible.**
  We can cover your collection for breakage without the hassle of a deductible.

- **Simplified inventory.**
  Inventories and schedules are not required except on collections valued at over $50,000. We have pre-printed inventory forms if you need them.

- **Quality coverage backed by Aetna.**
  Your collection is protected by Aetna Life & Casualty***— strong, stable and experienced.

Ask for your FREE Collection Protection Insurance Kit today!

RL&G Collection Protection Specialist Patty Rickey is a licensed agent and a collector herself, so she understands your needs and is qualified to meet them. Please contact her today at: RL&G Agency, P.O. Box 426, Norwich, CT 06360 or call toll-free 1-800-962-0431.

* This insurance program may not be available in every state. Please call for an updated list of eligible states.
** ENESCO is not associated with, nor does it support, sponsor, or promote this insurance program.
*** Includes: The Aetna Casualty and Surety Company; The Standard Fire Insurance Company; The Automobile Insurance Company of Hartford, Connecticut; Aetna Casualty & Surety Company of Illinois; Aetna Insurance Company; Aetna Insurance Company of Illinois; Aetna Lloyds of Texas Insurance Company; and Aetna Personal Security Insurance Company.

RL&G
AGENCY, INC.
PROFESSIONAL INSURANCE SERVICES

CARING MEANS SERVING—SINCE 1944

Gifts International

Specializing in the Secondary Market
For Past Years' Precious Moments® Collectibles

We Buy to Resell!!

SATISFACTION GUARANTEED!

Serving the Collector since 1984

Send your "For Sale" list with prices!

22341 E. Wells Rd.
Canton, IL 61520

ALSO OLDER:

Cherished Teddies®
Boyds Bears ♥ Hallmark Ornaments
Star Trek Toby Jugs: Captain Kirk & Borg
Barbie™ Dolls and Ornaments
Bradford Collector Plates
Disney Classics
Swarovski and More!

1-800-445-8745

8 am - 8 pm Monday - Thursday
8 am - 5 pm Friday ♥ 9 am - 3 pm Saturday
IL residents add 6.25% Sales Tax

U.S. Funds Only